The Liberty Tree

The stirring story of Thomas Muir
and Scotland's first fight for democracy

Murray Armstrong

To Richard
with best wishes,
Murray Armstrong.

WP
BOOKS

Published by Word Power Books 2014
43–45 West Nicolson Street
Edinburgh EH8 9DB

www.word-power.co.uk

Reprinted 2015

Printed and bound by Bell & Bain Ltd
Designed by Leela Sooben

British Library Cataloguing in Publication Data.
A catalogue record for this book is
available from the British Library.

ISBN 978-0-9927392-2-5

The publisher acknowledges support from Creative Scotland
towards the publication of this title

ALBA | CHRUTHACHAIL

In memory of my parents

Margaret Matthews
(1923–2007)
Sandy Armstrong
(1915–1952)

and my stepfather
Jimmie Sutherland
(1908–1991)

ACKNOWLEDGEMENTS

I owe a considerable debt to many people who assisted me in the preparation of this book, but first I have to thank my whole family for their encouragement, in particular my daughter Beth Armstrong and friends Laurie Flynn and Allan Borrell for their consistent support and enthusiasm for a book on Thomas Muir since the thought was first formed in my head.

My friends and former colleagues at the *Guardian*, Mike Sumner and Douglas Morrison, offered constructive criticism of early drafts of the story and Mike used his considerable sub-editing skills to ensure consistent style and to make my syntax, grammar and spelling acceptable to the discerning reader.

Thanks are also due to Elspeth King, curator of the Stirling Smith Museum and Art Gallery, Michael Donnelly, author of the 1975 pamphlet, *Thomas Muir of Huntershill*, Neil Davidson, historian, author and lecturer at Glasgow University's School of Social and Political Sciences and Christopher Harvie, historian, journalist, and politician. They were good enough to read my manuscript and all four offered valuable advice and criticism.

John, Alex and Jimmy Watson of the Friends of Thomas Muir, who live and work across the road from the Muirs' old family house at Huntershill, also took the time to read and comment on my manuscript and, in addition, Alex provided local topographical knowledge and information about James Muir's will that might otherwise have remained hidden.

My thanks are due, too, to the friendly and helpful staff of the National Archives of Scotland and the National Library of Scotland, both in Edinburgh, and at the London Library, the British Library, and the former Colindale Newspaper Library, all in London, and the National Archives at Kew. Thanks, too, to the staff at the Mitchell Library in Sydney, the State Library of New South Wales, for both personal attention at McQuarrie Street and for their long-distance email service. My friend Fiachra Gibbons deserves a special thanks for rooting around in the National Archives in Paris for me. And thanks also to Dr Joanna Meacock, curator of British art at the Glasgow Museums Resource Centre, and Mark Dell in the Glasgow City Council press office, for assisting me in my (unsuccessful) search for the missing portrait of Thomas Muir. This book would not have been possible without its eager adoption by Tarlochan Gata-Aura and Elaine Henry at Word Power Books. Special thanks are due to Elaine for her accurate and painstaking editing of the later iterations of the manuscript.

But my greatest debt of gratitude is to my wife, Catherine Trow, who has given me wonderful moral and material support throughout, and who has uncomplainingly accepted the presence of another man in her marriage – Thomas Muir of Huntershill.

Murray Armstrong,
London, August 2014.

CONTENTS

Thomas Muir Junior of Huntershill, 1765–1798.
Engraving by Thomas Holloway after Thomas Banks, 1795.
By kind permission of the Scottish National Portrait Gallery.

Heard ye o' the Tree o' France,
I watna, what's the name o't;
Around it a' the patriots dance –
Weel Europe kens the fame o't.
It stands where ance the Bastile stood,
A prison built by kings, man,
When superstition's hellish brood
Kept France in leading-strings, man

Wi' plenty o' sic trees, I trow,
The warld would live in peace, man;
The sword would help to mak' a plough,
The din o' war would cease, man.
Like brethren in a common cause,
We'd on each other smile, man;
And equal rights and equal laws
Would gladden every isle, man.

From *The Tree of Liberty* by Robert Burns,
probably written in late 1795 but unpublished until 1838.

INTRODUCTION

"Too often events in England in the 1790s are seen only as a reflected glow from the storming of the Bastille... It was an English agitation of impressive dimensions, for an English democracy... It was, of course, in an even more intense form an agitation for Irish independence and for Scottish democracy."

EP Thompson, *The Making of the English Working Class*, 1963.

From the summer of 1792, Scotland experienced an astonishing burst of political activity. The call for a vote for every man in the country, and election of members of parliament every year, was a popular response to the corruption, nepotism, favouritism and elitism of landowning nobles who controlled the nation's parliamentary representation at Westminster. An organisation called Friends of the People, led by Thomas Muir, a lawyer from Glasgow, and William Skirving, a farmer from Fife, grew from a meeting in an Edinburgh tavern to a nationally linked movement that touched most Scottish towns and villages in the space of a few months. Separate but similar societies were formed in England and Ireland around the same time. The enthusiasm of the movements was met with tremendous and determined government opposition in London, Edinburgh and Dublin, and the radical but self-consciously legal and loyal campaigns for parliamentary reform were mercilessly killed off within four years. However, their bravery planted seeds from which others would harvest strength and inspiration.

The ground in which the Scottish seeds were sown had been well prepared by a mixture of Presbyterian theology and government, enlightenment philosophy, union with England, and unashamed manipulation of political and social opportunities by Henry Dundas, who was commonly known as King Harry the Ninth because of his vast power of patronage. He was home secretary and the political manager of Scotland, acting on behalf of George III of Hanover and his prime minister, William Pitt the Younger.

Presbyterianism demanded doctrinal independence and organ-isational freedom from the state. In theory its ministers were equal, unlike those in Catholic or Anglican hierarchies, and its government was by elders elected by congregations to appoint and supervise clergy and develop policy through kirk sessions, district presbyteries, regional synods and on to the national general assembly. Democracy was no stranger to most Scots.

One of the significant figures in the Scottish Enlightenment was Francis Hutcheson, professor of Moral Philosophy at Glasgow from 1730–46. An Ulster man from an Ayrshire family, he, like many other Presbyterian or Dissenting Irish, had also been a student at Glasgow. He taught the Presbyterian dictum that government was for the good of society as a whole and is a contract between the people and the gover-nors, who can rightfully be resisted if they fail to fulfil their side of the bargain. This right of resistance, in Hutcheson's teaching, extended to colonies and his thinking was a major influence in America before the War of Independence. This intellectual revival had spread by the early 1780s to the professional and commercial classes of Scotland and Ireland under the guidance of David Hume and Hutcheson's pupil, Adam Smith, who, according to a historian of Scottish radicalism, "had been eminently successful in arousing among his students in Glasgow and his friends in Edinburgh an interest in what was then termed 'the mechanism of political society'; and his opinions gained even wider currency under the teaching of John Millar [Muir's teacher] and Dugald Stewart [a friend of Robert Burns]".

In the 1790s the union with England, enacted in 1707, was by no means accepted by the bulk of the population as a good thing. Burns's anti-union poem, *Such a Parcel of Rogues in a Nation*, was published anonymously in August 1792 and probably reflected a state of mind common until the final triumph of pro-Union Scottish Toryism in the early to mid-nineteenth century and championed in the writings of Sir Walter Scott. The Act of Union preserved the feudal supremacy of Scotland's nobles, including the power of "pit and gallows", the right to punish and execute in their own fiefdoms. It also maintained the essentially medieval privileges of royal burghs. Scotland was allowed forty-five members in the Westminster House of Commons, just one more than Cornwall, and sixteen representative peers in the Lords. England had 513 MPs and 185 peers, so the Scots, with twenty percent of the population of England, were asked to accept nine percent of English representation. But this was also a financial calculation; poverty-stricken Scotland was only expected to raise two and a half percent of the land tax that wealthier England could supply to the exchequer.

"The immediate impact of the Union on Scottish trade," says one historian of the Treaty, "was to depress it rather than boost it. Aid for development in Scotland had in the end to be separately legislated, but it would not happen for twenty years... To Scots, the Union looked within a distressingly short time to have been a terrible mistake. No economic boom followed, not for now nor indeed for half a century. Businesses closed down rather than opened up in the new British common market." So the union was essentially a conservative measure that protected the northern flank of England, with a dominant capitalist market, ensured the Hanoverian succession and preserved the feudal rights of Scottish lords, including the right to call out tenants for military service. This was to prove crucial in the Stuart challenges to the Hanoverians in 1708, 1715, 1719, and 1745, particularly in the '15 and the '45. All of this legislation stayed intact until after the defeat of Charles Edward Stuart at Culloden in 1746, when military feudalism and "heritable jurisdictions", the right of pit and gallows, were swept away in several acts of parliament in the following year.

Although these privileges of the aristocratic families were brought to an end, their dominance was not. Most, however, were impecunious and depended on meagre rents squeezed from poor peasants, so they relied on place-hunting and patronage dispensed from London, which from 1784 was contingent on a loyalty test by Scotland's political manager, Henry Dundas. Government, customs, revenue, legal, and clerical posts and sinecures were all in his gift, as well as some naval appointments and colonial positions. A loyal MP could nominate to minor official posts falling vacant in his constituency but Dundas would distribute the positions in constituencies that chose an opposition MP. "He did, however, have a greater or lesser say in almost all the *major* revenue, church and judicial appointments made in Scotland between 1784 and 1806," according to one authority, who goes on, "Dundas is, of course, notorious for his use of East Indian patronage in Scots politics…perhaps an average of a dozen jobs a year in his personal gift between 1784 and 1801 was put to good use in his Scottish operations."

By this means Dundas gradually extended his reach from the Lowlands in the 1780s to the Highlands where, by the general election of 1790 (in which the franchise was confined to 2,665 county voters, half of whom were fictitious ciphers of the nobles, and to the self-selecting councils in the burghs), he could present Prime Minister Pitt with a cohort of thirty-nine loyal MPs from forty-five returned, although he had some difficulty in controlling the Treasury-sponsored King's list of nobles to be approved by their peers. At the general election in 1796, however, forty-three of the forty-five MPs and all of the peers were loyalists. Little had changed since the observation made by a member of an Edinburgh club in 1762, that the franchise was "a privilege now engrossed by the great lord, the drunken laird, and the drunkener baillie". After his retirement Dundas wrote to a family member, "The whole patronage of Scotland was concentrated in my person…during the whole time of my political connexion with Mr Pitt. He nor no department of government gave me a moment's trouble on that score."

The right of presenting ministers of the kirk to congregations in vacant parishes had been protected by the Act of Security at the time of the Union, but a Patronage Act of 1712, enacted to appease Episcopalian nobles in the north of Scotland, violated this by restoring that right to landowners who were heirs of the original donors of ecclesiastical properties. This was accepted by the Moderate faction in the Kirk but led to perpetual squabbles, secession, and resentment.

Further resentment was stoked by the presence of English customs houses and officials, even in small ports. New taxes were backed by the military might of the British state and customs houses became a popular target for attack and plunder in times of hardship or rebellion. "Alas!" wrote Robert Burns to a friend, "I have often said to myself, what are all the boasted advantages which my country reaps from a certain Union, that can counterbalance the annihilation of her independence, & even her very Name!" Burns's friend, the radical aristocrat Basil Douglas, Lord Daer, thought much the same. "I believe most deliberately that had no Union ever taken place we should in that respect have been more emancipated than we are," he wrote in a letter to the young Northumberland MP Charles Grey, who would later become prime minister and introduce the first Reform Act in 1832.

There was one other important influence on the reformers in Scotland that was common to their counterparts in England and Ireland, the Real Whigs. This was a loose grouping of radical thinkers who had distanced themselves from the ruling Whig oligarchy of the early eighteenth century whom they believed had neglected political liberties and had instead allowed the influence of the crown and the executive to be extended to the point where it had corrupted the representative part of the constitution. Their theorist was the seventeenth century philosopher John Locke, whose *Two Treatises of Government* outlined the theory of the social contract. "The community perpetually retains a supreme power of saving themselves from…their legislators, whenever they shall be so foolish or so wicked as to…carry on designs against their liberties and properties," he had written. Real Whigs in Scotland included Hutcheson and Andrew Fletcher, a leading opponent of union with England.

Usually educated at either Glasgow University or the English dissenting academies, Real Whigs preferred a federal constitution for the British Isles, but above all opposed corruption of the legislature by government patronage.

From the early 1780s Scots Whigs were active in promoting reform in burgh and county government and, by extension, their control of parliamentary representation. Various conventions met in Edinburgh and the playwright Richard Sheridan became their (largely unsuccessful) champion in the House of Commons. In 1784, for instance, half of the royal burghs were represented at a reform convention in Edinburgh under the leadership of the prominent Whig advocates Archibald Fletcher and Henry Erskine.

This, then, was the Scotland in which Thomas Muir and William Skirving tried to pull together different strands of dissatisfaction in the summer of 1792. The apparent successes of the American and French revolutions gave practical embodiment to these ideas and sentiments as well as providing added enthusiasm and optimism.

*

They were news. The story of the men and the movement was told in contemporary newspaper reports and pamphlets, along with reports of the government's response of increasing repression and restriction of political and individual liberties. In Scotland, as the "martyrs" were brought to trial, convicted and sentenced to transportation – first Muir and Thomas Fyshe Palmer, a Unitarian minister in Dundee, then Skirving and the London wine merchant, Maurice Margarot, and finally Joseph Gerrald, a lawyer from the West Indies – the transcripts of the court proceedings sold in many editions and in many thousands. Their enforced voyage to Australia was recorded in letters and in a pamphlet written by Palmer and published in Cambridge in 1798.

The first biography of Muir was written by Peter Mackenzie in 1831 and was essentially a polemical work, part of the campaign for the Reform Bill which was passed into law the following year. He said little about Muir's time in either France or Ireland, and gave rise to the myth about Muir being rescued from Sydney Cove by a United States ship expressly sent there by sympathetic Americans and with the blessing of George Washington. He also wrote, incorrectly, that Muir was shipwrecked off the coast of Vancouver Island and lived with Native Americans there before walking the length of America's west coast, about 4,000 miles, to Panama City, before being sent by ship to Spain. This is surprising because Muir told the authentic version of his journey to the French newspaper *Le Moniteur* in 1797.

Little more was written about the radical movement in Scotland until early in the twentieth century. Muir and his associates slipped from being significant historical figures to mere footnotes. For the growing labour movement in an industrialising country, the radical democracy of Muir or the democratic republicanism of Tom Paine were no longer sufficient, and new problems were addressed by new theories of social democracy or socialism. At the same time the triumphant, centralised British imperial state regarded the unity of Britain and Ireland, and later Northern Ireland, as its natural political geography and strenuously resisted each attempt at further reform. There could be no important place for the radicals of the late eighteenth century in a Unionist history because they had been branded as traitors, conspirators, deranged, or a combination of all three.

Henry Meikle filled out more of the story of the reform movement in his masterful *Scotland and the French Revolution* published in 1912 but had little to say about Muir's transportation and escape and only five pages on his final days in France. In 1920, Tom Johnston wrote a sympathetic account of the radical movement amounting to twenty pages in his *A History of the Working Classes in Scotland*, but repeated the errors of Mackenzie in Muir's story. After that, new information came largely from abroad.

In the early 1920s, Marjorie Masson at the University of Victoria in Melbourne and JF Jameson in Washington were collaborating on details of Muir's journey from Sydney Cove to Cadiz. Masson was searching the Australian archives while Jameson was combing American and Spanish sources in Washington, Mexico, and Seville.

They ruled out an intentional involvement in Muir's escape by President George Washington, or by groups of friendly supporters with the means to equip a ship for the purpose. There was not a scrap of evidence to support Mackenzie's fanciful rescue claims, and they gave us much new detail about a merchant ship, the Otter, and its captain Ebenezer Dorr, his negotiations with Muir about the rescue, and the subsequent voyages of Muir from Nootka Sound at Vancouver Island to Monterey, San Blas and on to Mexico City, Vera Cruz, Havana and Cadiz. *The Odyssey of Thomas Muir* was published in the *American Historical Review* in October 1923.

A second collaboration, or at a least helpful exchange of letters, between historians George Insh in Scotland and John Earnshaw in Australia in the late 1940s, led to a deeper understanding of the Pacific journey. Both had rediscovered the abridged diaries and memoirs of the Otter's first mate, Pierre Francois Péron, who became a close friend to Muir. The two volumes had been published in 1824 in Paris, which is where Insh found his copies, while Earnshaw discovered another in the Mitchell Library in Sydney. They independently translated *Mémoires du Capitaine Péron sur ses Voyages*. Earnshaw published a small volume, *Thomas Muir, Scottish Martyr*, in 1959, which added some detail of life in Sydney Cove as well as providing a colourful description of the Pacific voyage to add to the work of Masson and Jameson. He translated Muir's letters from Monterey and shared them with Insh.

Insh went further and by 1952 had prepared a biography, *Thomas Muir of Huntershill*, which unfortunately was never published and remains a typed manuscript in the rare books section of the National Library of Scotland. However, Insh requested all of the material on Muir from the archives in Paris, Seville, and Mexico, the ageing photographs and photocopies of which are stored with his manuscript. In 1969 another Australian, Frank Clune, pulled much of this together in *The Scottish Martyrs*, and added biographies of Skirving, Palmer, Margarot and Gerrald.

In 1981 the first biography of Muir to benefit from this previous research appeared in *Muir of Huntershill* by Christina Bewley, who claims to be a descendant of the Muir family. She, though, found it "difficult to assess Muir's importance, if any, as a political reformer. The reform agitation of the 1790s was premature, supported only by a minute section of the population, submerged by the French wars. Muir is at most a minor historical figure..." Hector MacMillan set out to disprove that view in *Handful of Rogues*, published in 2005, emphasising the unprecedented growth of the movement at a time of social and cultural regeneration in Scotland. "It was a vigorous movement," he argued, "rooted in democratic principle, greatly influenced by the recent revolution in France and driven on by many of the best minds of the day." MacMillan reset the compass and, re-examining much of the evidence from government informers, showed how determined the authorities were to use any means possible to resist the perceived threat to their great privileges.

I have had the benefit all of these sources as well as a rich seam of recent academic interest in eighteenth century radicalism, from scholars such as Bob Harris, John Brims, Emma Vincent Macleod, Patrick Scott Hogg and Liam McIlvanney in Scotland, and John Barrell, Geoffrey Claeys and Jennifer Mori in England. I have also revisited original documents and records, contemporary publications and newspapers to help reconstruct a picture of the wider movement and its context, its internationalism through important links in England, Ireland, and France, and its metamorphosis from an open campaign to a secret society in the face of unyielding opposition from government.

The new academic interest in the period happened alongside the waves of literary and artistic renaissance that enriched Scotland as the politics of neoliberalism, beginning with the government of Margaret Thatcher, was rejected for its profound economic and social failure in the country. That in turn sparked the desire for devolution of some powers to a Scottish Parliament, which was approved in a referendum of 1997, and the subsequent constitutional debate about whether to remain within the Union has led to a second referendum, this time on independence, to be held this year. However, that debate is more than simply about reorganising the furniture. It has provided an opportunity for Scots to imagine a different way of living, from rights and responsibilities enshrined in a written constitution to the kind of government that Francis Hutcheson recommended, one for the good of society as a whole. It has become a debate about social as well as political objectives, which was of course what Muir saw in his vision of a democracy to end unmerited privilege and social exclusion. He would have recognised the recent statement of Elliot Bulmer, research director of the Constitutional Commission in Scotland, "The electoral system for the House of Commons is unrepresentative, the composition of the House of Lords is indefensible, the powers of the Crown are excessive, secretive and unaccountable, rights are fragile, and privileges rife."

There has recently been renewed interest in a public statue being erected to Thomas Muir in Edinburgh (where are you in this Glasgow?), and the beginnings of a campaign to have him posthumously pardoned of his crime of seditious libel. If the atmosphere engendered by the independence debate, no matter what the outcome, provides a space for Thomas Muir and the radical movement of the 1790s to be reinstated as a significant part of Scotland's story, some justice will have been done. If they help to inform that debate then so much the better.

I was in a quandary about how to write this book from the off. On the one hand I felt that Muir deserved a proper, new biography but was aware that the dearth of personal papers and documents made this pretty difficult. On the other hand I could see there was a mountain of circumstantial documentation which, layer by layer, could provide rich context and lots of room in which to tell the story from the points of view of the participants. Not being a historian I didn't want to engage in a debate with that profession about the veracity of this or that interpretation of the 1790s, but being a journalist I instinctively wanted to reveal the narrative of the period as it unfolded. So where, for instance, some historians might argue about

Muir's later plans for a rising being unrealistic, I was concerned to let the reader know what *he* and the people around him thought, and what risks they were prepared to take.

One of the things I did want to achieve from the start, though, was to write a version of the story that was easy to follow and understand. I was dumbfounded by the ignorance about Muir and the radical movement, even among Scots. So I have sometimes resorted to a little imagination to drive the narrative along but not, I hope, at the expense of the historical record. It is unusual, I think, in a reconstructed narrative such as this to list sources in an academic sort of fashion but I wanted to share those with readers as much as the story itself. So there are lots of page notes at the back and I have indicated in them where imaginative reconstruction has taken place.

CHAPTER 1

Riot

"The mob of Edinburgh, when thoroughly excited, had been at all times one of the fiercest which could be found in Europe; and of late years they had risen repeatedly against the government, and sometimes not without temporary success."

Sir Walter Scott, *The Heart of Midlothian.*

His Majesty's Ship Hinde, with a company of marines on board, docked in the port of Leith, a short distance from Edinburgh. The Hinde had been on a routine tour of duty under the command of Captain Cochrane who, on hearing of fears that celebrations planned to mark the birthday of King George III might be marred by riot, generously offered his soldiers to the lord provost of the city, James Stirling. Lord Adam Gordon, commander in chief of the army in North Britain had, at the request of the provost and magistrates, also drafted in dragoons to reinforce the regiment of foot soldiers, garrisoned in the great castle looking down on the town from its high rock.

Thomas Muir, a young advocate in the city, sensed the tension in the tenements as the big day approached. Handbills had been circulating announcing that an effigy of the home secretary, the Right Honourable Henry Dundas, would be burnt at the town cross on the evening of the birthday celebrations on Monday, 4 June 1792, and the lord provost had complained to his magistrates of having received threatening letters warning him that the incineration should be allowed to go ahead without interference.

On Monday morning the *Caledonian Mercury* confidently announced, "Yesterday and today, a number of dragoons arrived in town. They are at present parading the streets in order to keep the public peace, which, for some time past has been strongly apprehended would be interrupted by a riot; but, from present appearances and the exertions of the magistrates, it is hoped, will be prevented."

The day was quiet but tense. The show of force by the military had done little except remind the townspeople how effectively they were excluded from the birthday celebrations. The nobility and the well-to-do would toast the distant monarch on whom they relied for their exalted positions and would ensure, by musket and bayonet if need be, that their polite assemblies would take place away from the envious and avaricious *hoi polloi*.

The hooves of dragoons' horses rang on the cobbled streets of the Old Town throughout the afternoon. The snorts of chargers, the slap of their harnesses and the jangle of swords and spurs provided reassurance to one part of the population while reinforcing a sullen, resentful feeling in the denizens of the crowded tenements in the town's wynds and closes.

Muir was aware that at around six o'clock important city officials, along with prominent lawyers, ministers of the kirk, senior members of the Scottish judiciary, several aristocrats, landowners and a sprinkling of wealthy businessmen, were meeting in the old Parliament House to drink a birthday toast to King George and the House of Hanover. Soon after, the city's governing caste dispersed, some to common taverns, as was still the practice of the times for the upper orders, others to private birthday functions.

At the same time a small crowd gathered in the High Street around the Tron Kirk. Some brought firecrackers, determined to play a part in the celebrations, but were constantly moved on by the town guard or scattered by the rising clatter of dragoons' horses coming to the trot. Major Robert Matthews brought down the 53rd infantry from the castle and drew them up in ranks at the crossroads by the kirk. Stones were thrown, and loud bangs and flashes of squibs thrown under the horses caused them to skitter across the cobbles. Muir sensed that the soldiers were losing control. So did the crowd, which swelled in the street until it snaked up the hill to the Lawnmarket, squeezed in the pass in front of the town jail and into the Krames, a tiny alley behind the Luckenbooths, small lock-up shops jammed between the old cathedral of St Giles and the main road, creating a narrow bottleneck at the top of the wide High Street.

Sheriff John Pringle, the chief law officer of Edinburgh, was called out of a private party in the house of the lord advocate by one of his officers, William Middleton, who told him of the disturbances. Pringle ran to the town centre and collected Provost Stirling, in convivial mood, from Hunters Tavern in Writers Court. Muir's apartment was close to the cross, where the provost and sheriff stood facing the unruly crowd as it jeered at the soldiers and pelted them with stones. The provost appealed for calm but the crowd ignored his pleas. A stone thudded into Sheriff Pringle's leg. The foot soldiers closed ranks and Provost Stirling ordered the sheriff to read the Riot Act. Dragoons were ordered to ride their horses down the pavements to clear people away but the crowd continued to pour in and out of alleyways, now disappearing into Bell's Wynd, now reappearing at the mouth of Old Assembly Close. The horses were vulnerable in the side streets and had to keep to the main road for safety. The crowd grew greater and began to transform itself into a mob or, as the burghers called them, the *canaille*, pack of dogs.

From the alleys more stones were launched at troopers by young men and boys; rubbish, cinders, urine and excrement were showered on the soldiers from high tenement windows. Frightened horses were spurred to the gallop by desperate riders trying to recapture the streets. One of the town guard, tamely standing sentinel by the guard house, was chased away and his sentry box dragged to the middle of the road, broken into pieces and set on fire. A great cheer went up. A second sentry box at the Tron church was consigned to the flames, together with signboards ripped from shop fronts and anything else the mob could collect and burn.

The 53rd, the dragoons, provost, sheriff, and magistrates did everything in their power to disperse the rioters, but without success.

They were hesitant in employing their weapons for fear of transforming a riot into an insurrection. The rioters fought on with sticks and stones, setting bonfires and breaking windows till past midnight when, as if by a prearranged signal, they separated, melted away and disappeared into their tenement homes. Fourteen of the rioters had been arrested and sent as prisoners to the castle.

*

Most of Tuesday passed quietly and the authorities, hoping that riotous intentions had subsided, sent the dragoons to their quarters outside the city. But at about six o'clock in the evening, what was described as "a very great mob" assembled in the neighbourhood of George Square, a most fashionable district near the green and spacious open parkland known as The Meadows, to the south of the castle rock and the Old Town. Tonight the mob had not come to celebrate but to show those who ruled over them that they wanted something better: some clutched handbills urging democracy; some had loaves on the ends of poles and called for cheaper bread; others shouted for a stop to the grain ships taking much needed food away for sale in foreign countries; and some had just come to riot again, in the way their kind had done for centuries, the only way open to people with no other means of making their needs and wants known.

The protesters shouted their slogans, sang their songs and waved branches, the symbols of liberty trees that had been planted in towns and villages throughout Scotland in celebration of the overthrow of tyranny in France three years before. They burst into the square and came to a stop outside number five, the town house of Henry Dundas, home secretary, president of the Board of Control for India, treasurer of the navy, and political manager for the nobles of Scotland and most of their forty-five subservient members of parliament at Westminster. Dundas was in London but his mother, Ann, Lady Arniston, was at home. She looked from her window with anxiety as the crowd swept into the square bearing an effigy of her son, which was paraded in front of her house.

On the other side of the square, her grandson, Colonel Francis Dundas, looked out of the window of the house of the lord advocate, his brother. He ran outside and pushed his way through the crowd to the front door of his grandmother's house. He found her in the drawing room upstairs, terrified. Minutes later he was joined by Admiral Adam Duncan, also a resident of the fine square who had married into the Dundas dynasty. A window in the elegant Georgian casement of the drawing room shattered. Then another. The effigy of Lady Arniston's son was once more held up before the house on its makeshift gallows and set alight, amid the shouts and cheers of the now tumultuous mass filling the square, and the blackened remains were insolently tossed on Dundas's front steps.

An angry Francis Dundas grabbed one of Lady Arniston's wooden crutches while Adam Duncan selected a golf club from a bag in the hall. They ran outside to beat back the crowd, feeling protected by their family's unquestionable right to rule. But the mob ignored this assumed immunity and Duncan saw Dundas knocked to the ground; the crutch was taken from him and he was pounded in the face with it; those nearest to him buried heavy boots into his side. Duncan pulled his relative to his feet and dragged him to the shelter of the house in a hail of stones and sticks. Young Dundas had a deep cut across his nose and he would have two very black eyes before morning.

Sheriff Pringle rushed from his home to George Square, where he first commanded and then pleaded with the mob to disperse. They took no notice but instead, as the sheriff later testified, "They seemed rather to grow more enraged, so that I found it absolutely necessary to send for the military to prevent them from going to greater extremities."

The mob had by now turned its attention to the house of the lord advocate, on the opposite side of the square. Robert Dundas, a mediocre lawyer and MP for Midlothian, had been given the Westminster seat along with the top law job in Scotland by his Uncle Henry. He was just thirty-one. The mob had smashed many of the windows and doors of his town house when the 53rd foot arrived.

"I again exhorted them to disperse but they paid no attention to my admonitions and continued to throw volleys of stones at myself and the military," Pringle later reported. "I then informed them that unless they desisted I would be under the necessity of ordering the soldiers to fire upon them. This, having no effect, I went forward a considerable way in front of the soldiers and repeatedly, in a loud voice, called 'silence!'; and told them I was to make a proclamation of the Riot Act." The mob dispersed.

Pringle was relieved, thinking the crisis had passed, until in a short time a magistrate's messenger found him with news of disturbances in the New Town, the fashionable streets and squares to the north of the castle rock. The messenger requested that a party of soldiers be sent immediately to St Andrew's Square, "as the mob were very tumultuous there". The rioters had found new targets for their ire. The lord provost lived in the square, as did Lord Braxfield, Robert McQueen. Braxfield was president of the Court of Session, the chief judge in Scotland's supreme court, and known by his straightforward motto, "Hang a thief when he's young and he'll no steal when he's auld." He, like Lord Provost Stirling, was another of the many men raised up by Henry Dundas.

A party of soldiers hurried to the other side of town, leaving behind a twenty-strong detachment of the 53rd in the command of Ensign George Hay. It was now a little after nine o'clock. The main party of infantry was marched at the double to the New Town only to be told that the crowd had turned back to George Square and was about to attempt to demolish Lady Arniston's house. Pringle took the infantry back to the south of the city and once more appealed to the rioters to go home. He told them he would soon "be under the disagreeable necessity of ordering the soldiers to fire if any more mischief was attempted." The mob answered with a volley of stones and the sheriff gave the order to fire.

Muskets flashed and a report of the deafening explosions echoed back off the precipice of the castle rock. The rioters stopped. They looked around. No one was hurt. The mob took courage in the belief that the soldiers' pieces were charged only with powder. As Ensign

Hay was later to tell an inquiry, "So soon as the smoke cleared away the mob advanced a little and they immediately commenced the throwing of stones at the party and they cried out to the soldiers 'fire ye buggers' and this was cried out repeatedly." More taunts and another shower of stones were hurled at the ranks and the soldiers fired again. Seven people fell wounded. The crowd retreated into the side streets and dissolved into the gathering darkness.

Only four of the names of the wounded were recorded that night. The *Caledonian Mercury* listed, "Robert Richardson, carver and gilder, shot through the loins, dangerously; George Graham, shoemaker, wounded near the collar bone; Samuel Ringen, tailor, shot through the right arm; John Morrison, watchmaker, wounded in the thigh; and three others whose names we have not learned." But the tally afterwards drawn up back in the Old Town tenements rose to sixteen. One more name came to be known later, that of a young man, no more than a boy: Robert Ritchie, an apprentice to a carver, who died in the Royal Infirmary of a musket ball wound on the following Sunday morning, 10 June, 1792.

Muir witnessed much of the disturbance. He read the reports in the papers and shook his head. He was sympathetic to the desires of ordinary people and, like them, wanted political change that he believed would improve conditions. Real representation at Westminster and in towns and counties throughout Scotland would neutralise the corrupt power of the gentry and the Dundas clan. Riots would not do. Muir thought they would only strengthen the resolve of the privileged and that legal and constitutional change could be brought about only by peaceful methods.

That night, Lady Arniston sat at a desk to write to her son in London. "To say I was not a little frightened would be false," she told him, "but I happily was supported by friends and expect a good night's sleep to remit my spirits." Her optimism came a little too early.

*

Wednesday had begun like the previous day. Everything was quiet until evening. A reporter from the *Caledonian Mercury* recorded, "The mob then assembled and continued pelting one another with dead cats, &c till half past nine o'clock, when, in an instant, they left the High Street and went directly to the lord provost's house in St Andrew's Square, which they endeavoured to demolish by breaking the windows, doors, &c."

Once more, the *canaille* gathered in the fashionable New Town, where proud, neo-classical mansions and apartments had been built during the past two decades, carved sandstone monuments to a new prosperity. These elegant buildings were testaments to a modern way of thinking, an enlightenment in science, reason and progress, and many of those ideas, clothed in notions of freedom and liberty, had not escaped the notice of the common people.

The mob took its revenge on Provost Stirling. Cobblestones were pulled from the ground and thrown through the long windows of his imposing house as Mrs Stirling and her daughters cowered in terror in a cellar. Once more the 53rd was hurried down from the castle. A warning fire was lit in the Half Moon battery of the fortress to alert the marines on the frigate and the dragoons camped on the other side of the city. Two cannons were fired from the battlements to reinforce the urgency of the request. In a short time, marines entered the city from the broad boulevard of Leith Walk and began patrolling the streets. From the west, dragoons rode in with drawn swords and resumed their gallop from street to street. No shots were fired and, around midnight, all was quiet. Most of the infantry returned to their garrison in the castle, the dragoons withdrew to their encampment, and the marines were quartered in Parliament Close. Ten people were arrested and sent to the castle prison.

That night, an exhausted Provost Stirling sat at his desk, lifted a pen, dunked it in an inkwell and prepared a report for Home Secretary Dundas. He described the events he had witnessed during these tumultuous days and in one sentence was unwittingly prophetic: "An evil spirit seems to have reached us which I was in hopes John Bull would have kept to himself."

A hurried public meeting was organised by the authorities on the following morning, Thursday, in the New Church, with the lord provost in the chair and addressed by the lord advocate. Robert Dundas said, with certainty, that one person had directed the violence on these last two nights; he had seen him "pass and repass the front of my house and, by a wave of his hand, direct the mob with as much regularity as if they had been under military discipline." Lord Adam Gordon, commander of the northern army, said he was ready to use strong measures again. A resolution was passed in support of the actions taken, and it called on all inhabitants to do their utmost to prevent a recurrence of such outrages, offering a reward of £100 for information leading to the arrest and conviction of the ringleaders. The marines were asked to remain in town for now, and moved into quarters in the Excise office.

This was not the first riot in Scotland that year, nor would it be the last. A bad harvest and the sorry state of the people was the cause of much of the unrest. But always the disturbances were tinged with political urgency. Just two weeks before the birthday riots, the king and his government had issued a proclamation banning seditious meetings and publications, in response to the popularity of a new book by Tom Paine called *Rights of Man*. The book was the second part of Paine's defence of the revolution in France, a criticism of monarchy and a plan for a democratic society, and it sold in hundreds of thousands. It was translated into Gaelic. Norman Macleod, the MP for Inverness, one of a handful not ensnared in Dundas's patronage, said of the government's ban, "It set people of all ranks a-reading and as everybody in this country can read, the people are astonishingly informed." He condemned the government for the "odious" proclamation and added his distaste at the handling of the Edinburgh riots. "The pension of £100 a year," he objected, "given immediately to

Pringle, the sheriff who ordered the troops to fire, and creating the provost a baronet, have greatly aggravated the insult."

Effigies of Henry Dundas had already been burnt in Aberdeen, Perth, Dundee and "almost every village in the north of Scotland", according to a contemporary newspaper report. Other reports sent to the home secretary noted that in Lanark there was "a very disagreeable state of tumult and disorder", while "at Peebles, the Rt Hon Secretary has twice undergone the fire ordeal".

Among those arrested in Edinburgh were two young men in servants' liveries. One, Alexander Lockie, had been standing by the Tron church in High Street as the soldiers rushed from George Square to the New Town. An infantry officer, thinking he recognised Lockie's clothing – he wore a short blue jacket and had on boots and spurs – ordered two of his men to arrest him. A second young man was plucked from the crowd in George Square and arrested. John Bertram, a servant, wore a white coat, with a blue collar, trimmed with blue at the pockets.

The reward offered for information about the ringleaders of the riot was unsuccessful so Lockie and Bertram were selected and brought to trial on Wednesday, 18 July. Bertram, who wore the white livery most common for servants in Edinburgh, could not be positively identified and was acquitted. Lockie, a coachman who worked for a chaise hire company, was defended by Thomas Muir who, at twenty-six years of age, had just four years' experience at the Scottish bar. Lockie admitted to being present in the Old Town at the time but the evidence of his having been one of the organisers was insubstantial: he could not properly be identified, there were so many young men in livery of similar sorts on the streets that day; his employer confirmed his alibi, he had sent Lockie to collect his daughter from another part of town. The arresting soldiers were hopelessly ill-informed, neither of them being able to swear they had seen Lockie in the riot, or that he had been caught with stones or other missiles outside the Tron Kirk. They were following orders given by Lieutenant Robertson.

Mindful of the political nature of the trial and the inflamed opinions of the respectable burghers of Edinburgh, Muir addressed the jury, not only on the lack of evidence, but also with strong arguments about the dangerous tendency of mobs who often defeated the cause they meant to serve. In summing up, the lead judge, Lord Braxfield concentrated the minds of the jury (selected by him, as was the custom, from a list of names supplied by town and county officials), solely on the evils of riot rather than on the facts of the case before them and they brought back a guilty verdict. Lockie was guilty, the jurors decided, "of throwing one stone".

"My lord," objected Muir, "the members of the jury have found my client guilty of throwing one stone. Where in the indictment is he charged with that offence? The charge relates to mobbing and rioting and identifies Mr Lockie as a ringleader. He has not been found guilty of those charges as stated."

"Ech! He's guilty enough Mr Muir, leave it be," replied Braxfield.

"My lord, new charges cannot be brought in a jury room and accepted by this court," insisted Muir. "If a charge of stone throwing had been brought then it would have had to be tested by evidence and cross-examination. My client ..."

"Enough, Mr Muir," shouted Braxfield. "Stone throwing is implicit in the indictment, which we found relevant at the start of this case."

"My lord!" said Muir.

"Your objection has been repelled, Mr Muir!" Braxfield insisted. "Now attend to the business of the court."

Muir expected Lockie to be sentenced to some time in the local jail, the Tollbooth, or maybe, at worst, be whipped on the public platform on the roof of the two-storey extension at its gable end. But when Braxfield declared transportation to Botany Bay for fourteen years a shocked silence smothered the advocates' tables and the whole of the public gallery. The bench was keenly aware of the strength of the Edinburgh mob but in the past it had typically been manipulated by contending ruling factions. This mob was different, the times were different, ripples from the French revolution were lapping at the shores of Scotland. The judges knew that a terrible threat had to be answered with a terrifying punishment. Alexander Lockie had been convicted simply of "throwing one stone" during a riot but, nevertheless, his sentence had to be exemplary.

CHAPTER 2

The Association

"Here's freedom to him that wad read,
Here's freedom to him that wad write!
There's nane ever feared that the Truth should be heard,
But they whom the Truth wad indite."

Robert Burns, 'Here's a Health to Them That's Awa',
possibly December 1792.

The light was fading inside Muir's lodging rooms. He took a length
of ribbon from the roll on his table and tied together the documents
from last week's case. He thought he had given a good performance
before the bench in Alexander Lockie's case, but not good enough.
He stared down from his window in Carrubber's Close into the darkening High Street, part of the crowded mile of tenements, shops and
taverns, punctuated by churches and public buildings, running east
to west from the Palace of Holyrood House in the parkland at the
bottom of the rock, up its volcanic spine to the castle. He had worked
on young Lockie's plea for mercy – there was no appeal to a higher
court from the Scottish Court of Justiciary and the only avenue left
open was to apply for a royal pardon – and would lodge it in court in
the morning, before the summer recess.

Tonight, though, other business was pressing. It was, admit-
tedly, the same business that the mob had given voice to. In the early
months of the year, all across Scotland, many local reform societies
had grown, often in the same places liberty trees had been planted
in celebration of the revolution in France. These new ideas, though,
had been circulating long before that. Some of them had come from

America and the successful war of independence, concluded in a peace treaty with the humiliated Hanoverian monarch, George III, just nine years before. The European Enlightenment was strong in Scotland and the Calvinist tradition had deep roots reaching back into the politics of the Reformation, which held that resistance to oppressive government was morally justified. But now the overthrow of absolute rule in France had given people another living example of those ideas. In England, local reform organisations in London, Norwich, Manchester and Sheffield had been founded. An older group, the Society for Constitutional Information, had been revived after having closed its door ten years before, following a brief prospect of reform, unsuccessfully taken to the floor of the House of Commons by William Pitt, then a young, ambitious MP; now the prime minister.

Even some of the Whig aristocrats and their dwindling group of opposition members in parliament, seeing the growth of popular opinion, had formed themselves into a reform society in London called the Friends of the People. This cost three guineas to join and was intended only for those with breeding or connections. There was one organisation that was different, though, and it called itself the London Corresponding Society. It had been formed in January by an expatriate Scottish shoemaker, Thomas Hardy, who lived in Piccadilly, at the heart of the capital. Its difference was that it was open to all; it was not exclusive to wealth; it was not a secret society; it was not confined to a trade or occupation; it just required a commitment to amend the system of representation in the House of Commons and the payment of a penny a week, well within the reach of most artisans and shopkeepers. The first of its rules stated simply, "That the number of our members be unlimited." It was this idea that Muir was taking to a meeting in the Fortune Tavern that night in Edinburgh.

He tied back his shock of auburn hair, straightened the cravat at his neck, pulled on a coat and ran down the three storeys of narrow twisting stairs to the close. Carefully avoiding the piles of human dung in the alley – the practice of throwing sewage out of windows, with a warning cry of "gardez loo!", had been banned some twenty years before but the habit still remained and excrement sometimes lay in the wynds for days on end – Muir picked his way to the High Street and turned downhill towards the tavern in Canongate. The great tenements on either side contained people of all social classes. The drift of the wealthy to the New Town had recently become a flood but its streets and squares were still insufficient to accommodate all of the gentry and nobility who could afford the move to classical pediments and running water. In a few more years the well-to-do would have completed their move but, for now, rich and poor still lived together in the same buildings of the medieval town, in a strictly observed sequence. Most "respectable" floors were on the second and third storeys, above the worst of the smell but still a fairly easy climb.

The Fortune tavern was full. Muir stood on the threshold and wondered if it could be true. Had the growing radicalism of recent months, not to mention the hard work of discussion and persuasion that he and William Skirving and other friends had undertaken, really brought all of these people together? Skirving lived in Edinburgh and had a farm at Strathruddie in Fife. He was one of the new breed on the land, an "agricultural improver" and had just published a book entitled *The Husbandman's Assistant*. His desire for reform also had its practical side. He was a small landowner but had no vote. In the archaic feudal land system of Scotland, the Crown and the great families held land "in superiority", no matter who owned the title deeds. They controlled the political power that flowed from land and often parcelled out this power to followers who would vote for their interests. These "parchment barons", about half of the 2,662 voters in the counties, sent thirty of Scotland's forty-five MPs to Westminster. Reform was not just a question of political ideals to people such as Skirving, it was a desire to have a say in the laws governing them, and in particular they resented the disastrous laws concerning the import and export of corn, introduced the previous year, that benefited none but the great landowners. Small farmers were hurt and poor folk were hungry as grain was shipped abroad by wealthy merchants who were paid handsome government bounties for doing so.

Muir spotted Skirving talking to a group in the corner. He elbowed his way through a clutch of tradesmen and farmers. All of them had been involved, in one way or another, with local clubs. From the far end of the bar, Muir's good friends and fellow advocates, William Moffat and Robert Forsyth, waved to him above the heads of the crowd. Forsyth, unlike Muir, was from a well-connected, wealthy, landowning family, as were most advocates in Edinburgh, including Moffat. But the Forsyths and Moffats were not beholden to the Dundas dynasty. They were Whigs, reformers who wanted the excessive power of the executive curbed and a wider representation in parliament and in the corrupt and self-serving burghs and counties of Scotland. Forsyth had introduced Muir to many of the Whig families of the city.

Muir could also see some merchants and other professionals but mostly the tavern was filled with ordinary people, artisans, teachers, shopkeepers. He squeezed through the press of bodies towards Forsyth and Moffat. He was hoping they had used their connections and persuaded the senior Whig lawyers Henry Erskine and Archibald Fletcher to attend. Erskine and Fletcher were central to the cautious but extremely influential and widespread movement for burgh reform and they could hold their own against the conservative establishment who not only supported, but made a pretty living from the pensions and places handed out through the Dundas machine.

Moffat and Forsyth had disappointing news, Erskine felt that the time was not right, and feared that a new organisation would raise people's hopes only to be dashed by the government. He thought the present situation was too delicate and he wouldn't even have anything to do with the London Friends of the People, although both of his brothers were leading members there. Fletcher held much the same view and both of them were advising Whig friends and legal colleagues to stay away from the Edinburgh meeting. A burgh reformers' convention had taken place the day before and rejected the proposal for a general association. They were afraid that it might harm their chances of success even though they had achieved nothing on their own so far.

In the crowded upstairs room Skirving proposed they should elect a chairman and offered the name of a former army officer. Captain William Johnston accepted the nomination and was elected by acclaim. Another friend of Muir, the solicitor James Campbell, was elected as secretary. Skirving then explained that since spring, particularly in June, members of reform societies in Glasgow, Edinburgh, Dundee, Perth, and other smaller towns had begun a regular correspondence with a view to setting up an associated society, like the one in London. He and Thomas Muir had drawn up a plan of organisation. Unlike the London association run by the parliamentary Whigs, this was to be unlimited in membership, in the same way as the London Corresponding Society.

The proposed rules were read, debated amended and agreed. Johnston explained that the first task was to forge their national organisation and then begin to organise a petition to parliament seeking their aims, an equal distribution of seats and a more representative franchise. Later in the evening, after more expectant and excited discussion about how to reform the corrupt county and burgh constituencies that sent the country's forty-five representatives to the Commons (it was said at the time that Scottish MPs often changed their minds but never changed their votes), the meeting broke up in a mood of optimism. They left the Fortune tavern in the belief that the weight of public opinion was gathering in their favour; that the opinions of ordinary people would be carried in a solemn and historic petition to parliament; that those who presently ruled the land would see the reason and necessity for fundamental change for the benefit of all; and that in a very short time a part of the constitution guaranteed in the Bill of Rights that accompanied the Glorious Revolution of 1688 would be amended and modernised to give voice to the people engaged in building a new age of enlightenment, science and industry. As Muir walked home, back up to the High Street on that cool summer night, he would have realised that, in a small room, a handful of animated and idealistic young men had just thrown down a challenge to Old Corruption. And Old Corruption was at the heart of the mightiest empire in the modern world.

*

Two days later, early on a bright Saturday morning, Muir heaved his bag up on the roof of the Glasgow stage, where it was stowed with other luggage by the guard of the four-horse coach. On the previous day he had lodged a plea on behalf of the unfortunate Alexander Lockie, completed odds and ends of outstanding business and, in the evening, enjoyed an end-of-term dinner with his friends Moffat, Forsyth, and Campbell. Now he clambered into the carriage and smiled at the prospect of spending the next two months of the summer recess with his family and friends in Glasgow, and at his father's small estate in Huntershill, just north of the city.

After the last of the passengers was settled, the coachman shouted encouragement to the horses and flicked the long leather reins. They got in step and found a comfortable trot, west out of the city towards the toll road that connected it to Glasgow, its growing and prosperous rival, just 50 miles away, across the thin strip of rich farmland that separates the Forth from the Clyde, on the other coast of the country.

Muir looked out to his left across the new gardens built on land reclaimed from the ditched and drained Nor' Loch, a dank, swampy, cistern of diseased water, used for centuries as a moat, but mainly as a fetid pond in which rubbish and animal entrails from slaughterhouses were dumped, or in which witches and fornicators were punished. High above the green of the gardens, the grey castle slipped by on its precipice, while on Muir's right the grandeur of the New Town slid behind him. He opened that morning's copy of the *Caledonian Mercury* and, as his eyes fell on a notice inside, a small, excited but apprehensive shiver ran through him. The notice read, "Fortune Tavern, Edinburgh, July 26, 1792. At a meeting of many well-wishers to the cause of the people, assembled from different parts of the country, a unanimous wish was expressed, that a permanent society should be formed in order to adopt such measures as they shall judge most expedient for collecting the real unbiased voice of the people on the subject of their parliamentary representation, and for taking into consideration the means best adapted for restoring our constitution to its original purity. W Johnston, Chairman. JA Campbell, Secretary." In that way, the Associated Friends of the People announced themselves to the world.

He folded the newspaper and closed his eyes in anticipation of the seven hours or so of slow progress towards Glasgow, completed in stages where horses were changed or rested. The turnpike roads that had begun to cover the lowlands of Scotland during the past fifty years were another sign of growing prosperity, a prosperity, many argued, that would not have been achieved without the union with England and her empire at the beginning of the century. That, though, was only one part of the story. The administration of the roads, like much else in public life, was in the hands of self-seeking cliques, local gentry and merchants who could sponsor private acts of parliament establishing turnpike trusts, which allowed them to raise additional capital by charging heavy tolls. Only that week, new toll bars in Duns, Berwickshire, had been destroyed by a mob who shouted accusations of misappropriation of the tolls by the self-elected council. This form of protest was common.

But today the roads were quiet and the weather was mild. The coach made good progress through the Lothians into Lanarkshire and by early evening was passing bleachfields and print works in the eastern suburbs of Glasgow, where cotton and linen were printed and finished. Soon the expanding city came to meet them in the new tenements of Calton and Gallowgate and presently the coachman reined in his beasts opposite a statue of King William III, in front of the arcaded piazza beneath the Tontine Hotel in Trongate, near the heart of the city, Glasgow Cross. The horses steamed and snorted and stuck their noses eagerly into buckets of water brought by small boys as Muir jumped from the carriage to the "plainstanes", the pavement, and took his bag from the guard on the roof. He walked a little to the east and rounded the tall, slender, square tower of the Tollbooth steeple, with its arched crown covering twenty-eight bells that hourly reminded the population of the progress of each day. Hoisting his bag to his shoulder, he set off up the High Street to his father's small warehouse where his family still kept a town home in the rooms above the grocery shop, a little way short of the university. He had arranged to meet his father there and travel the extra three miles with him to Huntershill in the pony and trap.

CHAPTER 3

Huntershill

"My Name's Jamie Lapslie, pray mind what I say,
In the clachan each Sunday I preach and I pray.
Ye men of my parish I pray you take heed,
While I give you a sketch of my orthodox creed,
With my black coat and my cravat so white."

Anon, 'The Clerical Informer's Creed', published in
the *Edinburgh Gazetteer*, Tuesday, 10 September, 1793.

Muir came to a halt outside his father's shop at the point where the
hill of the High Street began to rise towards the Old College. The
sight of its two quadrangles and handsome clock tower, its high
chimneys and stepped gables, were familiar to him. Not only had he
been born and brought up next to the university, he had been enrolled
there as a ten-year-old and attended classes until he matriculated and
went on to study theology at the age of fifteen. It was only later that
he had turned to the law. Muir knocked on the closed door of the
shop and it was answered by Ann Fisher, a young servant employed
by the family.

Fisher lived at Huntershill and sometimes helped in the shop.
She had been taken in by Muir's mother two years before, after her
parents had fallen on hard times. The whole Fisher family had been
supported by Mrs Muir after Ann's father found that the money he
earned from weaving at his loom in the back of their home was less
than a living wage. His arthritic hands and back meant he could no
longer work as fast as he used to, while the price for a piece of finished
cloth had fallen so low that the family sank deeper into poverty. In

time, he found new employment tending a room full of water-driven looms in one of the new factories near the town. Ann remained with the Muirs as a scullery maid.

Muir thanked her and made his way upstairs. The rooms above the double shop front were kept as a fully functioning house, although the family spent as much time as they could in Huntershill. In summer they could travel back and forward but in winter they often had to stay in town for weeks on end. Muir gently opened the door to the drawing room and saw his father, now in his late sixties, reading by the fading light in the window overlooking the street.

James Muir was the younger son of a small landowner near Kirkintilloch. He had established himself as a grocer and, relatively late in life at the age of 39, married Margaret Smith in 1764. He had become successful enough to buy Huntershill House and its forty acres when young Thomas was 16. The house and estate stood about three miles north of the city on the old post road to Edinburgh.

Father and son embraced in genuine friendship. James and Margaret Muir doted on their son; they had made sure he had the best education they could afford and had expected Muir to become a minister of the kirk. The family was old-school Calvinist, hard working, frugal, with faith stronger than reason, and destined for salvation. They were immensely proud of their son the lawyer, called to the bar in Edinburgh, a feat not many sons of shopkeepers could achieve. James and Thomas agreed to hurry before the long summer evening lost more of its trailing light. The pony was already in the shafts of a trap in the courtyard.

The two men made their way downstairs, collected Ann Fisher, and left by the back door of the shop to the cobbled yard with its stable, privy, midden and washhouse. Father and son climbed on the seat and Ann jumped on the tailboard. James tugged the reins and the pony, from the memory of numberless journeys before, set off through the great entry in the tenement, a storey high and the width of a house, that led to the High Street. The pony turned up the hill without prompting, towards the medieval cathedral, now stripped of its idolatry and gradually adapted for modest worship during the three hundred and more years since the upheaval of the Reformation. The travellers turned left along the ridge of the hill overlooking the city, bringing into view the reflected light from the waters of the River Clyde at the bottom of the valley. At the end of Rottenrow the trap reached the open road heading north for Huntershill.

Muir told his father about the Edinburgh meeting and of the efforts he and William Skirving had made in organising the association. James Muir was sympathetic to his son's vision of a wider franchise. He belonged to the Auld Light fundamentalists in the kirk and, while not having fully embraced the age of reason, he was a democrat in kirk politics. His faction, also called the Popular Party, stood for the rights of congregations to elect their ministers, a right taken away by the infant parliament of the union eighty years before and fought over ever since. Landowners now had power to appoint ministers. This kept the church at the centre of Scottish politics. The patron in a third of the parishes was the Crown, in effect the powerful Henry Dundas. In many of the others it was the great noble families but the Dundas hand was again often the controlling influence in the background. Muir's father had early on schooled him in theological democracy with the words, "What difference does a piece of land make between man and man in the affairs of Christ's kingdom?" James Muir was aware that the ordinary folk of Scotland were denied even the limited franchise many had in England. He had land but no vote in the county; a thriving business but no vote in the town; and he paid taxes in both.

James Muir's feudal "superior", the Earl of Selkirk, had exercised his ancient feudal powers and had long ago appointed a "parchment baron" to exercise the vote in this part of his vast estates. Glasgow, too, was closed to democratic control. All of the old royal burghs were run by the urban gentry, the magistrates, merchants from the chartered companies, and some selected representatives from the incorporated trades. There were no elections to the councils, which appointed their own successors. These sixty-six burghs that once had seats in the Scottish parliament now shared a total of fifteen MPs in London. They were grouped in districts of four or five, so that Glasgow, Renfrew, Rutherglen and Dumbarton had one member chosen by the thirty-two town councillors. Edinburgh was the only town with its own representative, chosen by thirty-three people. The fifteen burgh MPs were selected by ninety-eight individuals in all, each one self-appointed. James Muir, unsurprisingly, was a keen member of the burgh reform movement. Ann Fisher listened to the conversation from the back of the trap with interest.

As the last of the light was wrapped in the darkness creeping towards the western horizon, the pony turned its trap away from the old Edinburgh road and into Huntershill driveway. The windows of the stone house were already bright with welcoming candles. Built with two storeys, it had a central door with a Greek pediment, a pair of windows on each side and a symmetrical row of five windows on the upper storey. There were rooms for servants in the attic, with skylights in the roof between the two tall chimneys at each gable. Muir could still pick out the elms and beeches around his home but would have to wait until morning to see once again the panoramic view to the Clyde in the south and the first range of Highland mountains to the north.

The mahogany door, with its large etched glass panel, swung open as the trap crunched to a semicircular finish on the gravel in front of the house. Muir's mother, Margaret, and his young sister Janet came down the steps with welcoming embraces. His mother was overjoyed and filled with pride at the sight of her boy. She looked into his blue eyes, her gaze briefly darting to his long face with the high forehead, round chin and aquiline nose, and she held him tightly to her, as mothers do.

She had paced around the house and knitted and darned more than usual, until this moment. Like her husband, she had nurtured this boy, made sure he was educated in a private school, even though every parish in Scotland had its local school. There he had learned not just the elementary skills but also the rudiments of Latin. She had also employed a private tutor from when Muir was five until he went to the gowned school at the Old College at the age of ten. He meant everything to her.

The table was set for supper in the dining room. James and Margaret, young Janet, and the weary Muir sat down to eat. It was already late and the family, as usual and as expected, would be up early on the sabbath for kirk. Muir finished his food, said his good-nights, climbed the stairs to the first floor and opened the door to the bedroom he had known since adolescence. He slowly pulled off layers of clothes that he dropped on a chair one by one, before dropping into the well-remembered bed in the centre of the room.

*

On Sunday the family returned from Cadder parish kirk in time for lunch. Muir had been made welcome there, too. He had been an elder in the church until the previous year and had represented the parishioners in a long legal battle over the appointment of a new minister, which went all the way to the Court of Session, the highest court in the land, in Edinburgh. A large coal owner, James Dunlop of Garnkirk, led a group of other substantial landowners in attempting to appoint a young man who was chaplain to an important family in the area. But the congregation wanted the vacant pulpit filled by the popular Mr Provan, who had worked in the parish and preached there from time to time over the years. James Dunlop began creating parchment barons on his estate to outvote those freeholders who supported Provan. Muir won the case for the parish in the teeth of opposition from the conservative establishment.

As the pony and trap approached Huntershill on its way home from kirk, a figure appeared over the horizon on the post road, bobbing towards them on an old grey mare. Margaret Muir muffled a groan. "Oh," she breathed, as her sharp eyes picked out the familiar tall black hat on the man on horseback with the dog collar at his throat and the long, ankle-length, black clerical coat flapping behind.

The Rev James Lapslie was minister in the neighbouring parish of Campsie. He regarded himself as an old friend of the Muirs and often invited himself to dinner, sometimes staying overnight at Huntershill, and occasionally taking advantage of their hospitality for a week or more. James and Margaret Muir had befriended and supported him in his early days at the Campsie manse, some fifteen or sixteen years before when church funds were short, but he had become more eccentric as the years passed. He was now a bombastic and opinionated man who defended every established institution, and was servile to his betters, while being haughty and patronising to those beneath him. James still loved to pick an argument with him.

Lapslie was an active member of the ruling faction in kirk politics, the Moderate party, and often goaded James Muir for his too literal interpretation of the bible. The Moderates, in fact, embraced the ideas of the Enlightenment and valued reason over blind faith, allowing that scientific discovery and philosophic inquiry might simply reveal the wonders of God's creation more clearly. But the Moderates also accepted, enthusiastically, the rule of law and, although they kept up an annual token fight against church patronage, argued that as long as the act of parliament was there it had to be obeyed. In practical terms, they were as deep in the pensions and places machine of Henry Dundas as the judges, nobles and politicians of the country. For Lapslie, patronage was at the centre of his world, some progressive ideas being an annoying accessory to the business of individual advancement.

Lapslie waved and the family waved back. The minister slid from the saddle of his mare at the entrance to the driveway. He brushed away the long dark hair, tinged with white, from his full face, "Why Mrs Muir, you're looking as radiant as the day you married James. I trust your cooking is still as refined! And Janet, a perfect flower, just waiting for a young laird to pick. And whit hae we here?"

Muir shuddered inside. Janet threw him a secret glance of sympathy.

"Why, it's the young radical, the man who would be Lord Protector of a French republican commonwealth. Ha! Ye'll grow out of it

Thomas, when you start to enjoy the benefits of this the most glorious constitution the world has yet witnessed."

"Oh, aye, Mr Lapslie, I've no doubt you have the best of it," said Muir, drawing the sting and declaring an early truce. Muir knew he had to be ready for an argument with Lapslie. He had seen his entire display of histrionics at the general assembly of the kirk in Edinburgh, as the tall, bony, muscular minister tore open his waist-coat for emphasis, bellowed, sobbed, and wept, and finally sat down at the end of his harangue, trembling to his finger ends. The man was known for his weeping during his hellfire and brimstone sermons. One parishioner had remarked, "Mr. Lapslie is an awful man for greetin'. Man, he would greet reading an Almanac."

They took the horses to the back of the house to be fed and watered, before going to the dining room through Muir's respectably stocked library.

"Ha! The secret chamber of Jacobin tracts, no doubt," teased Lapslie.

"That's true only if you see a Jacobin in Plato, or in Rousseau," replied Muir, a little testily, "or, indeed in Shakespeare or Locke or Hume."

James and Margaret smoothed over the emerging dispute and Janet went into the kitchen to tell Ann and the cook that there was one more for Sunday lunch, and to warn them to keep the kettle hot. Lapslie was noted for the vast quantities of tea he would consume at a single sitting. As they settled down to their meal, Lapslie announced that he was about to be married. "Miss Lizbeth Stirling of Glorat has accepted my suit and we are to be wed in September," he announced with a broad smile.

James and Margaret were first to congratulate him. "I thought it would never happen," said Margaret, thinking to herself that the minister was already forty-two years of age. Janet and Muir exchanged knowing glances. Both of them knew of Lapslie's love of patronage. Now he had reached his goal by marrying into one of the richest families in the area. Lizbeth Stirling was the daughter of Sir

John Stirling, present head of a family that had lived on the Glorat estate for more than 150 years.

Lapslie asked if they had read of his other success in the Glasgow presbytery. He explained that he had given notice that he meant to move a loyal address to his majesty for his "late gracious proclamation" against seditious meetings and writings. "I told them I was giving them a month's notice so that none of them could say they were taken by surprise," he said with glee. "I said I hoped there would be a full attendance and that they would be unanimous in expressing their thanks to his majesty, and their attachment to the constitution as established at the Glorious Revolution. Then, at the July meeting, why, they all turned up and voted to a man for my address." Lapslie had directed his words towards Muir.

"Yes, very loyal I'm sure, Mr Lapslie," said Muir. "But did you take the same question to the parishioners and did you allow them a full discussion of all the opposing points of view? You know as well as I do that the Dundases in London and Edinburgh are encouraging such resolutions from 'respectable' people. They're doing it to scare folks into opposing reform."

"*Folks*, as you call them," replied Lapslie with a sneer, "don't need to be scared into it, Thomas. Nobody in decent, polite society thinks this is the time for reform; not when dangerous ideas about equality are being spread far and wide by Tom Paine and others. They'd do away with the established kirk if they could, like the damned Americans! They might have no king and no kirk but they still turned to Popish France for money and guns to fight their war against established government."

"Well, you certainly have turned your coat inside out, Mr Lapslie," Muir responded. "It wasn't so long ago, I remember, when you were preaching reform to me even before I came of age. That was when Mr Pitt was preaching the same urgent need for reform when he was a new member of parliament. Four years later he became prime minister and suddenly he saw the error of his ways. I assume you had the same blinding epiphany?"

"No, Thomas. Our constitution can't be faulted. Don't forget that such public opinion as counts is represented in parliament. Wealth is in land and that's where the main say should come from. Competent men govern and we, by acquiescing, give our consent. Where's the need for crude and levelling democracy? It can only lead to tumult."

"And *polite society*, as you call it," responded Muir, "will not just vote self-serving addresses of thanks to Dundas and the king but are also prepared to sit back and allow tumult to keep their privilege intact. Who among them came to the defence of poor Dr Priestley last year?"

"Bah! Yon Unitarian rascal!" barked Lapslie. "He doesn't even believe in the father, son and holy ghost. And he was at a dinner in support of Frenchies."

"Yes, but there's nothing unlawful in either of those charges," said Muir, straining to keep his annoyance in check. "Dr Priestley and others held a dinner in Birmingham to celebrate the second anniversary of the fall of the Bastille, an event which brought the French into the same century as us. It was a group of prominent Tory magistrates and clergy that organised a mob and sent them on a three-day rampage to selected targets, targets chosen by those *polite* and *respectable* people responsible for ensuring law and order. Not only did the so-called Church and King mob wreck the tavern where the dinner was held, but they sacked two Unitarian churches and a Baptist meeting house, burned and looted a score of houses and many shops of supposed Dissenters or radical sympathisers, then went on to destroy Dr Priestley's home and laboratory, so that now he's had to flee to London. But the scandal is this: the magistrates did nothing about it. Nothing! A full day after the riots finished, the military managed to come to town. And it's all because Dr Priestley publicly opposed a supporter of the government, Edmund Burke, in his views about the revolution in France and the future of liberty. That's tumult for you," concluded Muir, embarrassed as he realised he may have raised his voice too much to a guest at their table.

"And what about the disgraceful behaviour of the Edinburgh

canaille on the king's birthday?" continued Lapslie, undeterred. "Is that the kind of respect that Jacobins and Democraticals would have us suffer if the mob controlled parliament?"

"With respect Mr Lapslie," interrupted James Muir, "did not Thomas in his defence of the young coachman make the very point that riot is no way to achieve progress?"

"Aye, you can speak every fine word in your vocabulary but they'll not stop the mob in their criminal, levelling, envy of respectable folk," replied Lapslie, who was working himself into a lather. "Even in my parish licentiousness has begun to prevail, owing to high wages in new factories, and due respect for rank is almost totally forgot!"

"Do you not think, Mr Lapslie," said Janet, "that the actions of government ministers might have caused anger in ordinary people?"

"And how do you make that out, Janet?" said Lapslie with a patronising smile.

"Well, for a start," she began, "the petitions for burgh reform that were subscribed to all over Scotland were ignored by the House of Commons in the spring. Mr Sheridan introduced them and Mr Dundas ridiculed them and called on the vast majority of his and Mr Pitt's supporters to vote against them. Maybe that's why his effigy was burnt."

"Janet has a good point," said James. "People now expect a political change and they know that Dundas controls the patronage and the politics in this country. A reform would lose him his exalted position."

Margaret, who had been listening in silence until now, said quietly, "Many people in this country have joined in the activity against the slave trade, Mr Lapslie. We, as you know only too well through the kirk, have petitioned these past five years against that accursed traffic of humanity. But at the same time as Mr Dundas spoke out against burgh reform in the commons, he also opposed Mr Wilberforce's motion on abolition and caused the proposal to fail. It's no wonder he is universally reviled by all those who are not tied to him by strings of obligation."

"I know what you're getting at, Margaret," answered Lapslie. "I opposed the involvement of the Glasgow presbytery in this year's petitioning campaign because it's political, and the kirk should not become involved for fear of future interference in its affairs by the state. I feel that it is dangerous to foment the spirit of dissatisfaction which is too prevalent in the present day. The church should check and moderate the present national frenzy and I hope the legislature will take measures consistent with the interests of the colonies and the safety of private property."

"But people are not private property, Mr Lapslie," countered Margaret Muir. "The General Assembly voted in favour of the petition, and rightly so. Poor Mr Vassa, the emancipated slave, describes the treatment of slaves by Europeans as un-Christian, and so it is. His book clearly shows the heartless cruelty towards African slaves in the Caribbean and America, and in the unimaginably harsh journey there."

Gustavus Vassa, who had been captured at the age of eleven and sold into slavery, was a national figure in the anti-slave-trade campaign. He had been in Glasgow in April that year and sold signed copies of his book, *The Interesting Narrative*, from an inn in Trongate. He travelled all over Scotland that summer and his presence was noted in many newspaper articles. Vassa was also a member of the London Corresponding Society and a personal friend of Hardy, to whom he wrote from Edinburgh in May that he had, "sold books at Glasgow & Paisley, and came here on the 10th ult. I hope next month to go to Dunde (sic), Perth & Aberdeen... My best Respect to my fellow members of your society. I hope they do yet increase. I do not hear in this place that there is any such societys (sic)." That was soon to change.

Thankfully for the Muirs, Lapslie decided to leave just before dusk. While James and Thomas made their way to fetch the preacher's mare, Lapslie went to the scullery to take his leave of young Ann Fisher. As minister and mare clopped slowly out of the drive into the gloaming of the post road, Muir remarked that it was unusual for Lapslie to take an interest in Ann. James guessed that he might have some parochial attachment to the Fisher family. Muir shrugged, extinguished the lantern in the yard and closed the door behind them.

CHAPTER 4

Equal representation

"The peasant seems to be equally knowing in politics with the peer, and supports his arguments with as much force and keenness... Societies are everywhere formed and clubs instituted, for the sole purpose of political debate."

Morning Chronicle, Saturday, September 29, 1792.

Muir spent most of the summer and autumn at the Glasgow house. When he arrived in July there had been little organisation but great interest in France and liberty. The second part of Tom Paine's pamphlet, *Rights of Man*, had been published and became a sensation. It was to be found in every workman's cottage. Paine had a feel for the historic moment. "Never did so great an opportunity offer itself to England, and to all Europe as is produced by the two Revolutions of America and France," he wrote. "By the former, freedom has a national champion in the Western world; and by the latter, in Europe. When another nation shall join France, despotism and bad government will scarcely dare to appear. To use a trite expression, the iron is becoming hot all over Europe." Recognising the same moment, in May Henry Dundas had introduced a royal proclamation in parliament that banned the book, but without naming it, for being "wicked and seditious". It was not only forbidden to print it or sell it, but it was everyone's duty to report those who did. Paine had had to flee to France to escape prosecution.

One September afternoon Muir was reading in the large coffee house in the piazza at Trongate. He flicked the pages of *The Bee*, a literary and scientific magazine edited by James Anderson, an

Edinburgh economist and agriculturalist, and stopped at the editorial. "I know," wrote Anderson, "that in a small town in the north of Scotland before the proclamation, there was just one copy of Paine's pamphlet; and the bookseller of the place declared three weeks ago that he had since then sold seven hundred and fifty copies of it. And a bookseller in Edinburgh told me he had before the proclamation a good many copies of it that lay so long on his hand that he would gladly have sold them all at two shillings a copy. He has since then sold the whole of these and many more at three shillings and sixpence each."

Muir admired Paine but felt that the republican programme he advocated was not right for the campaign in Scotland. A much wider movement for reform of the House of Commons could, he felt, have a greater chance of success than a call for the abolition of monarchy and aristocracy. He did not object in principle to republicanism but calculated that a representative parliament could curb the power of the executive and achieve much the same result.

In taverns and coffee houses the discussion had been about little else. Some were already beginning to fear the government's over-reaction while others were swayed by the arguments in a book by a former radical MP turned government supporter, who warned that the revolution in France would end in anarchy and bloodshed. Edmund Burke had presented exaggerated evidence for his predictions but his *Reflections on the Revolution in France* had been in circulation for two years and was widely read by those who could afford it. It sowed doubts.

Muir looked up from his magazine to see an old acquaintance, the grammar school teacher Daniel McArthur, who had been a supporter of reform but was having second thoughts. "Do you not think this is a wrong time to insist on a reform in parliament," said the teacher, "seeing what has happened in France?"

News of the September massacres of royalist prisoners in Paris jails had been in all of the newspapers. This had been described in some as a panic reaction by a populace in fear of certain death on the bayonets of invading armies. These were no hysterical imaginings. A proclamation by the Duke of Brunswick, commander of the Prussian army, warned all Parisians to expect their city to be razed and their lives forfeited for their insult to royalty, and this probably gave an excuse to the cruel, the bloodthirsty, the psychopaths and the fearful to eliminate those whom they saw as a fifth column at their backs.

"There is no comparison between this country and France," Muir replied. "And you surely cannot lay the actions of a small group at the feet of a whole nation. How many atrocities have been carried out in these islands or overseas by our people, or our armies at the command of our governors? In France they sought a revolution and brought it about. We need no such convulsion, our monarchy was limited while theirs was absolute; the number of our aristocracy did not equal the thousandth part of theirs; we had trial by jury while they had none; our persons were protected by the laws, while their lives were at the mercy of every titled individual. Our constitution is a contract and in 1688 we removed James II because he failed in his part. The present king recognises a limited monarchy but the House of Commons has been so corrupted that it no longer represents the people. That is what we wish to reform, and that only."

"But, again, surely this is not the right time for such a reform," countered McArthur.

"So when is the right time, Daniel?" asked Muir. "The enemies of reform say it is not right because of revolution in France. But we are at peace with France. It was not right a decade ago because we were at war with America. We have been at peace with the republic there for nine years. They will never find a right time. This is surely it; we not only have the blessings of peace and prosperity but people want it." Muir explained that a new reform association was soon to meet in Glasgow and that Daniel would be welcome to attend. McArthur said he would consider it and took his leave.

Muir looked out of the large round window and through the colonnade to the bookshop of Brash and Reid on the other side of the street, where the first copy of a new newspaper, the *Edinburgh*

Gazetteer, was eagerly expected. He rose and crossed the street. William Reid welcomed him into his shop waving a copy of the broadsheet.

"Look, it's arrived, Thomas," he said. "Another voice for reform."

"The proclamation against wicked and seditious writings seems to be having the opposite effect," said Muir with a smile.

Reid agreed. In the space of ten years the number of Scottish newspapers for sale in his shop had grown from eight to more than thirty. Pamphlets and broadsides were being published daily. "People are reading as never before," he said.

Muir told Reid how he had returned to Edinburgh for discussions about the *Gazetteer* with its owner William Johnston, chairman of the Friends of the People, and how the poet Robert Burns had written to Johnston supporting the paper. The letter from Burns had stated, "I beg leave to insert my name as a subscriber; and if you have already published any papers, please send them to me from the beginning. Go on sir! Lay bare, with undaunted heart and steady hand, that horrid mass of corruption called politics and state-craft."

Reid gave a whistle of appreciation. He asked Muir what he thought, as a lawyer, about continuing to sell Paine's *Rights of Man*. He had had it on his shelves since it was published in February, and although the proclamation was announced in May, nothing much had been done to enforce it, at least not in Scotland although book-sellers in England had been mightily harassed. It had now become the most popular book in the shop.

Muir recommended caution. There were many people who, for a place or a pension, or even for a few government pounds, would tell anything to the authorities. Muir added that he would not be recommending it, much as he admired Paine and what he had to say, in case it could be used as a stick to flay the infant reform movement and trap it in legal difficulties.

Muir walked home to his father's store in High Street and found his Uncle Alexander in the back shop. Ann Fisher was serving him tea. She looked up from the table and said, "Your uncle asked me to look in your room for a copy of *Rights of Man*, Mr Thomas."

Alexander corrected her. "That's not quite so, Ann," he said. "I asked you if you knew if Thomas had any copies of the book here, and you ran off to look without answering."

"I'm sorry, uncle, but I only have one copy of my own, which you can borrow with pleasure," said Muir.

"I'll go to the bookshop in the Trongate for you, Mr Muir," volunteered Ann. "Brash and Reid have lots of copies on their shelves."

Alexander thanked her, gave her the price of the book, and Ann skipped out of the shop and headed down the hill to the busy Trongate.

Ann's behaviour had been unsettling Muir all summer. She used every possible opportunity to tidy his rooms, both here and at Huntershill, and was constantly rearranging his papers and books, and volunteering to take his manuscripts to the local printer. She was always around when he had visitors and would attend to their every need, especially if it meant running to Brash and Reid's for copies of newspapers or pamphlets. Muir's sister, Janet, had taken to teasing him, saying that Ann was flirting with him, that she was intent on "marrying up", and that her coquettish and attentive behaviour was all directed to that end.

*

Since that evening in July when the Society of the Friends of the People was established in the Fortune Tavern in Edinburgh, the growth of the reform movement in Scotland had been astonishing. As well as widespread resentment at the government's arrogant dismissal of petitions requesting reform of burgh councils and abolition of the slave trade, the desire to extend a democracy that people were well used to in the kirk was stoked by the stunning success of the revolution in France. The despotism of centuries was ended in August when Louis XVI was handed a historic opportunity to become a constitutional monarch, a chance that he failed to understand. The

French people rallied to the flag when Prussian and Austrian armies invaded their country with threats of fire and sword. The invaders were turned back, the king tried to escape to the enemy lines, and a republic was declared. Just as Americans had earlier shown it was possible to govern without the apparatus of pomp and privilege, so the French had taken the torch of liberty and now offered it to the rest of Europe.

Muir spoke at meetings in all parts of the Lowlands and he was particularly impressed by the people of Paisley, when he, with Colonel William Dalrymple, president of the Glasgow association, addressed the several societies there in the late summer. Paisley, like other manufacturing towns such as Airdrie, Renfrew, and Dumbarton, was a centre of radical strength. There was a culture of popular enlightenment across the west and central Lowlands and in most sizeable towns reading societies were common. People clubbed together to buy books and newspapers and read them aloud or borrowed them to read in their own homes. Paisley, though, was particularly important. It was a large, prosperous burgh, made rich by cotton and linen weaving. Its trademark was checked cloth but now that had been overtaken by thread spinning in 137 mills. Its silk cloth, Paisley pattern, had become famous all over the world. Immigrants flooded into the town, some from England, more from Ireland, great numbers from Ayrshire, and many more from the Highlands, where people were being displaced by sheep at an alarming rate. Paisley was now the third largest town in Scotland, with about 12,000 people weaving silk in the factories and another 11,000 tending looms in its suburbs.

After one evening meeting there, Muir and Dalrymple called at Sinclair's Inn while waiting for the coach to Glasgow, and came across a group in a back room listening to one of their number read from a book. "I must dare to be plain on this part of the subject, that the corruption of the state ought not to be winked at: every defect in the manoeuvres of government should be as public as the noon-day sun," declaimed the reader. A chorus of voices cheered and boots thudded the floorboards.

Dalrymple turned to their companion, William Orr, a local manufacturer. "What's going on in there?"

"Oh, that's the regular Thursday night meeting of the Encyclopaedia
Club," explained Orr. "It's called that because its small collection of
books, all bought by subscriptions from members, includes a set of
Encyclopaedia Britannica. Some say this club has been meeting here
for at least twenty years now."

"Impressive," said Dalrymple in admiration.

*

Muir tugged at the girth strap of his saddle to secure it and pulled
up the collar of his greatcoat. He stood on a mounting block by the
back door of Huntershill and climbed on his horse. It was just four
miles to Kirkintilloch and he'd be there in half an hour to meet with
a local group, mostly weavers, who wanted to join the campaign for
equal representation. He coaxed the horse out of the yard into the
cold wind and reined its head round towards the Campsie Fells in the
distance. The Saturday afternoon light was fading and Muir pulled
down the brim of his hat to shield his eyes from the November blast.
The road passed through fields sharp with the stubble of summer's
harvest of barley and oats, and crossed over the new canal on one of
its four bridges in the parish of Cadder. The Forth and Clyde canal
had been opened just two years before and the demands of the great
cities of Edinburgh and Glasgow filled its barges with grain and cloth
and coal.

Presently the smoke from coal fires in Kirkintilloch's hearths
reached Muir and he pulled round his horse's head to direct it off
the turnpike. He rode along a lane towards the small town of about
fifteen hundred people, while going over in his mind what he would
say at the meeting. He would start with the Fortune Tavern meeting
in July and explain how, since then, reform societies bearing a variety
of names had been established in all parts of Scotland. Muir had
spoken individually to some of the people in Kirkintilloch before
tonight. He had already helped new societies into life in the Campsies,

at Milton and Lennoxtown, in spite of some hostile opposition from James Lapslie. That problem wouldn't arise here. The Kirkintilloch minister, the Rev William Dunn, was a reformer and sympathetic to the campaign.

They would want to know about the founding meeting for the Glasgow association, held the month before in the Star Inn in Ingram Street, where Dalrymple was elected president and Muir became vice-president. The meeting contained artisans and labourers as well as better-off Glaswegians. Major Thomas Maitland MP, brother of the reforming Earl of Lauderdale, had joined, as had David Dale the manufacturer and abolitionist campaigner. In Edinburgh, Col Norman Macleod, the MP for Inverness, had become a member, as had Lord Daer, a radical Whig aristocrat who had been in the Burgh Reform Movement and had been present at the main events in France since 1789. Many saw Lord Daer, or Citizen Douglas as he preferred to be called, as the potential leader of a reformed Scotland. Daer was the link between the grandees of the London Friends of the People and the London Corresponding Society, of which he was also a member.

Many popular societies were now growing. Perth was one of the strongest centres for reform with 1,200 members in October, including a "vast number" of weavers and other operatives. Muir had been elected, on his return to Edinburgh in September, as chairman of the new organising committee, the General Association of the Friends of the People, with his friend William Skirving as secretary. In the west, Paisley and Kilmarnock had followed Glasgow in setting up new societies and this quickly spread throughout Lanarkshire, Renfrewshire, and Dunbartonshire, and down the coast to Ayrshire, Dumfries and Galloway. The Glasgow society had held its third public meeting a month ago, and four hundred people had turned up and crushed into the hall.

Muir was jolted from his thoughts when he became suddenly aware he had reached the centre of Kirkintilloch. Nosing his horse round a tight corner into a row of weavers' cottages he stopped and dismounted outside Henry Freeland's.

"Come into the warm, Thomas," said Freeland as he threw open the door of the cottage to reveal about thirty men, young and old, inside. Freeland was president of the meeting, and he introduced Muir to their vice-president, Robert Weddell, and James Baird, the secretary. He was greeted by the others in the room and set to work repeating all he had been rehearsing on his journey.

He explained how the campaign was about shortening the duration of parliament, which at present was elected only once in every seven years, and obtaining a more equal representation in the House of Commons. He went on to describe the unequal representation in rotten boroughs and the counties, the unjustified influence of aristocratic patronage in parliament, at the last general election in 1790 only fifty-seven seats out of 558 in the House of Commons had been contested, and noted that in France the people were now better represented than in Britain. Republicanism was probably the ideal but not essential if the executive was controlled by true representatives of the whole people. The British constitution comprised the Crown, Lords and Commons and the campaign was to affect only the Commons. The purpose of the societies was to gather signatures on a petition to be presented to parliament. The young Northumberland MP, Charles Grey, had given notice in April that he would present a motion for parliamentary reform next May, basing his proposals on a petition drawn up by the Friends of the People in London, which would highlight the extent of electoral patronage and influence, the small number of voters in many constituencies, and the lack of representation for newer commercial and industrial towns. It had been proposed that delegates from all of the Scottish societies should meet together in a convention in Edinburgh next month, December, to coordinate the campaign throughout the country.

Muir also reminded the meeting of the king's birthday riot in Edinburgh, and the fact that in many towns and villages throughout the country liberty trees had been planted in celebration of French achievements, but often accompanied by disorder and burning of effigies, sometimes of local magistrates but more often of Henry

Dundas. Newspapers had reported that in June, Aberdeen, Perth, Dundee and almost every village in the north of Scotland burned Dundas in effigy. He reminded them of the riots at Peebles and Lanark and recommended "order and regularity", stressing that disorder could ruin their common cause. "There is no other mode of procuring redress but by applying to parliament," he concluded, before resuming his chair next to Henry Freeland.

The meeting declared itself a reform society and formally elected its officers. Requests were made for reading materials and petitions to be sent from Glasgow or Edinburgh, and the men dispersed in optimistic mood. A number of them made their way to the local tavern run by William Wallace, who had been in the meeting. He invited the small group into a private room. Muir followed Wallace, along with Freeland, Baird, Weddell, William Muir, a former servant of Muir's father, and Robert Boyd. When they were settled with ale on the table before them Boyd asked Muir's opinion of Paine's *Rights of Man*.

"I think it is a book quite foreign to our purpose," said Muir, explaining that their present campaign was to gather together as many of those who were reform minded as possible, not just the committed republicans. He went even further and said that Paine's book "had a tendency to mislead weak minds".

"I haven't seen it," said Freeland, "but I am curious to see a book that is so much spoken of. Isn't the king's proclamation directed against it?"

Muir replied that it was, although the book wasn't mentioned by name.

"Well, I'd like to read it," said Freeland, "even if we think it's not right for our campaign."

"I have a copy, over there in the pocket of my greatcoat, if you'd like to borrow it, Henry," offered Muir, and Freeland took it from the coat on the back of a chair.

As the innkeeper fetched more drinks, they talked about other books to read, such as Benjamin Flower's book on the French constitution, *Henry's History of England*, James Thomson Callender's

The Political Progress of Britain, which had appeared in serial form in *The Bee*. They all liked the English newspaper, *The Patriot*, which was printed in Sheffield and consumed in great numbers in Scotland. And they discussed the Paisley Declaration, based on the French National Assembly's 1789 *Declaration of the Rights of Man and of Citizens*. This had been included in Paine's *Rights of Man* but the Paisley societies had decided to print cheap copies locally.

Wallace brought more ale and the discussion moved to representation. Two opinions flew round the table, some saying that the vote should be restricted to landed property, but small enough and broad enough for the average cottager or householder to qualify, and others were firmly for a universal franchise. Muir gave no opinion on the franchise, only that it should be more equal, which was the objective that would be stated on the petition to be introduced in parliament by Grey.

The innkeeper's generosity ran to yet another bumper of foaming ale and the talk turned to the power of the executive. Alcohol played its usual part in heightening emotions and loosening tongues and soon all the company imagined themselves elected to the House of Commons on a truly popular vote.

"You'd be MP for Cadder, Thomas," said old William Muir.

"And you, William, would coast home with a grand majority in Kirkintilloch for your well-know wisdom and good judgment!" replied Muir.

"What about Campsie?" asked Freeland. "Lapslie would want to stand. He'd get the local bigwigs to back him. And he has a fierce tongue in his head. When they're singing the first hymn on a Sunday morning he walks over to the cottages opposite the church to harangue those who haven't attended!" They all laughed at the thought of it.

"No, no," said Baird. "The folk of Campsie are sensible enough. They'd elect an honest young man from the bleach fields, one of their own who knows what they need and want."

"That's the key, James," said Muir. "None but honest men would be members of parliament. They would keep the constitution clean; they would give new councillors to the king, who would have to govern with justice."

*

The night was crisp and clear and a bright moon lit Muir's way home to Huntershill. He thought of his sister Janet's teasing about Ann, the servant, and his mind, fuzzy with drink, flipped to memories of Basil Douglas, Lord Daer. It was a strange association but the two worries were somehow intertwined. Muir thought about his friend Daer, "Citizen Douglas", who was already ill. He coughed constantly and many people thought he had consumption. Muir and Douglas were almost the same age, he 27 and Daer 29, and they had met when they were introduced by Anna Barbauld, the poet and educationalist. Barbauld was also a reformer and had been toasted as one of the "lady defenders of the French revolution". She was on a visit from London to Scotland when she introduced the two young men. Daer had been educated at her school in Palgrave, Suffolk, before studying at Edinburgh University under the moral philosopher Dugald Stewart. Daer was, if not unique, then rare among the Scottish aristocracy. A friend of Robert Burns, whom he had met in Dugald Stewart's home in Ayrshire six years before, the poet described him in the friendliest fashion, "Nae honest, worthy man need care, To meet with noble, youthfu' Daer, For he meets but a brother."

Muir urged his horse on down the moonlit road as he remembered the connection between his thoughts, it was Anna Barbauld, whom Muir had first met on a visit to London while in his early twenties. In her company was a young, attractive, intelligent, cultured, well-informed young woman with whom Muir immediately fell in love. She fell as quickly and they spent the summer writing notes, composing poems, making assignations, and trying to avoid chaperones, mostly unsuccessfully. Then she disappeared. One final note informed him that her parents had found out about their love. She was an aristocrat. He was a commoner. It could not be contemplated. Muir was wounded and broken-hearted. He had not been able to look at another woman since that day. His family, his male friends, his law and his politics inhabited his whole world. The most flirtatious servant in the whole city of Glasgow could never penetrate that part of his emotions reserved for an impossible dream.

CHAPTER 5

Wimbledon

"After [Pitt] had once forsworn the errors of his way and said to corruption 'thou art my brother' and called power, or rather place, his god, the sight of a reformer became a spectre to his eyes – he detested it as the wicked do the light."

Edinburgh Review, April, 1810.

Secretary of State Henry Dundas pushed the letter across his desk to his assistant, Evan Nepean. "Read this, copy it, and send it to the Lord Advocate in Scotland," he said.

Nepean picked up the letter. It came from Edinburgh and had been posted a week previously, on 31August, 1792. "Societies are forming in this city and in other parts of the country whose sacred principles strike at the very vitals of the constitution," the writer explained, "and I cannot as a friend to my country but inform you of their proceedings and intentions."

An informer, thought Nepean. Part of his daily routine was to deal with those wishing to find favour or fortune as agents of the government. Nepean had been running spies and informers for ten years, ever since his spectacular promotion at the age of 29 from purser on HMS Foudroyant to permanent under-secretary of state at the Home Office.

This correspondent wrote that he had been visited by a William Johnston at his home and invited to attend a meeting in Mather's Tavern. "Mr Johnston," he explained, "was an officer in the 70th regiment of foot. He is a most seditious man." He went on, "They propose to accomplish their hellish designs by pretending at first moderation in their demands and proceedings and by degrees skilfully to infuse their sentiments into the minds of their adherents and when they suppose themselves sufficiently powerful then to attack by force the throne and the friends of the constitution. This they think they can do with more ease and safety than even the French." A meeting of 200 people had taken place in Edinburgh on 28 August to begin this revolution. The correspondent promised more information and asked, "I trust sir that you will not reveal my correspondence with you to any but such as you can positively confide in. Be assured that I will with the utmost secrecy inform you from time to time of the men's proceedings." It was signed Robert Watt.

Nepean had it copied and sent to the home secretary's nephew, Robert Dundas, with a recommendation that Watt be contacted. Robert, who was married to Henry Dundas's daughter Lizabeth, looked after some of the interests of the clan in Scotland, being the country's chief law officer. Dundas had appointed him to high office eight years previously, aged just 26.

In the early afternoon Henry Dundas left his office and walked to his carriage. He called to his driver to take him home to Wimbledon. "But call at Downing Street and pick up Mr Pitt first," he added. The young prime minister and Dundas were close friends, and Pitt often stayed at Warren House, Dundas's Wimbledon mansion, Pitt's own country residence in Kent being too far from the capital. Dundas was 50 and Pitt only 33, he had been the chief minister since the age of 21, but despite their age difference the two men shared a total immersion in politics, a love of the countryside and a taste for strong drink.

The tall, slightly awkward and angular figure of the young prime minister loped from the door of 10 Downing Street and climbed aboard Dundas's carriage and four. Pitt was relaxed in the company of Dundas. He was famously unable to make small talk but with a few close friends he lost his social awkwardness. In public he was aloof and unapproachable, rarely even acknowledging a bow or nod from a colleague in the Commons. The artist George Romney had remarked that Pitt's nose was "turned up at all mankind". He held few dinners for his loyal MPs but occasionally met government supporters in White's club in St James's. Most party management was carried out by Dundas and Pitt's other close friend and cousin, William Grenville, the foreign secretary.

Dundas poured two large glasses of port from a bottle in a food hamper that also contained Pitt's favourite Belamy's pies. He explained that his paramour, Lady Anne Lindsay, was at Wimbledon this weekend and they would be joined later by Lord Thurlow, the Lord Chancellor, and his daughters.

Dundas had pursued Lady Anne, aristocratic Scot and daughter of the Earl of Crawford, for close on a decade. She was almost forty years of age and still unmarried but their relationship was tangled and their affair drifted. Sometimes she showed him great affection but at other times showed more to William Windham, a young, favoured politician who had deserted the opposition and had been marked out for future preferment. Dundas had been single since his divorce from Lizabeth Rannie, the mother of his four children, fourteen years before. She had complained of his neglect and had begun an affair with a young army officer. He divorced her and kept her property and fortune.

As well as Dundas's long affair with Anne Lindsay, there were many others. A verse often repeated in the capital's ale houses went:

> What various tastes divide the fickle town!
> One likes the fair, and one admires the brown;
> The stately Queensberry, Hinchbrook the small;
> Thurlow loves servant maids; Dundas loves all.

Dundas showed Pitt the letter from Edinburgh and explained that intelligence showed that reform societies were forming all over Scotland; that the former infantry officer, Johnston, was planning a newspaper supporting reform; that Paine's *Rights of Man* was being reprinted in cheap copies, in spite of the king's proclamation; and that Charles Grey had given notice of a reform motion in the House for next May and the reform societies were petitioning to support him.

Pitt refilled his glass. His long face and pointed nose turned to the window and his eyes clouded over with thought. At length he explained that in spite of having proposed mild measures for reform in the past, which failed, the time was now different. "The revolution in France has gone beyond our settlement," he said. "Reformers here have now adopted France as a model and any reform proceeding from the impracticable principles of the revolution can only end in a wild state of nature. Any reform now will threaten the peace and security of the nation."

But it was the radical movement rather than revolutionary France that occupied them. "With France we have to wait and watch," offered Dundas.

"More than that, Harry," said Pitt. "We have to keep ourselves quiet. In recent years the French have backed rebellion in Ireland, Scotland and America and we must not support any faction there, not even the royalists, until we see more clearly how our interests lie."

Dundas agreed but pressed home the point that they must do more than wait and watch at home. Reform societies in England had been formed among some of the aristocratic Whigs as well as among common folk. The popular societies were strong in London and Norwich, Manchester, Nottingham, Derby and Sheffield. He handed Pitt an eight-page printed handbill headed, "Address from the London Corresponding Society to the inhabitants of Great Britain on the subject of parliamentary reform". It began with the dangerous, democratic words, "Fellow citizens", and argued for "a restoration of annually elected parliaments, unbiased and unbought elections, and equal representation of the whole body of the people".

"We have regular reports from spies in these societies," continued Dundas, "but our information from Scotland is irregular and our law officers there are unprepared."

The port glasses were refilled to wash down some Bellamy's pies, and finally the carriage came to a halt outside Dundas's home in its 150-acre estate on the west side of Wimbledon Common. The two men were helped from the coach and climbed the wide steps to the hall of the classical house, two storeys high, five front windows wide, with matching lower side wings. They had covered the seven miles from Whitehall at a lick.

In the formal garden at the rear Anne Lindsay put down her pencil and sketch pad. "Why Henry, Mr Pitt, welcome to a little plot in paradise." They sat beside her at a small table in the sun. Anne was an accomplished painter who had exhibited in London and Edinburgh. She recorded Dundas's newly landscaped gardens in oils.

Wine was brought to the table but Dundas sent the serving girl back for beer. Although he was a prodigious consumer of claret and port, Dundas loved English beer. He sipped from the glass. "When I go every year to my own country," he said, savouring the taste, "I find no beer that I can drink, it is such weak, disagreeable and poor stuff. Here it is so fine, so pleasant, so swelling a liquor, that I care little if I taste no other beverage all the while I stay here."

Pitt stuck to the port. He had been a heavy drinker from his youth and suffered from gout. On the advice of his doctor, at least a bottle of port a day was consumed as a palliative.

Soon Edward Thurlow, the Lord Chancellor, arrived with his three daughters. He had never married but kept the daughters close to him. The political relationship between Thurlow and Pitt was fragile but Pitt kept him in his post at the head of the courts and the House of Lords because of Thurlow's close friendship with the king. When Thurlow sat down, he complained, as always, about his piles.

Dundas was known for entertaining "with burgundy and blasphemy" and tonight was no different. The party ate in the late afternoon, drank deeply, and listened to Anne Lindsay and the

Thurlow ladies play harpsichord and sing until nine o'clock when, as was the custom with Dundas and Pitt, they saddled up for a ride. Thurlow went with them. He stood on the mounting stone, slipped his foot in the stirrup, swung his other leg over the horse and came down heavily on the beast's back.

"Damn you, Dundas!" he slurred. "I can't feel my ruddy piles! Bugger me if you weren't born upon a rock. You could drink up the ocean!" Pitt climbed quietly but unsteadily on his mount. He was feather light. He was so skinny his bum couldn't fill his trousers and, behind his back, some called him Bottomless Pitt. Dundas, his broad, genial face cheerfully tinged with imbiber's purple, settled himself in the saddle. "Tally-ho!" he shouted, and the three raced off into the fading light of the Surrey countryside, clods of grass flying behind their heels.

Presently it was dark. They had come to a trot and were sharing songs and jokes.

"What's that ahead?" asked Pitt. "Is it a turnpike?"

"It is," replied Thurlow. "Do we have coins?"

"I have none," said Dundas.

"Nor I," said Pitt.

"We have no money," concluded Thurlow. "What shall we do?"

"Come on!" cried Dundas, spurring his horse on.

The three came back to the gallop and rushed toward the white gate by the toll keeper's cottage. The thunder of hooves surprised the keeper inside and he caught a glimpse of the riders leaping the gate. Thinking they were highwaymen he grabbed his blunderbuss and ran outside, shouting "Stop thieves!" He fired a shower of pellets after them. All he could hear above the clatter of horse-shoes on gravel was giggling and laughter fading into the darkness.

Later, Dundas tiptoed past family portraits lining an upstairs corridor of Warren House and slipped into Anne Lindsay's room. She was awake and waiting. He flopped on to the bed.

"I have to go away for a while, Anne," he announced. "We decided, Pitt, Thurlow and I, that the Scots democrats are having

too free a run of it. I'm going north to help my nephew put a stop
to them."

She stretched her arms across his chest and pulled herself closer
to him. She thought of her brother's scorn at her casual relationships. "That man Windham uses you like a dog," he had said,
"and you use Dundas like one."

CHAPTER 6

Mad ideas

"The Rights of Man is now weel kenned,
And read by mony a hunder;
For Tammy Paine the buik has penned,
And lent the Courts a lounder [beating]."

Alexander Wilson, 'Address to the Synod
of Glasgow and Ayr', 1792.

Henry Scott, the Duke of Buccleuch, greatest landowner in Scotland, looked from the windows of Langholm Lodge, his new mansion near the borders town after which it was named. He saw the dust from an approaching party of horsemen as it entered the valley. Presently he made out a carriage protected by an escort of dragoons as the group followed the course of the River Esk towards the lodge. He had been expecting them.

He turned to his wife, Lizabeth, and suggested they meet the home secretary at the front door. The duke and duchess, foremost nobles in Scotland, complete with their retinue of staff, watched the brightly uniformed riders rein in their mounts, allowing the official carriage containing Henry Dundas and Sir William Pulteney to go on ahead and come to a smooth halt by the white stone steps in front of the substantial house, their new hunting lodge that had been completed only three years earlier.

The 46-year-old Buccleuch was the leading supporter of Dundas and Pitt in Scotland and used his influence in his Scottish and English estates to return loyal members of parliament. Dundas was anxious to call on him on his way north and was pleased to learn that the duke was here, just off the main route from Carlisle to Edinburgh, rather than in his main residence at Dalkeith Castle, outside the capital. He wanted to share his fears with Buccleuch and find out what the duke could add to his information about the Scottish radicals.

Dundas had eventually managed to quit London by the end of September. He had asked his friend and ally William Pulteney to join him. Pulteney, aged 63, had been an MP for 24 years, first for Cromarty and then Shrewsbury. He was a loyalist and a shrewd organiser and he knew Edinburgh. Pulteney had started life as William Johnstone, son of Sir James, an MP from Dumfriesshire. He had been an Edinburgh lawyer from his admittance to the bar as a young man in 1751 and he had moved in the city's literary and intellectual circles. Eleven years later his wife, Frances Pulteney, unexpectedly inherited the immense fortune, if not the title, of the deceased Earl of Bath. The couple moved to London and adopted the Pulteney name.

Dundas planned to stay in Edinburgh for a month or two but asked Pulteney to stay as long as necessary, to be his eyes and ears, but also to make sure his nephew Robert implemented measures strong enough to rout the radicals. Dundas had planned ahead and had written to Robert asking him to set up a meeting with the spy, Robert Watt, in a safe place, and to assemble a group of powerful men to discuss tactics.

That evening Dundas and Pulteney dined at Langholm Lodge with the Buccleuchs and another guest, Sir William Maxwell of Springkell, who also had considerable landholdings in Eskdale. Buccleuch explained that he had invited Maxwell because the two had been talking recently and had found the county quiet. However "facts of an alarming nature" had come Sir William's way in the past few days.

"I have come upon information showing that unknown emissaries of sedition have been at work in this part of the kingdom, sowing seeds of discontent, faction and rebellion," explained Maxwell. "A riot recently took place in Langholm, new taxes on the registration of christenings and burials seems to have been the spark for it, so I engaged a few people as spies. They found that Paine's pamphlet, or the cream and substance of it, is now in the hands of almost every countryman. Liberty medals are being handed round and powerful arguments are working upon the minds of ignorant people. I cannot, sir, help dreading the consequences that may arise from the present discontent, this absurd doctrine of equality which seems everywhere to prevail in these kingdoms, amongst the lower classes."

"That's very useful, Sir William," said Dundas. "It strikes me the more forcibly as a proof of the speed with which these mad ideas have made their progress. Information from elsewhere shows that the radical societies are growing, in fact they are increasing daily."

"Furthermore," interrupted the duke, "Sir William tells me that those same emissaries of sedition are working to convince many that the king is a useless and burdensome member in the community, that he ought to be dethroned, and that he and his family should be set adrift, for taxes are only levied to support their luxury and extravagance."

"We must find a way, home secretary," added Maxwell, "to impose peace, regularity, good order and subordination and try to persuade the common people that they live under a glorious constitution with the mildest and happiest government that ever was in the world."

The company nodded in agreement.

"Scots peasants," Pulteney said by way of explanation, "understand nothing of parliamentary reform, equal representation, and other grievances. But they may be tempted to unite their strength and risk their necks in the hopes of bringing about a division of the landed property and of getting ten acres each."

"The French!" Maxwell said with rising anger, "The French are behind this! The French, who were formerly papists, are now absolute infidels, ruffians, and murderers, intent on abolishing Christianity!"

*

Dundas peered into the gloom of a storeroom beside the stables at the rear of Melville Castle and presently recognised the shape of a man in his thirties dressed in the threadbare clothes of a gentleman.

"Watt?"

"Yes, home secretary," replied the figure, "thank you for sending for me. It is an honour to meet you."

Dundas had arranged for the would-be spy, Robert Watt, to be brought to his home near Dalkeith, judging this the safest place to conduct a private interview. He had sent one of his military escorts, dressed in civilian clothes, on a modest pony and trap to rendezvous with Watt in the Meadows at the southern limit of Edinburgh.

"What makes you want to inform for me, man?"

"I explained in my letter to you, sir, of my concern for the constitution," said Watt, "but I cannot deny that my motive is also financial. I am in the wine trade and times are hard. However, being in that line of business takes me to all the major towns in the country without suspicion and allows me to mix with gentlemen as well as the labouring kind. My contacts are extensive."

"Very well, Watt, what can you tell me now?"

"I have last month been in Dundee and Perth, sir," he replied, "where the number in reform societies is about forty for Dundee and upward of a hundred in Perth. I also visited Glasgow where some have been intimidated by the recent accounts from France but their present number is very considerable. In Edinburgh, I understand the societies have gained another hundred members in three weeks." Watt passed a handbill to Dundas advertising Captain Johnston's new paper, the *Edinburgh Gazetteer*, published every Tuesday and Friday. It promised serious reporting allied to no particular party "except that of the nation", and to correct "those glaring misrepresentations of events upon the continent". It also declared its attachment to the British constitution but "not to those defects produced by time and by the efforts of the bad men which now dishonour it".

Dundas was only mildly impressed by the quality of the information and dismissed the informer. "Oh, there is more, home secretary," Watt said quickly.

"Go on, man."

"I heard reports that four gentlemen of the Friends of the People had gone to the Register House where soldiers were on guard and tried to suborn them," he said. "I'm told one of the men said 'Damn the king! None but the nation!' I also learned that the pretended Friends of the People now correspond with similar societies in London and other towns in England."

Dundas's interest was renewed. "Do you know who these four men are?" he asked.

"I don't know their names yet but I found this out from one of the gentlemen in the association and I can question him further," replied Watt.

"Do that," said Dundas, "and from now on report to the lord advocate and not to me. You may also report with equal safety to the sheriff, Mr Pringle."

"Thank you, home secretary, sir. Thank you most kindly. It has been an honour." Watt hesitated at the storeroom door and turned again to face Dundas. "One more thing, Mr Dundas."

"Yes?"

"With respect, sir, please inform your mother, Lady Arniston, that her bookseller, Mr Elder, attends the radicals' committee. He also sells seditious publications." Dundas smiled inwardly, and dismissed the spy.

He returned to his apartment in the castle to prepare for the evening meeting in Edinburgh. He had decided to use his Gothic pile, formerly part of his ex-wife's fortune, as his headquarters. His presence there had not gone unnoticed. London's *Morning Chronicle* on Thursday 11 October noted, "Yesterday, the Rt Hon Henry Dundas arrived at his seat of Melville Castle from London." Pulteney had gone ahead to apartments in the city.

*

"Good God, sir," said Dundas as he entered his nephew's house in Edinburgh's George Square, "the town is plastered with hand-bills calling for reform. Some of them even make threats to my person!" Dundas was shown into Robert's study where he greeted

Pulteney, Sheriff Pringle, Provost Stirling, William Scott, the chief prosecutor, and Lord Adam Gordon. Glasses were filled with claret.

The lord advocate, explained that he had received a flood of confidential letters from respectable people in all parts of the country outlining their fears about reform associations. "Here, for example, is a despatch from Glasgow, which reads in part, 'The success of the French Democrats has had a most mischievous effect here. Did it go no further than give occasion for triumph for those who entertain the same sentiments here there would be little harm, for they are very few in number, and but two or three of them possessed of any considerable influence or respectability. But it has led them to think of forming societies for reformation in which the lower classes of people are invited to enter, and however insignificant these leaders may be in themselves, when backed with the mob they become formidable.' As we know, gentlemen, lately the west of the country has seen so-called Friends of the People societies formed in most towns. At the third meeting of the Glasgow association there were four hundred present, addressed by the lawyer Muir and Thomas Maitland MP, brother of the Earl of Lauderdale. The same is happening here in the east of the country."

"I had an interview with that fellow, Watt, today and he said the same thing," reported Dundas.

"We are receiving intelligence from the provosts and sheriffs across the country," continued Robert Dundas, "but closer to the people are the Rev James Lapslie in the Campsie towns, and three more in the societies who pass information directly to me, a young divinity student by the name of Patrick Moir and someone whom I have never met but signs his letters only by the initials JB. I fancy he may be Watt, who is in desperate need of money."

"I am more and more satisfied, gentlemen," said Dundas, "that unless something effectual can be done to check the indiscriminate practice of associations, they will spread the fermentation of the country to such a height it will be impossible to restrain the effects of them. Talk to Lord Braxfield, Robert, find out what charges can be brought against those who encourage disaffection."

"You know Braxfield's motto, uncle," replied Robert. " 'Let them bring me prisoners, an' I'll find them law,' he says, and usually adds, 'They'd be nane the waur o' a hangin'." They all laughed. Braxfield was the last judge on the Scottish bench who insisted on using the old Scotch. He could speak very well in plain English but preferred the vernacular of his fathers.

Dundas turned to Sheriff Pringle. "Who can you bring us to make an example of?"

"Well, there are printers and booksellers all over the city selling pamphlets advocating equality of representation in parliament," replied Pringle.

"Then sheriff, you and the Lord Advocate and the procurator fiscal should between you prepare some sound cases to bring before the courts," ordered Dundas. "In the meantime I shall write to sheriffs across the country reminding them of the May proclamation against seditious literature."

He then turned to the commander of the army in Scotland. "Adam," he said, "what is the strength of our forces?"

"As you know, secretary of state," began Lord Gordon, "in January parliament made the first of what had been intended as many budget cuts for the army and navy. But now we are being augmented again and barracks are being built in many parts of the country. At the moment the work is progressing in Glasgow, Aberdeen, and elsewhere. There is, however, much local opposition to the barracks." Gordon pushed across the table a four-page pamphlet printed in Glasgow, which made the popular argument against barracks and standing armies. "It seems that people who were unhappy about soldiers being billeted upon them are equally unhappy about permanent quarters in their midst. In dangerous and restless times like these I much prefer to have our soldiers kept apart from the people."

"And can you give us an audit of arms and men in the country?" asked Dundas.

Lord Gordon shuffled the leaves of the notes he had brought from his official residence in Holyrood Palace. "We have 10,310 muskets and men available in Scotland; 2,623 of them are in the Highlands; 6,221 in Edinburgh Castle; 454 in Stirling Castle; 412 in Dumbarton Castle; with another 600 in minor outposts. There are none in the Fife, Perth and Dundee area. The castle at Dumbarton needs attention in case of disturbance in the west of Scotland or in Ireland, and we could use the four companies temporarily stationed in the Isle of Man, as well as another company of artillery. We could also use two companies of marines."

"A ship in the Clyde and one in the Forth?" inquired Dundas.

"That would be sufficient and also a permanent reminder to the radicals in both cities," replied Gordon. "You may also like to consider this for the future, Henry, we have no militia in Scotland and no provision for such a force, unlike in England. A few private regiments of fencibles, soldiers for home defence such as we had during the American war, would greatly increase our strength."

"I'll consider that, too," said Dundas. "In the meantime, what do we know about attempts to suborn our soldiers outside Register House? The spy Watt gave me some information that four radicals had tried to engage infantry on guard there."

Neither Gordon nor Pringle had any more knowledge of the incident.

"Very well," said Dundas, "It might be a good idea to send an anonymous letter to the papers telling of this. It would divide the revolutionists from the reformers. Sir William, will you do that?"

Pulteney agreed. "And that brings us to the newspaper campaign," he went on. "As you know, it has been the policy of the administration to give limited support, sometimes with finance, to anti-reform papers and some individual writers in London. Here in Scotland we have no such arrangement at present, although we already have a special relationship with Henry Mackenzie, who I believe also lives here in George Square. Is that so, Robert?"

"Just a few doors away," replied the lord advocate. "He's well known for his sentimental novels and he writes and edits some periodicals. I understand he has close links to Mr Pitt, for whom he has written several political pamphlets."

"Precisely," said Pulteney, "and he also has ties to other important individuals involved in anti-radical polemics in London. I do believe he has an annual pension from the government. But, crucially, he has close relationships with newspaper editors in Edinburgh and Glasgow, and should be a starting point for our campaign."

"We have secret service funds available," said Dundas.

"In that case I'll see Mr Mackenzie tomorrow," said Pulteney. "He is friendly with Mr Sibbald, editor of the *Edinburgh Herald*, who has been pursuing a strongly loyal line from the middle of last year. We could offer Sibbald an annual pension of, say, £100 together with a sum for the principal proprietors." They planned support for other likely papers such as the *Glasgow Courier* and the *Dumfries Weekly Journal*.

"The anti-radical items in the *Glasgow Courier* have been part of a wider loyalist propaganda campaign led by the lord provost," explained Robert Dundas, "who has responded well to direction from us." Pulteney thought that approaches to more independent papers might bear fruit, the *Edinburgh Advertiser, Aberdeen Weekly Journal, Glasgow Mercury, Caledonian Mercury,* and the *Edinburgh Evening Courant*.

"At the very least we could try to supply them with information," he said. "And that leaves us with Captain Johnston's *Edinburgh Gazetteer* and John Mennon's *Glasgow Advertiser*," he went on, "both of which open their pages to the Friends of the People."

"Watch them with special care," said Dundas, turning to Robert and Sheriff Pringle. "If they put a foot wrong bring them to court in front of Lord Braxfield."

As they were about to break up for the evening, Dundas remembered his conversation with Watt. "Just one more thing gentlemen," he announced. "The spy Watt told me an interesting piece of tittle-tattle. He said that my mother's bookseller is a radical and sells seditious publications. Maybe prosecution alone is not sufficient. Maybe my mother will withdraw her custom. Maybe others can be persuaded to do the same. If we deprived radical businessmen, shopkeepers, artisans and lawyers of their income we should bring them to their senses in no time. Do you agree?"

There was general approval. Provost Stirling promised to oversee the tactic by way of the council members and their families.

CHAPTER 7

Panic

"His Majesty has commanded me to communicate to you his directions, that you make diligent enquiry respecting all wicked and seditious writings published and industriously spread within your jurisdiction, and report the result of such enquiry to His Majesty's Advocate in order that the authors, printers, publishers and distributors of such writings may be severally dealt with according to law."

Henry Dundas to all Scotland's sheriffs, 1 December, 1792.

As the tall man with blue-stained fingers stepped into a woman's gown, his workmates laughed. "Ye might laugh but it's the best way to stay unknown," he said, pulling on a white mob cap and tying an apron around his waist. He hoisted an effigy of Henry Dundas on his shoulders and led the crowd from the tavern by the dye works where many of them had finished their shift. They headed away from the factory by the River Tay on Watergate and into the High Street of Perth, gathering more young men and boys on the way.

"The French have beaten the tyrants!" they cried. "Reform parliament now!" That day a conscript army of French peasants had defeated the professional armies of Austria and Prussia in the small Belgian town of Jemappes. The victory, and the name of its hero, General Dumouriez, had been announced with jubilation in parts of the town.

At a high window in the town hall, the sheriff turned to the provost and remarked gloomily, "The lower class of people talk of nothing but liberty and equality, 'No Dundas! No Bishops! and no King! Nothing but a republic for us!' Such is the spirit of the times."

Beneath them, a leader of the procession shouted, "A victory for the whole family of the human race!" Dundas's effigy was hoisted on a pole and set on fire. The crowd cheered and a young man stepped forward with a fir sapling, which he jammed into the soft earth by the side of the footpath. "A liberty tree!" he cried. The crowd cheered louder.

The provost looked at the sheriff. "Can you find out who's behind this? The Friends of the People is now strong hereabouts. I'm told as many as 1,200 in Perth alone. See if you can unearth the ringleaders."

"They're the most inflammatory set of scoundrels I've ever heard of," replied the sheriff, "and it is astonishing the notions they have instilled into the minds of the common people. Liberty and equality. Pah!"

Eight days later, on 14 November, Brussels fell to the French. This dazzling victory resounded not only in beleaguered France but across Scotland, too. Trees of liberty were once more planted in celebration at Stonehaven, Aberdeen, Fochabers, Auchtermuchty, and Strathmilgo. A bonfire was lit near the Buccleuch holiday home at Langholm Cross and three public toasts were drunk, "Success to the French Revolution", "George the third and last king", and "Liberty and equality to all the world". As each toast was drunk, guns were fired, and in the evening candles were lit in windows. Disturbances were widespread, but what most concerned the authorities were Perth and Dundee. At Perth the crowd assembled again and another tree of liberty was planted, this time with great solemnity. A huge bonfire was lit, bells were rung and windows were illuminated with brightly burning candles and lamps. Twenty miles away and two days later, on Friday, a young fir was brought to the centre of Dundee and planted as a liberty tree. It was removed on Saturday, but Monday saw handbills circulating urging people to meet to replant the tree.

A stocky man with a leather apron and well-worked biceps lifted a flaming barrel of tar and sat it on his head. It was five o'clock in the afternoon and already four or five hundred people had assembled. They cheered and formed up behind the smoke and flames to walk to the home of one of those who had uprooted the tree, where they threw stones at the front of the house and demolished its gate. The mob moved on to stone the lodgings of Lieutenant John Fyffe who, it was reported, had insulted the Rev Thomas Fyshe Palmer, a prominent Dundee reformer. Fyffe had refused to play whist at the same table as the Unitarian minister and had threatened him in public. "If ever he presumes to mention reform in my presence," he had said, "I will break every bone in his body." Effigies of those who had uprooted Friday's tree were carried to the town centre and burnt to great applause and laughter. The procession then followed the flaming barrel to the house of the provost, Alexander Riddoch.

"Mr Riddoch," they cried, "ring the town bells!" They kept up the chant until an assistant meekly opened the front door and explained that the provost was not at home. "Give us the keys to the bell tower, then!" they demanded and eventually coaxed them from the frightened man peering from behind the stout wooden door. A bonfire was lit in the High Street and the town bells tolled throughout the evening. The fire was kept burning all night, while young men paraded around it with a tree of liberty. In the small hours a group stole away from the celebration and attacked the rooms of some excise officers. Later, an attempt was made to break into the Custom House in protest at a shipload of meal from Berwick had that stood in the harbour for more than two weeks, stranded because of the despised Corn Laws. As dawn broke those still keeping vigil by the victory bonfire gathered up the liberty tree and fixed it to the town hall door. It was taken down later but another appeared in the market place. Provost Riddoch ordered that one to be removed, too, before the arrival of troops, at his request. A frigate and a sloop had been despatched from Newcastle.

*

In Edinburgh, Thomas Muir and William Skirving walked up the hill toward the castle and turned off Lawnmarket through a low, narrow close into James Court, where Lawrie's dancing school had a large meeting room. Tonight, delegates from all the reform societies in and around Edinburgh were to meet to make preparations for a national convention.

Both men were alarmed at the news from Perth and Dundee. They understood why people would want to cheer on the French but were afraid riot would undermine their campaign. Already the Unitarian preacher, Palmer, was being blamed for the Dundee riot in spite of having condemned it in public. As a result a detachment of the army had been garrisoned there. Skirving and Muir agreed that a public statement from the meeting should distance the reform association from the disturbances.

They entered the door of the meeting room, which was already filling with people, excitedly talking about the French advances and the celebrations throughout the country. The *Edinburgh Gazetteer* later reported a celebration in Sheffield after the battle at Jemappes, where several sheep were roasted, and when Dumouriez entered Brussels an ox was cooked on a spit and distributed to the poor and to those in debtors' prison. About twenty thousand marched through the town waving flags topped with red republican hats.

Skirving brought the meeting to order. At the back of the hall, Robert Watt made a note that there were around 300 people in the room. Hugh Bell, a brewer, was elected chairman and Colonel Norman Macleod MP spoke in support of the organisation and the need for a great petition to parliament on reform of representation. Muir then voiced his concerns about rioting and Johnston echoed his anxiety. He proposed that the views of the Friends of the People be published in all newspapers as soon as possible.

"First," he declared, "that any person or persons belonging to the Associated Friends of the People, if found guilty of rioting, of creating or aiding sedition in the country, his name shall be expunged from the books of the society. Secondly, that any person acting properly, who may be persecuted and oppressed by the arm of power, be protected by the society to which he belongs."

A member from nearby Belhaven rose. "I agree with Captain Johnston," he said. "Our reform society was founded to obtain a full, free, and equal representation of the people and shorter parliaments. A meeting in our village this week agreed that all persons who attempt to precipitate the people of Scotland into riot and sedition are the enemies of this country and ought to be refused admittance as members."

Skirving pointed out that he had received similar sentiments from Stirling and many other societies in recent correspondence. Johnston's proposal was agreed with warm applause. His resolutions would be published in as many newspapers as possible. A delegation was elected, led by Skirving and Muir, to approach the authorities and offer the help of the reform societies in keeping good order and preventing riots.

It was reported that loyalist declarations uncritically supporting the king and constitution were being posted in towns and villages around the country and that the wording in each seemed to be the same. Meetings to approve them were being called by local churches or councils in an effort to give the impression there was overwhelming opposition to equal representation. It was suggested that members attend these meetings and try to amend the proposals. William Dalrymple from the Glasgow society had attended the Lanark loyalist county gathering and proposed a motion in support of reform. It was defeated, but Dalrymple had won the support of eighteen people at the meeting.

A delegate from Queensferry told how his local loyalist meeting had gathered to approve the usual paragraphs but they were successfully amended by society members. "They now say we enjoy freedom, that the constitution is a good one, that reform should be by legal and peaceful means, and that people agree to co-operate with the civil power to preserve the invaluable blessings of true liberty," he explained. "But that is not the whole story. Another two resolutions had been intended by the loyalists, one censuring us and another disapproving of seditious writings. Both had to be abandoned. The people crowded in and the minister of Queensferry became doubtful about trying a vote."

Skirving announced that he had had letters from other societies that had done the same in Perth, Dundee, Montrose, Forfar, Dalmeny, Strathaven, Hamilton, Kilmarnock, Linlithgow and Glasgow. "The Perth loyalist resolutions, following an amendment put forward by George Meliss, include specific reference to reintroducing triennial elections, as well as the need for more general, as well as more true representation. Still in Perthshire, it's reported that Lord Kinnoul proposed some resolutions in the county but can get nobody to sign them but his gardener." The hall erupted in laughter.

William Johnston of the *Gazetteer* held up his paper and read from an article. "At the instigation of the Earl of Kinnoul," it reported, "the parish of Aberdalgie were assembled at the church to subscribe to the resolutions of the gentlemen in Edinburgh, which are transmitted to all the villages in the county for signatures. The minister harangued the people from the pulpit. His lordship made a long speech, in the usual style, for supporting the constitution without any qualification. After he was done a sensible farmer opposed the measure, and when the paper was offered for subscription the people quitted the church, declaring they would have nothing to do with it, nor any other paper which tied them up from Reform." Laughter and applause resumed, before the delegates ratified arrangements for a general convention of all Scottish societies to be held in the same place on 11 December, and elected the necessary committees to organise it.

CHAPTER 8

Liberty restrained

"From the serious alarm betrayed by the government,
one would suppose that the Society for Constitutional
Information, with Horne Tooke at their head, had encamped
upon Blackheath, and that Mr Paine with a detachment of
the Jacobins, had landed at Dover."
Edinburgh Gazetteer, 7 December, 1792.

Henry Dundas sat in the drawing room of his mother's house in
George Square. Around him were Robert Dundas, Pulteney, Pringle,
Stirling and Gordon. "Perth and Dundee," Dundas said sharply.
"What do we know?"

"Perth is a very dangerous place," said Lord Gordon. "Two
troops of 4th dragoons have arrived there and one is now on its
way to Dundee. I have also ordered four companies of the Royal
Highland regiment to be brought from Fort George. In the rest of
the country, a troop of the 3rd has gone to Hamilton and a second
to Kilmarnock. Stirling Castle has been made ready to receive four
hundred men if necessary. A troop of the 4th dragoons is in the
castle and three companies of the 53rd foot are marching there
now. I have also ordered two companies of the 42nd at Dunkeld
to Aberdeen, to deal with a strike of all the seamen there, at the
request of the provost."

"I have information from the sheriff at Perth," said Robert
Dundas. "He names those involved in burning an effigy of you,
uncle, along with the leading gentlemen of the society there. The
coat was provided by James Wylie, a merchant, and president of the

Friends of the People in the town. A Mr Meliss, a man of considerable property, is the leading man in the society. Most others are
shopkeepers and journeymen." Looking down at the letter, the lord
advocate added, "The sheriff also says, and I quote, 'The whole of
the lower class appear to be at the command of these men. I am told
it is not uncommon in the west end of town, which is mostly inhabited by them, to hear the boys crying liberty, equality and no king'."

"And isn't the estimate of society members in Perth now more
than a thousand?" asked Pulteney.

"That's right, Sir William," answered Robert. "The sheriff
informs me that a sergeant and two soldiers in a recruiting party
for Colonel Macleod's regiment were in Perth and attended a
Friends meeting. Twenty or thirty soldiers stationed there seem to
be regular attenders."

Lord Gordon was outraged and vowed to bring the soldiers back
into line with severe discipline.

Pulteney reported on his anti-reform organisation. "We have
made a good beginning," he said. "I attended the first meeting of
the Friends of Order in Goldsmiths Hall and, although there was a
shyness about standing in public at first, there was no want of general
zeal. That matter is now in good train and they have asked me to
attend the committee. We had one meeting today and I see it will
now be necessary to moderate their zeal. John Wauchope is secretary.
He holds a minor government office and he's good. Without him I
wouldn't have succeeded."

"Just as John Reeves's Crown and Anchor association in London
is seen to be independent of government," said Dundas, "so must
this one. Make it clear to Wauchope and the others that we can't
offer official backing, only private encouragement, because of the
delicacy of being seen to encourage one sort of association and not
the other reform ones."

"Already, subscriptions have been established to raise funds to defray
the costs of producing loyal pamphlets and distributing them in large
numbers among the artisan and labouring classes," said Pulteney.

The association had already subsidised a pamphlet called *Look Before Ye Loup* by "Tam Thrum, an Auld Weaver." Its real author, William Brown of Dundee, had been established in Edinburgh as editor of the *Patriot's Weekly Chronicle*. A hostile *Life of Paine*, published under the pseudonym Francis Oldys, was being distributed by the committee. It was written by George Chalmers, chief clerk of the Committee of Trade in London.

Robert Dundas outlined the cash required to continue the campaign, £400 to be paid to the *Edinburgh Herald*, plus half-yearly payments of £50. Payments to individual writers on the *Caledonian Mercury* would come to £134. The Glasgow lord provost had already spent £40 on popular loyalist literature and had to be reimbursed. "And £100 more will be necessary to reward informers," added the lord advocate. "Watt, for instance, should get something in hand to reward and encourage him." There was secret service money available for counter-reform activity and propaganda. By the winter of 1792 Pitt's administration was already subsidising seven of the fourteen London daily papers, and individual writers and publishers were also on the payroll. The total expenditure was nearly £5,000 a year.

Pulteney proposed the next move in extending the influence of the loyalists of Goldsmiths Hall. "I have suggested something to the advocate," he said, "and I think that in a little it'll work." He explained how a loyal resolution in support of the constitution should be left for signature at Goldsmiths to encourage all the respectable people of Edinburgh to declare themselves.

Dundas said correspondence of leading reformers should be intercepted and he would ask Nepean, his assistant, to contact the Post Office in London. Letters to colonels Dalrymple and Macleod and Captain Johnston should be objects of particular attention.

"I understand from the postmaster," offered Provost Stirling, "that since September the letters of several leading local radicals have been opened and copied. They include Captain Johnston, William Skirving and Thomas Muir."

"Now, Mr Pringle, do we have news of actions against seditious publications?" asked Dundas.

"Indeed, Home Secretary," replied the sheriff. "But first, there was an incident at the castle last night when three young journeymen printers drank a subversive toast in the soldiers' canteen. They were arrested by the duty officer and handed to me. They have been charged with sedition. We are also about to make a series of arrests of writers, publishers, and printers, both here and in Glasgow."

"Very good, sheriff," said Dundas. "Now, gentlemen, I have to tell you that I must away to London. As you might have noticed, on the very evening of the Perth riot the French opened the River Scheldt to all commercial ships. This brings us nearer to war. That act breaks the Treaty of Utrecht, which assures the navigation of the river to the Dutch. We are their allies and this affects our interests. The Admiralty has met to commission ships and men; the War Office has ordered regiments to be placed at an hour's march from London; a cabinet council met throughout the night and issued a proclamation calling out the militia in England and summoning parliament; defences at the Tower are being strengthened and the troops in every station are directed to hold themselves in readiness for immediate action. Gentlemen, unless France explains satisfactorily to our court, her conduct on the Scheldt, a fleet of twelve ships of the line will be instantly ordered, in addition to the ten frigates already put into commission, which fleet will be followed up by more force. The Cabinet is meeting almost daily. In this hour of alarm, I must return to London. I have assured Mr Pitt I will be back by December 3rd or 4th at the latest. I have told him no consideration shall detain me. You must now make up your minds to act upon your own judgment and discretion."

"It appears to me, gentlemen," added Pulteney, "that if mischief is to be set to work, it is likely to begin in Scotland or Ireland, or in both, and that great vigour to extinguish the first flame is of very great moment, for which purpose, preparatory measures cannot be too soon taken. The period of Christmas, when the work people are idle, is a likely time for beginning a riot."

*

Muir, Skirving, Campbell and Forsyth were in the Fortune tavern in front of a blazing fire. All four agreed they would visit Sheriff Pringle in the morning and decided that Muir should have one more try at bringing Archibald Fletcher into the reform society. Muir agreed to visit him the following evening. But now they had other worries to consider. Word had reached them on the legal grapevine that three young men had been arrested and charged with sedition for allegedly drinking a toast to 'King George the Third and last' in the soldiers' canteen in the castle. Two were journeymen printers and one still an apprentice. They were to be defended by Alexander Wight, a leading counsel at the Edinburgh bar, the constitutional expert on Scottish electoral law, and associated with the Whigs. Wight had briefly occupied the position of solicitor general, taking over from Dundas's man Islay Campbell, but was ousted a year later by the young Robert Dundas, as Henry Dundas regained his grip on appointments.

They had also heard of a slew of other sedition charges laid against printers and booksellers immediately after Dundas reissued the proclamation against seditious writings. James Tytler, editor of the *Historical Review*, had been charged with writing a seditious libel addressed to the people. It argued that petitions to parliament would achieve nothing and that withholding taxes would be more effective. It was simply an expression of opinion and thought by most lawyers to be harmless. However, the four reformers had no doubt that in the present circumstances the Dundas faction saw danger everywhere.

Two men had also been arrested in Glasgow by the Lanarkshire sheriff William Honyman: John Mennons for publishing a resolution of the Partick reform society, called the Sons of Liberty, which defended the works of Tom Paine, and James Smith, the person who introduced the proposal. Then John Elder, the Edinburgh bookseller frequented by Dundas's mother, who had a shop on North Bridge, was arrested by Sheriff Pringle for printing and selling the French

National Assembly's *Declaration of the Rights of Man and of Citizens*; William Stewart, a merchant from Leith, was charged with sedition along with him; James Callender was charged with the same offence for writing an article published in *The Bee*, about the faults in the constitution; and two booksellers who handled the magazine were also charged, Walter Berry of South Bridge Street and James Robertson of Horse Wynd, a neighbour of Skirving.

*

On the following morning Muir, Skirving, Campbell and Forsyth sought out the lord provost in his office in the tangle of buildings off Parliament Close to inform him of the society's resolution the previous night and offer help in preventing disorder in the city. Stirling was gruff and unwilling to talk. He dismissed them with a single sentence. "I do not recognise a legally constituted society under that designation," he barked.

*

That evening Muir left his digs in Carrubber's Close and walked down to the New Town. In Hill Street he stopped before the door of the recent newly-weds Archibald and Liza Fletcher. He hoped to bring Fletcher to the side of the Friends of the People. A previous attempt, in the summer, had failed. Fletcher, along with Henry Erskine and other influential Whigs in the city, had set their faces against supporting the parliamentary reform campaign, even though they had been leaders of the burgh reform movement for almost a decade now. Muir thought the differences between the two camps was not great. Bringing them together would strengthen the petitioners and also, he reckoned, weaken opposition within the old elite.

He pulled on the brass doorbell mounted in grey sandstone. Liza Fletcher answered. She was young, just 22, and already a popular Whig hostess in the town. Muir introduced himself and she invited him to wait in the spacious hallway. Presently Fletcher appeared and welcomed his visitor. The two entered the door to a book-lined study.

Fletcher guessed why Muir had come but was adamant that his answer was the same as it had been six months before. Muir explained the impact his support would have on the campaign but he was unmoved and said Henry Erskine would still refuse to sponsor the petition as well, in spite of his brothers, Thomas, the barrister and MP for Portsmouth, and David, Earl of Buchan, both being members of the Friends of the People in London.

"We think that two evils will result from the propaganda of your societies," Fletcher said. "You will light a flame of reform that you will be unable to extinguish. The lower classes will be alienated by frustrated hopes, and so the real leaders will lose authority at a later date when reform is practicable."

"Sir," countered Muir. "You must be aware of the arrests now taking place for sedition. At the same time, the enemies of reform are circulating rumours that the object of the societies is to introduce a system similar to that of France. This is an untruth of a most atrocious nature. It terrifies moderate men from joining us, when our real object is to mend the constitution and correct abuses. You could have a most beneficial effect in correcting these misapprehensions."

"As you know, Thomas," Fletcher continued, "I have denigrated the major political parties in the past, especially those political jobbers on the Treasury bench. Unless parties arise possessed of higher and nobler views than any of these, it is in vain to talk of public spirit or to think of accomplishing any objects of extensive public utility in this country. True, the association of the Friends of the People seemed to me at one point to be the only party that merits the attention of the people at large. But times have now changed. There is panic in London. The gates of all government offices are locked at 10pm. The Bank of England guard has been reinforced with fifty extra men. Several 'French Jacobins', they say, were arrested last Saturday night in different coffee houses 'for speaking rebellion against our happy government' and a learned doctor was taken before Lord

Grenville on Sunday last, for some 'improper conversation' in the shop of a bookseller in Piccadilly. It is preposterous. Even here in Edinburgh people are expecting a French fleet in the Forth, now that the National Assembly has promised 'fraternity and assistance' to all those fighting for liberty.

"The government is preparing for war, Thomas," he went on, "and all the while talking neutrality. Many ships of the line and frigates are being fitted out and the press gangs are hard at work. I hear that two noblemen were discharged from military service for having signed their names to the Revolution Society, I believe they are Lord Sempill and Lord Edward Fitzgerald, and two colonels and a major are struck off the army list. This may all be an over-reaction but it is clear, to me at least, that no one can win a reform in such a climate of fear."

Muir thought for a moment. "With respect, Mr Fletcher," he said, "you are known to be a supporter of republican government in America. You celebrate the anniversary of the fall of the Bastille every year. You are a key figure on the Edinburgh committee to abolish the slave trade. And you have devoted the last ten years of your life to obtaining for Scotland the burgh reform which you believe will lead to parliamentary reform. The rejection by the House of Commons of Richard Sheridan's motion in favour of burgh reform last April, the point-blank refusal to countenance even a committee of inquiry to investigate the notorious maladministration of Scotland's royal burghs, was more than just another setback. It was a massive rebuff and it forces us to reassess that whole strategy. Even Mr Sheridan admitted it would be easier to reform hell! And that was all in peacetime."

"You forget, Thomas," interrupted Fletcher, "that I declined membership of the Friends of the People because I do not approve of universal suffrage and annual parliaments, which some advocate, and from a conviction that such claims will increase the alarm among the higher orders and therefore strengthen Mr Pitt's administration. Leading Foxites are already advocating a temporary cessation of campaigning in both England and Scotland and Charles Grey is being pressed to withdraw his proposed reform motion in the next session of parliament. The French revolution has raised among the upper classes such a feeling against all liberal movements, and it was suggested to the movement for burgh reform that it would be prudent to abandon the project for a time. I see the wisdom in that suggestion. Here in Scotland, there is considerable Whig opposition to your inaugural convention. The matter is, I am afraid, closed."

Muir had run out of argument and time. He knew his welcome in the Fletcher home was at an end. He took his leave of the couple and stepped back into the cold, dark night in Hill Street, with a feeling of dejection, desertion and betrayal. His hopes for a reform campaign encompassing all of the classes in Scotland were withering. He realised he would have to rely on the common people more and more.

Back in the Fletcher home, Liza questioned Archibald about the loud voices she had heard coming from his study. "Muir quitted me much dissatisfied," he told her, "because he could not persuade me to join the society. Liza, I believe him to be an honest enthusiast but he is an ill-judging man. These violent reformers will create such an alarm in the country as must strengthen the government. The country is not prepared to second their views of annual parliaments and universal suffrage."

CHAPTER 9

The Scottish convention

"My sov'reign, if I might advise –
Our just petitions don't despise,
If John and Sandy e'er arise,
Pitt fair will Rue that mornin'."
'Rhyme of a Perth Weaver',
Scots Chronicle, 26 May, 1797.

The assembly of ordinary Scots who, for the first time, were attempting to take an active part in the government of their country, met on Tuesday 11 December, 1792. The meeting was small but significant; 160 delegates represented 80 societies in 35 towns and villages, predominantly from the manufacturing areas bordered by Glasgow, Edinburgh and Dundee. They comprised some lawyers and soldiers, some gentry, professionals and dissenting clergymen, but most were shopkeepers, printers, teachers and skilled artisans. They were clumsy in their procedure, feeling their way into a new kind of democracy, and sometimes their deliberations were unclear or even fanciful, but the convention was a milestone in the history of the reform movement and a fateful day for Thomas Muir.

Robert Watt once again sat near the back of Lawrie's large room in the James Court dancing academy, making notes of the proceedings. Basil Douglas, Lord Daer, was speaking. "Fellow citizens," he began. (Good, thought Watt, making a special note of the French form of address.) "There is no need for a formal election of office bearers. Although there ought to be some person in the chair whom speakers might address, there is no occasion for a president, a vice president, etc. We are all met on the great principles of liberty and political equality and therefore ought to be jealous of all men that set up in a permanent situation. I move that there should be no regular office bearers or leaders. It is proper, while the ministry has their eye on those whom they consider as leaders, to divide the responsibility among many. At all events every appearance of establishing an aristocracy amongst us ought to be guarded against."

Colonel Dalrymple rose and shouted above the clamour and applause that he seconded Daer's motion. Muir suggested a daily election of office-bearers. Alex Aitchison, from Canongate, thought it necessary that the treasurer and secretary should be permanent, "to prevent the affairs of the association from going into confusion". Daer agreed and so did the delegates. Skirving was elected secretary and Dalrymple voted into the chair for the day.

The convention had been called to agree on the timing and content of the petition campaign but the political landscape had changed. Loyalist reaction had made the atmosphere hostile and, as the likelihood of war with revolutionary France grew, the pro-government press sensationally reported that plans for a London insurrection had been foiled. No evidence was presented for these claims but a cabinet meeting in the house of the foreign secretary, William Grenville, which had lasted until 1am on Saturday 1 December, had agreed a royal proclamation recalling parliament, calling out part of the English militia, and allowing extra regular troops to be available for the reinforcement of London.

John Morthland told the convention, "Loyalist placemen load us with obloquy, accusing us of an intention to subvert the constitution, that we are disloyal subjects, enemies to king, lords and commons and that we wish to plunge everything into anarchy. It is necessary to refute their calumnies by full, fair and free declaration of our principles." He proposed they show their support for the established constitution and its three estates. One delegate was on his feet immediately, objecting to the words "king, lords, and commons". A clergyman rose and said he wished that the resolution had not been moved, but he hoped that the convention would now adopt it, as the rejection of the clause of king, lords, and commons, "would give wing to the malicious slanders of our enemies".

Morthland continued, "It appears that very great abuses have arisen in the government of this country from a neglect of the genuine principles of the constitution; that these abuses have of late grown to an alarming height and produced great discontents. The essential measures to be pursued in order to remove these abuses and to do away with their mischievous consequences are, first, to restore the freedom of election, and an equal representation of the people in parliament; secondly, to secure to the people a frequent exercise of their right of electing their representatives. I move that to accomplish these constitutional objects, the proper and legal method is that of applying by petition to parliament."

The debate continued with objections reflecting the republican sympathies of many who, however, recognised the point of the campaign was for something less. Muir summed up. "Although the House of Commons voted many years ago that the influence of the executive 'had increased, was increasing, and ought to be diminished'," he said, "what is the source of these abuses? The royal influence? What! Are you to remove the King? Then, gentlemen, according to this, we shall find ourselves in the same predicament with those foolish fellows who got drunk with the soldiers in the castle the other week, and drank, 'George the Third and Last'." He was interrupted by laughter. "Our great business is to reform, not to alter, to hold up the constitution to the people, to get it restored to its original purity."

Morthland put the question "Shall this resolution pass?" and it was carried by a large majority on a show of hands. Delegates then agreed to assist civil magistrates to repress riots and voted for their resolutions to be printed in the Scottish and English newspapers and in handbills.

When the first day's session ended that evening, Robert Watt went home to North Gray's Close and sat into the night, transcribing his notes for a report he would deliver to Robert Dundas in the morning.

On the following day Muir presented a printed address from the Society of United Irishmen in Dublin, signed by the organisation's chairman, William Drennan, and its secretary, Archibald Hamilton Rowan. Daer was convention chairman for the morning and allowed Muir time to read it. Colonel Dalrymple and Hugh Bell protested against its being read, afraid that it may be judged treasonable. But shouts from the hall to allow it to be read were loud and Daer asked Muir to step forward.

"We take the liberty of addressing you in the spirit of civic union, in the fellowship of a just and common cause," Muir read aloud. "We greatly rejoice that the spirit of freedom moves over the surface of Scotland," the address went on, "... not by a calm, contented, secret wish for a reform in parliament but by openly, actively and urgently willing it with the unity and energy of an embodied nation." The address explained how the Protestants and Catholics of Ireland had found common cause "in the assertion of that liberty which is due to us all". "Our cause is your cause," read Muir. "... our rights and wrongs are the same. Out of 32 counties in Ireland, 29 petitioned for a reform in parliament, and out of 56 of the royal burghs in Scotland, 50 petitioned for a reform in their internal structure and government".

Muir read on for 20 minutes until he reached the conclusion, "Let delegates from each country digest a plan of reform, best adapted to the situation and circumstances of their respective nations, and let the legislatures be petitioned at once by the urgent and unanimous voice of England, Scotland and Ireland. You have our ideas. Answer us, and quickly. This is not a time to procrastinate."

Muir moved that the address should be answered by the convention and it should be debated the following day. His friend Forsyth said the document bordered on an attack on the British constitution with the words "inviolability of the people". "To mend the constitution is legal," he said. "To do more is to raise a standard against it. The legality of the paper is not certain but in my opinion it is illegal. At all events, to reply would be inexpedient. Mr Muir is so far responsible for it, but if the convention should make it their own by approving and answering it, we become responsible. I caution the members against it."

Muir protested that there was no danger. "The paper supports the constitution," he said.

Richard Fowler insisted it was treasonable. "It says, 'Not by a calm, contented secret wish for a reform but by openly, actively, and urgently willing it, with the unity and energy of an embodied nation.' These words might be construed into high treason," he argued. Daer ruled that the paper should not be answered nor even lie on the table, but delegates, seeing Muir wanted to reply to Fowler, called "Hear him! Hear him!"

"If I had made no reply to Mr Fowler," Muir said, "the report would have gone out and been spread abroad by the enemies of reform that I had spoken high treason. We will a reform, do we not? Colonel Dalrymple, Lord Daer, and all the honourable gentlemen will a reform. The lord chief baron and the gentlemen of the county willed it, the royal burghs willed reform. The whole nation wills it, and cursed be the man who wills it not!"

The applause drowned Muir out for a time. He continued, "I myself have studied the law, and am confident that the paper is perfectly constitutional. How ridiculous, then, will it appear if we send no answer to this address? If the people of Ireland send us a congratulatory address in our spirit, it is immediately construed as treason. The people of Ireland will a reform, the Scotch will a reform. Is the Irish nation to be considered as the scapegoat in this business? Is it treason to petition parliament? It is clear, to me at least, that the convention should answer it."

A vigorous debate continued until Forsyth moved that the address be returned by Muir with a private letter acknowledging their interest and support. Muir, frustrated, agreed.

Thomas Fyshe Palmer from Dundee moved that the convention

now consider a petition to parliament. He was supported by many, concerned that the main business of the meeting should not be forgotten. During that evening and the following morning it was agreed to co-operate with the Friends of the People in London over the wording of the petition, with Palmer further insisting that it should be done quickly. "It will strengthen the cause of reform all over the country and show the people that we are in earnest," he stressed. "There is a great deal of danger in letting the spirit of the people cool by procrastination."

Later on Thursday morning John Millar called the attention of the convention to an advertisement in the *Edinburgh Herald*, placed by the Goldsmiths Hall association that pledged their lives and fortunes to the defence of the constitution. They promised to "counteract all seditious attempts, and in particular all associations for the publication or dispersion of seditious and inflammatory writings, or tending to excite disorders and tumults within this part of the kingdom", to "maintain the public peace, and to act in support of the civil authority for suppressing all riots and tumults", and "to give such just and proper information to our fellow subjects as may tend to remove the false and delusive opinions that have been industriously circulated amongst them."

"This," said Millar, "is one of these insidious and malicious attempts of the enemies of reform to thwart the measures of the Friends of the People, and to bring the cause of reform into discredit with the public, as if we were the friends of riot and sedition. I propose that members of the convention should go down in small parties to Goldsmiths Hall and subscribe the declaration. It contains nothing that any friend to reform could disapprove of."

John Clark objected. "By subscribing to the resolutions of our enemies it would appear as if we have deserted the cause of the people," he argued. "If the convention, however, thought that it would serve the cause I have no further objection, provided every member should add to his signature, 'a Friend of the People'." Captain Johnston seconded this, and said that he himself would subscribe as that day's chairman. Johnston left for Goldsmiths Hall with Millar, Morthland and several others, adding their names and designations to the roll. On their return a second party went out with John Clark at their head but the town officials had by this time become alarmed and they were not allowed to subscribe.

Muir made the closing speech and congratulated the members of the convention on their conduct and their deliberations. He complimented them for the free spirit of their inquiry and the "jealous attention" which had pervaded all their debates. "You paid no respect to the authority of leaders. You did not assent to a single clause in the various resolutions in compliance to great names. You entered into the minutiae of everything, and scrutinised every syllable before you gave your consent, instead of tamely yielding your judgments to those of others. This is the true spirit of liberty which, now that it is fairly begun to be understood amongst our countrymen, I hope will never cease till it becomes universal, and till every object we wish for is accomplished."

Richard Fowler's enthusiasm brought him to his feet, where he moved that all present should take the French oath, "to live free or die". The whole convention rose as one and, holding up their right hands, took the oath then applauded and congratulated one another. Colonel Dalrymple called above the noise that though he was highly pleased with the spirit of freedom, he cautioned against too much enthusiasm of the moment. "We stand on perilous ground," he declared, "and must therefore take care to give our enemies no just ground against us. The oath, or rather vow, just now made is in itself harmless, but might be magnified by our enemies as sowing the seeds of sedition. I therefore hope that no notice will be taken of it in our minutes or in the newspapers."

Fowler acknowledged the danger, and said that he meant no more than simply to impress on all present their commitment to the cause of freedom. The convention was adjourned until April. It was Thursday 13 December, 1792.

CHAPTER 10

Phoney war

"There can be no harm in giving alarm,
And scaring the people with strange apprehensions;
By brewing this storm, we avoid a Reform,
And securely enjoy all our places and pensions."

Anon, 'National Alarm', 1793.

On the same day the Scottish convention ended, parliament was recalled in emergency session. In the king's speech, George III spoke of "a spirit of tumult and disorder" and "acts of riot and insurrection". The debate on the speech was held up for a time by Joseph Jeckyll MP, who demanded, "By what authority are we actually sitting?" He explained that according to law the king is only allowed to summon an extraordinary meeting of parliament in cases of invasion, rebellion or insurrection. "I wish, therefore," he asked, "that those who are best qualified to clear up what is obscure and doubtful on this head, will point out where and when this insurrection has taken place."

Henry Dundas replied that the king had the power to call out the militia but to do that he had to call a parliament within fourteen days, if it were not already sitting. What he did not say was that the militia in England could only be embodied for the same reasons, invasion, rebellion or insurrection. Nevertheless, the speaker, Henry Addington, ruled that the debate should continue.

The lord mayor of London, Sir James Saunderson, got to his feet to move the speech's acceptance by saying he had discovered information that convinced him that seditious practices "were renewed with augmented force", and that "numerous societies had been established within the city of London, corresponding and confederating with other societies in different parts of the united kingdoms, all formed under specious pretences, but actually tending to subvert the constitution of the country". He noted that "a spirit of tumult and disorder has shown itself in acts of riot and insurrection which required the interposition of a military force."

Thomas Wallace MP seconded the lord mayor and went even further. "The insurrections that have taken place in various parts of the kingdom are matters of such notoriety that it would be a waste of time to enumerate or specify them," he declared. "Publications have been circulated through the country calculated to inflame the minds of the people, to render them dissatisfied with the present government, and to induce them to pull down our happy constitution and establish in its stead another, formed on the model of the French republic."

The Earl of Wycombe wondered, "Where is the cause of the alarm? It is evident that it does not exist in England. Do gentlemen think it is to be found in Scotland? Certainly not, for what the people of that country look for is not a subversion but simply a reform of the constitution and the removal of certain abuses or defects in the representation of the Commons. They have no hostile intentions against either the crown or the House of Lords. Is it in Ireland that the cause for alarm might be discovered? Certainly not, for the claims of the catholics of that kingdom are neither unreasonable nor inimical to the constitution."

Charles James Fox, leader of the Whigs, raised his large frame from the opposition front bench and glowered at Pitt from beneath his large, black, bushy eyebrows. He challenged the king's honesty. "I state it to be my firm opinion that there is not one fact asserted in his majesty's speech which is not false, not one assertion or insinuation which is not unfounded. Nay, I cannot be so uncandid as to believe that even the ministers themselves think them true." He then turned to the threat to the state. "An insurrection! Where is it? Where has it reared its head? Good God! An insurrection in Great Britain! No wonder that the militia were called out and parliament assembled in the extraordinary way in which they have been. But where is it? Two gentlemen have delivered sentiments in commendation and illustration of the speech; and yet, though this insurrection has existed for fourteen days they have given us no light whatever, no clue, no information where to find it. The right honourable magistrate tells us, in his high municipal situation, he has received certain information which he does not think proper to communicate to us... we are now told that a municipal magistrate has information of an insurrection, which he does not choose to lay before the Commons of England, but which he assures us is sufficient to justify the alarm that has spread over the whole country! The honourable seconder tells us that the 'insurrections are too notorious to be described'. I will take it upon me to say, sir, that it is not the notoriety of the insurrections which prevents those gentlemen from communicating to us their particulars, but their non-existence."

Henry Dundas tried to rescue the government. He described sailors' strikes at Yarmouth, Shields and Leith as insurrections. "In Scotland, more particularly," he said, "a spirit of turbulence has appeared in several places. Mobs have taken place in Dundee, Perth and Aberdeen. At Dundee the pretext of the disturbance, at its commencement, was stated to be some discontents with respect to meal; but it was not long before shouts of liberty and equality were heard from every quarter of the mob assembled for the occasion. Some even called out 'No excise! No king!' and they concluded with planting the tree of liberty. Upon this occasion the magistrates had been obliged to make application for the assistance of the military, a part of whom, at an instant's warning, had crossed the Firth of Forth."

He explained that he had been in Scotland during much of the crisis. "During the last six weeks I spent in Scotland," he said, "I was visited from every quarter, by the great manufacturers, by magistrates, and by gentlemen from parts of the country where there were no magistrates, all expressing their alarm at the situation of the country, and requesting the interference of government to check the spirit which threatened such dangerous consequences. I desire, gentlemen, to attend to the tenor of the king's speech and then, from a view of the whole subject, to pronounce on the legality and propriety of the measures adopted by ministers in the present crisis."

Dundas was supported by the faithful and the supine by 290 votes to 50.

There were others who thought the panic undeserved. Sir Gilbert Elliott, a country magistrate and a supporter of Pitt, wrote to a friend, "The Scotch insurrections consist of the planting of the tree of liberty at Perth, and the Dundee mob, and some others of less note. This is certainly ridiculous to those who live in Scotland and know the truth. The conduct of the ministry imposes on those who wish to stand by the government the heavy task of defending, or at least approving of, an unconstitutional act relating to the military."

Colonel Norman Macleod, the MP for Inverness, thought the same. He wrote to his fellow reformer Charles Grey, "The conduct of government seems to be a mixture of timidity and cunning, they are really afraid of insurrections on the one hand and on the other they court and provoke them. On the slightest occasion the troops are put in motion…A few days ago some boys assembled at Dundee to plant the tree of liberty. One of the magistrates immediately announced an insurrection and it was industriously given out here that the inhabitants had risen, seized the Custom House and Excise officers and refused to pay taxes. In consequence the 42nd regiment is ordered to be quartered in Perth and Dundee."

The value of such alarmism was appreciated at the highest levels of government. The foreign secretary, William Grenville, spelt it out in a letter to Lord Auckland, ambassador in The Hague, about reports of French agents in Britain, "I send you the description I received of certain persons said to be coming over here to fire our ships and dockyards. The measures taken in consequence of this intelligence gave occasion to the alarm, which was not discouraged, as this is one of the cases where security arises out of a general impression of danger. But I strongly believe there was nothing in it. No such persons ever made their appearance anywhere in England where we could trace them."

Two days after the Commons debate, Henry Dundas received a package from Robert Dundas in Edinburgh. It contained Robert Watt's report of the Scottish convention, complete with thirty-four foolscap pages of minutes and the names of all the delegates. In an accompanying note the younger Dundas said, "I really think everything now goes on in this country as well as you could hopefully wish. Dalrymple is frightened out of his wits. The committee of our association ordered his name and that of about twenty of the leaders of these societies to be expunged from our subscription paper." Referring to the disputed address from the Society of United Irishmen, he wrote, "We are endeavouring to get hold of the letter which is alluded to as treasonable, and it may probably be furnished to me this evening. In that event, the solicitor and I are resolved to lay Muir by the heels on a charge of high treason."

*

Muir had gone home to Huntershill following the convention, to spend Christmas and New Year with his family and to prepare his defence for the polymath James Tytler – an apothecary by training, editor of the second edition of *Encyclopedia Britannica*, the first person in Britain to ascend in a hot-air balloon, and author of the article in *The Bee* advocating passive resistance against the Scottish landowning classes. He had been charged with sedition, had engaged Muir as his advocate, and was due to appear in Edinburgh's High Court on Monday 7 January.

At the end of the holiday season Muir waved goodbye to his mother, father and sister Janet at Glasgow Cross as he boarded the Edinburgh stage on the morning of 2 January. He settled into a corner seat and pulled his greatcoat around him against the cold. The first stop would be in two hours or so, at Holytown in Lanarkshire, where he looked forward to food and a hot drink at the staging post while the horses were changed. As they pulled into yard of the Holytown inn, Muir noticed a post-chaise with horses in its shafts. As he stepped from the stage a man called to him.

"Thomas Muir?"

"Yes. And you, sir, are?"

"Williamson, sir, king's messenger. I have a warrant for your arrest."

"On what charge?"

"That's unknown to me, sir. The warrant simply requires me to escort you to Sheriff Pringle in Edinburgh."

Muir was delivered to the Edinburgh Tollbooth at eight o'clock that night and brought before Sheriff Pringle an hour later. Sheriff Honyman from Lanarkshire was also present.

"Ah, Mr Honyman, you also have an interest in this affair?" noted Muir. Honyman made no reply but in fact had been investigating Muir's activities in the west of Scotland for some time, on the orders of the lord advocate, and assisted by Lapslie. "May I be informed of the charge on which you have brought me to this place?" Muir demanded.

"First of all Mr Muir," replied Pringle, "will you inform me whether or not, in the month of November last, you were in the towns of Kirkintilloch, Lennoxtown, or Milton of Campsie?"

"I decline to answer any questions in this place," insisted Muir. "Any declaration of this kind, obtained in these circumstances, is utterly inconsistent with the rights of a British subject. I have solemnly maintained this principle in pleading for others in a criminal court and in my own case I will not deviate from that principle."

"There is a material difference," objected Honyman, "between pleading on principles as counsel and acting on them as a private character."

"There may be a distinction," replied Muir, "but I don't know it. If principles are just they must apply to all cases."

He was asked about details of his meeting in Kirkintilloch and of publications produced there but again refused to comment.

"Were you a member of the convention which met in Edinburgh last month," continued Pringle, "and did you produce a paper entitled *Address from the Society of United Irishmen?*"

"Again," repeated Muir, "I decline to answer the question on the same principle. May I ask you the name of your informer? I am sure that any you might find as witnesses against me will have been impressed by the hope of places and emoluments."

Pringle didn't answer but committed Muir to the Tollbooth until bail could be found. Word was got to William Moffat, who posted bail in the early hours of the morning. No charge was brought against Muir and in a few days he decided he'd be safer in London, where he could explain the circumstances of Scotland and his arrest to his friends and fellow reformers there. He left his affairs in the hands of another friend, the solicitor James Campbell, and took the stage for the four-day journey south.

As the year 1793 began, the number of people who had joined reform societies in each of the main cities of Edinburgh, Glasgow and Perth reached between 1,000 and 1,500; Paisley, Stirling and Kilmarnock all had between 500 and 800; Dundee had a few hundred; and elsewhere smaller societies flourished. Saltcoats, on the Ayrshire coast, had 60 members just after its formation in December. The 80 to 100 societies that were in existence was the same number as in more heavily populated England. The *Edinburgh Evening Courant* declared on November 29, 1792, "The spirit of Association and Remonstrance is stronger in Scotland, as vegetation is most powerful in soil fresh and newly reduced from the forest." On Tuesday January 8, 1793, the *Edinburgh Gazetteer* reported that the reform society in the small fishing and market town of Wick, in the far north county of Caithness, had published its own address to the people.

In London, Muir met Fox and Sheridan, spoke to the Friends of the People in a meeting that included Lords Daer and Lauderdale and the MPs Samuel Whitbread, Charles Grey, Thomas Maitland and Norman Macleod. He met with Thomas Hardy and Maurice Margarot and addressed the London Corresponding Society. He then decided to take the opportunity to visit Paris and observe the revolution in France with his own eyes. He wrote to Skirving, "Tomorrow I shall set out for Paris. Idle curiosity is not my only motive. By a concurrence of circumstances, even my obscure and feeble voice and intercession may have a tendency to mitigate the fate of a great personage... If I am to be tried give me timely notice. I shall instantly return. If not, I shall be absent three weeks."

Muir embarked at Dover for Calais on Tuesday 15 January.

CHAPTER 11

Death of a king

"King Louis thought to cut it down,
When it was unco sma', man;
For this the watchman crack'd his crown,
Cut aff his head and a', man."
Robert Burns, 'The Tree of Liberty'.

The city walls of Paris rose up from the gloom of a cold, early morning mist as the Calais stage approached. These were not the ancient defensive walls, long gone now, but 17-foot-high obstructions erected by generations of tax farmers to stop all traffic in and out of the city and charge a levy on goods passing through their gates. The fat commissions were pocketed at ninety-six offices in the walls. These farmers had been swept away in the early days of the revolution and now the barriers were manned by armed citizens and National Guards.

"*Bonjour, citoyen!*" said a man who carried a pike.

"*Bonjour, ça va?*" replied the driver. A National Guardsman in blue uniform watched from the guardhouse, twisting the ends of his oversize moustache. He signalled for passports from the passengers.

Muir handed over his letters of introduction from the reform societies in Edinburgh and London along with his passport from Calais.

"There are many of you from overseas in Paris now," said the *sans-culottes*, the new name that artisans and shopkeepers of Paris had taken to distinguish themselves from the nobles and well-to-do who wore knee breeches and silk stockings. This citizen was dressed in the Republican fashion of long trousers and a short jacket decorated with a tricolour sash hanging from one shoulder across his chest. On his head was the red bonnet adopted by the working people of Paris in homage to the hat worn by freed slaves in ancient Rome.

Muir hoped to meet some of the overseas visitors. He knew that a British Club had been formed and met in White's Hotel, where Tom Paine made his home when he fled from London.

"You have come at a very dangerous time, citizen," the National Guardsman called to him. "Our convention talks and talks and brings us nothing. The price of bread rises without stop and anger is a daily companion to hunger in all of the *faubourgs* and sections of the city." He left the gatehouse and approached the carriage, propping his musket against a wheel, the more to use his hands for emphasis. "And right now they are debating whether to guillotine the king," he said, drawing his forefinger across his throat. "They've been at it for days and many of them refuse to accept that Louis Capet and his tribe are finished. They have tried to defeat our revolution by plotting with the Austrians and they deserve to die as traitors."

"But still the convention talks and talks," said the *sans-culottes*. "The assemblies that met before them were just the same until we forced spines into their backs. When the assembly was still at Versailles, it took a march there by the women of Paris to bring Louis the Last and his whore to the city. The women sang that they had brought back the baker, the baker's wife and the baker's son! Ha! Then, of course, the assembly followed behind them and left the royal playground deserted."

The guard nodded in agreement. He picked up his musket. "Louis said he was with us but organised against us all the time. Then the whole family of traitors tried to escape in the night to meet up with their *émigré* armies in Austria. But Lafayette," he spat contemptuously in the mud, "the bastard general who massacred our people on the Champ de Mars for daring to sign a petition for a republic, Lafayette and his royalist friends in the assembly still put Capet back on the throne. That is, until we burst into his palace at the Tuileries, put a *bonnet rouge* on his head, and made him toast the nation with our cheap wine."

The red bonnet of the *sans-culottes* bobbed back and forth in agreement. "But they were still blind to the strength of the people," he said quietly, with pride, "until the Prussians said they would burn Paris to the ground and massacre the lot of us if we touched Louis again. That's when we had to ignore the assembly, overthrow the king and fight his Swiss Guards in the palace. It cost us thousands of lives but we won a republic, and every man of us voted for a new National Convention."

The eyes above the guard's dark moustache showed a momentary triumphalist glint as he added, "And we kept the king. He's ours, locked in the tower of the old Temple. The convention might be wondering what to do with him but he belongs to our commune and that's where the power is, with us, not with them."

The Calais stage was waved through the barrier into the city. Although Muir sported neither the tricolour rosette, sash, nor red bonnet, he wore simple clothes, open at the neck, and had his hair in the French style, combed back and gathered at the rear. This appearance, and his letters of introduction, ensured him safe passage in a country held tense by the constant threat of royalist counter-revolution and foreign invasion, high on rumours of plots by returning aristocrats. The radical Whig, Lord Lauderdale, had told Muir in London that barely a month previously he was stopped on his way to Paris because the cloth cover on the luggage box of his carriage had coloured fringes. A sentry had pointed out that such distinction was contrary to equality and had it removed. A fragile fear filled the air.

The stage came to a halt in the Temple section of the city. Muir carried his bag through the narrow streets to a nearby hotel. He had heard that the tenements of Paris stood so close together you could only see the sky from the fifth floor, and that wasn't far from the truth in this neighbourhood, near where Louis and his family were held in the old fortress of the Templars. It was still morning on Friday January 18. Muir had disembarked at Calais on Tuesday and made Paris in three days' hard travelling through winter rains and sleet, passing through towns and villages with trees of liberty planted in market places and topped with red bonnets. He knew that the convention's debate on the fate of Louis had begun on Monday but he had no news of what had happened or why the convention was still talking, if the information from the guards at the city gate was correct. He made his way west to White's Hotel to look for the British Club.

The hotel was in a little street near what had been the monastery of the Austin Friars, known to the French as Petits Pères. The street contained both Hôtel des Etats Unis, as well as White's, sometimes called Hôtel d'Angleterre.

"I'm sorry, citizen, neither Deputy Paine nor Citizen Stone is here, they are at the convention," the clerk at the hotel told Muir. "This is a most important day. The president is to announce the final vote on whether the king should die." Muir had been advised in London to make contact with Tom Paine or John Hurford Stone. Stone had been resident in Paris since April 1792 and had established a small chemical factory there. He had been a member of Dr Price's Unitarian congregation in Hackney and was a close friend of Joseph Priestley. During Charles-Maurice Talleyrand's unofficial diplomatic visit to London in 1792, where he represented the convention and sought British neutrality in the European offensive against France, Stone was instrumental in helping him meet Fox and Sheridan. Stone was a prominent member of the British Club and had presided at some of its more important functions.

Muir thanked the concierge and made his way back into the Passage des Petits Pères, turned south and headed for the Tuileries Palace, home of the new National Convention and scene of the insurrection of August 10 the previous year that had brought an end to the monarchy. He walked through the slums of central Paris, past stone-masons' yards, tanneries, breweries, and dingy hotels, all within sight of the Tuileries and the ministries in their grand buildings with formal gardens laid out with rows of lime trees. The back streets swarmed with brokers and bird sellers, doctors, quacks, dentists, jugglers on the waste ground, dog gelders, blacksmiths, joiners, bakers and shabby wine shops. It was in these warrens that Marie Antoinette and her attendant had briefly, almost fatally, lost their way on the night of the royal flight, in June 1791.

The convention met in the old riding academy of Louis XV, the *manège*. Muir joined the crush in the public balcony that looked down on a steep hill of benches for deputies. The seats swept down to the oval at floor level where horses used to run. On the balcony were *sans-culottes* and *bourgeois*, men with workers' trousers and gentlemen with knee-breeches, ladies in fine frocks and women in rough shifts and pinnies, all jostling for a better view. Coffee, oranges and ices were on sale. Wines, liquers and brandies were drunk as if the convention was a common café. Many of these citizens felt free enough to shout their own opinions as speakers on the floor tried to make themselves heard. Some women had kept the score of past votes with pinpricks on cards as the deputies had mounted the tribune, one by one, to declare whether they were for or against execution of Louis. In both the gallery and in the cafés surrounding the Tuileries, bets were laid on the final outcome of the vote and on the numbers for and against.

Muir spotted Paine, looking tired and grim, on the deputies' benches. Along the public gallery he saw Stone, a fluent French speaker who knew many of the deputies from the Jacobins Club, especially those who grouped themselves around the writer and publisher Jacques-Pierre Brissot, and who were beginning to be known as Girondins.

Muir caught Stone's eye and worked his way though the press of bodies towards him. They shook hands. Stone had been expecting him for some time. "You are just in time for the announcement of the convention's president, Pierre Vergniaud, of the final vote on the king."

"Why now?" asked Muir. "What has gone on?"

"From early on Wednesday morning until late last night," Stone quickly explained, "the convention has been in permanent session, with every deputy going to the tribune to declare what punishment the king should have. Some simply said '*La mort!*' but many spelt out their reasons for wanting death or not. It seemed to take forever and the deputies were exhausted from the ordeal. Yesterday's vote, though, was counted differently by different secretaries, so the figures have had to be checked and now Vergniaud can tell us the true result."

The president called for order from his elevated chair on the other side of the hall, above the secretaries' table in the middle of the oval. He said, "Citizens, I am going to proclaim the results of the vote. You have exercised a great act of justice. I hope that humanity will lead you to maintain the most profound silence. When justice has spoken, humanity must have its place." He explained that twenty-eight deputies had not been able to vote, representatives from former colonies had not yet arrived in Paris, and others were ill, so the total cast was 721, and the simple majority required was 361. Some punishment other than death was asked for by 321 deputies; thirteen had voted for death with reprieve; twenty-six had voted for death with an amendment that a second debate should take place to consider a reprieve; and 361 voted unconditionally for death. The final tally was 387 for death and 334 for some penalty other than death. But those who voted for execution without any conditions at all had a majority of just one.

"I declare in the name of the National Convention," announced Vergniaud, "that the punishment it pronounces against Louis Capet is that of death."

The benches and the gallery remained silent and respectful, according to the wishes of the president. But when Vergniaud next ruled that, since twenty-six deputies had voted for an amendment requiring the decision to be reviewed and a new debate would be had the next day, the convention erupted in anger. Those deputies on the left of the president's chair were especially aggrieved. This was where the radicals sat and their numbers rose up the steep benches to the top rung. They were known as the Mountain, *la Montagne*, and they gathered around Maximilien Robespierre and Jean-Paul Marat. These deputies, like many in the Paris sections, saw no need for the convention to try the king in the first place, they were lawmakers, not judges. Louis was obviously a traitor and the law was clear on the fate of those who commit treason.

Although physically tired and emotionally exhausted, the deputies on both sides of the chair, Brissot's Girondins sat on the right, and those in the middle, who were known as the Plain, argued once again into the night until, at half past ten, the president placed his hat on his head, signifying that the session was adjourned. This was to the extreme, noisy and lengthy displeasure of the Mountain, who were prepared to argue once again into the early hours. The fate of the king was back on the convention's agenda for morning.

Muir was overwhelmed by the ferocity of the debate as well as the fierce reactions in the public gallery, but also by the very democracy of it. He had perhaps imagined a more restrained political democracy, such as the Philadelphia debates he had read of. On the way home Stone explained to Muir that the debate on the fate of the king had been going on since the insurrection of the previous August. Louis was finally brought before the convention on one day in early December, only after the commune had sent a delegation to announce that the patience of Parisians was running out and if the decision was delayed for much longer then the people might have to act as they had done with a reluctant assembly in August. Minds were concentrated but it was only at the start of this week that decisions had begun to be taken. On Monday the convention took 12 hours to decide that three questions would be voted on. First, is the king guilty? Second, if so, should this be ratified by a referendum? Third, what should the punishment be? On Tuesday the first two questions were put in a roll-call vote and the guilty verdict was nearly unanimous; the ratification by the people was rejected by a large majority. Then the marathon of Wednesday and Thursday took place.

Now, deputies and citizens drifted home to rest before the next day's continuing ordeal in the *manège*, all except one. Tom Paine, respected republican, English by birth, citizen of France and America, member of the National Convention representing the people of Pas-de-Calais, was filled with genuine sorrow at the decision to execute the king and he would tell the convention so in the morning. He would overcome his exhaustion to prepare a speech that might convince deputies to save France from destruction. He worked through the night, writing and rewriting, aiming arguments to try to prevent allies from deserting the cause of liberty or giving enemies added strength to destroy the fragile seedling of European democracy.

Paine had no political sympathy for the monarch. "Louis XVI considered as an individual," he had written, "is an object beneath the notice of the republic." But as a part of a band of conspirators he was dangerous. Paine had already told the assembled deputies, when he voted against the death sentence at noon on Thursday, that he thought the reaction to Louis's execution in America would act against France. Louis had supported the American revolution with arms and ships and was well regarded there. But more than that, contenders for thrones had always assassinated their way to a crown, and the death of Louis at the hands of the republic would simply remove an obstacle for his royal relatives abroad, who would nevertheless claim the title and rally support.

"It is our duty as legislators not to spill a drop of blood when our purpose may be effectually accomplished without it," he had told the deputies. Paine preferred exile and obscurity for the Capets, preferably in republican America. "There, hereafter, far removed from the miseries and crimes of royalty he may learn, from the constant aspect of public prosperity, that the true system of government consists not in kings, but in fair, equal and honourable representation." He had even won approval for the proposal from the American ambassador in Paris, the French ambassador in Philadelphia, and Pierre Lebrun, the French foreign minister.

He used the example of the Stuart dynasty in Britain. "Charles I lost his life," he argued, "yet Charles II was restored to all the plenitude of power, which his father had lost. Forty years had not expired when the same family strove to re-establish their ancient oppression; so the nation then banished from its territories the whole race.

The remedy was effectual. The Stuart family sank into obscurity, confounded itself with the multitude, and is at length extinct."

So Paine worked on without sleep to prepare his final appeal for what he thought was a calm, rational, humane policy and then, like the other deputies, took his seat once more in the *manège* at half past ten on Saturday morning. It was cold and dark in the hall, the winter chill reaching deep into the walls and the woodwork. The only light came from small clerestory windows running around the top of hall, just underneath the roof. And the only warmth was from a small porcelain stove, symbolically but humorously modelled on the old Bastille prison, placed in the centre of the room between the speakers' tribune and the president's chair.

All the old arguments were replayed with the usual antagonism and accusation. While one deputy called for exile of all the Bourbons before Louis's execution, another threatened a repeat of the September massacres if the sentence wasn't carried out immediately, and yet another asked for delay until a new constitution had been approved by the country. Then another round of the same furious disagreements would begin again. Paine caught the eye of the president and was invited to take the tribune. Although the veteran revolutionary was regarded with great affection and accorded much prestige, Paine's French was so bad that he couldn't take part in the debates and now, as always, he had to have his written speech translated for him. The philosopher Jean-Henri Bançal began reading while Paine stood mute beside him.

Bançal began, "The decision come to in the Convention yesterday in favour of death has filled me with genuine sorrow ..." when he was interrupted from high on the Mountain by Marat, wearing his trademark *sans-culottes* outfit, his hair tied back with a red cloth, and completing the theatricality of his appearance with two pistols stuck in his waistband.

"I deny the right of Thomas Paine to vote on such a subject!" he shouted. "As he is a Quaker, of course his religious views run counter to the infliction of capital punishment." Disorder erupted in the hall as shouts of agreement with Marat were countered by cries of "free speech!"

Bançal raised his voice above the hecklers and continued with Paine's speech. He read, "I may lay claim to the possession of a certain amount of experience. I have taken no inconsiderable part in the struggle for freedom during the revolution of the United States of America, it is a cause to which I have devoted almost twenty years of my existence… France's sole ally is the United States of America. It is the only nation upon which France can depend for a supply of naval stores, because all the kingdoms of northern Europe are either now waging war against her, or shortly will be. Now, it is an unfortunate circumstance that the individual whose fate we are at present determining has always been regarded by the people of the United States as a friend to their own revolution. Should you come, then, to the resolution of putting Louis to death, you will excite the heartfelt sorrow of your ally…"

Marat leapt to his feet once more. "I denounce the translator. Such opinions are not Thomas Paine's. The translation is incorrect." Paine had to shout to assure the convention, through Bançal and amid great noise and confusion, that the opinions were indeed his own.

As the commotion died, Bançal continued, "In the name of the citizens of the American republic, I beg that you delay the execution. Do not, I beseech you, bestow upon the English tyrant the satisfaction of learning that the man who helped America, the land of my love, to burst her fetters, has died on the scaffold."

Marat now leapt from the Mountain into the middle of the chamber. "Paine's reason for voting against the death penalty is that he is a Quaker!" Again he achieved the noise and fury he desired until Paine managed to call out over the din, "I have been influenced in my vote by public policy as well as by moral reasons!" He left the tribune deflated.

The arguments continued for the rest of the day and into the small hours of Sunday. One deputy, the unaligned Bertrand Barère, seemed to clinch the mood of the meeting when he argued that a reprieve would make the work of the convention impossible and that a "new diplomacy" would "stipulate the health or the banishment of a condemned man as the first article of a treaty". The fate of the king would be in the hands of their enemies, the crowned heads of Europe. "Citizens, do you want to expose this head to the chances and conjectures of military events?"

A vote was finally taken and at two o'clock in the morning the president announced that 310 had voted for a reprieve, while 380 had voted against. The fate of the king was sealed. The arguments of the Jacobins of the Mountain, that the revolution was in greater danger as long as the king was alive, had persuaded the majority in the Plain, along with many of the Girondin leaders, that the blade must fall on Louis's neck, and without delay. It was now Sunday 20 January. The guillotine would be made ready in the Place de la Révolution for the next morning.

Muir, who had sat in the gallery throughout the to and fro of the argument, felt the same deflation he had seen on the face of Tom Paine. He wondered what effect the decision would have on the radical movements in Scotland, England and Ireland, especially among Whig reformers whose support of popular democracy was lukewarm at best.

Paine went back to White's Hotel, sat at his desk and wrote to a friend, "If the French kill the king, it will be a signal for my departure, for I will not abide among such sanguinary men." But such a course was unlikely. Just a month before in an English court, Paine had been convicted in his absence for writing the most popular book since *Pilgrim's Progress*. Although Pitt's government was still officially neutral towards the new republic, all of the hostile powers surrounding France were Britain's allies. Escape by ship to America on seas controlled by the British navy was just too risky.

*

Muir and Stone made their way through the Tuileries gardens to the Place de la Révolution at dawn on Monday to witness the historic end of the French monarchy. It was cold and rain came intermittently through a freezing fog. The square was already filling with people and the whole city was armed. Antoine Santerre, a brewer by trade but now commander of the National Guard, had ordered the committees of the city's forty-eight sections to guard their own neighbourhoods. Suspicious groups of people were to be dispersed in case royalists made a rescue attempt. The city gates were closed and guarded. Every soldier and national guardsman in Paris was on duty, 80,000 under arms for Louis's procession to the guillotine.

This innovative machine of death had been moved from its usual place in the Place du Carrousel in front of the Tuileries to allow more space for spectators. It was a novelty, having been in use for only nine months, and had been proposed by Dr Joseph-Ignace Guillotin as a reform of the cruel and inhumane methods of capital punishment used by the *ancien régime*. Only aristocrats had benefited from the axe, other unfortunates being broken on the wheel or slowly hanged and disembowelled in a death of prolonged agony. Dr Guillotin, a member of the National Assembly, had brought his design before the deputies in December 1789 as a way of administering capital punishment according to the equality granted all citizens by the Declaration of the Rights of Man. This machine was egalitarian, swift, surgical and instantaneous, as far as the doctor could tell. Common criminals would now be treated with the dignity formerly accorded only to nobles, he argued.

Louis's carriage entered the place de la Révolution at ten o'clock to a thundering roll of drums. His escort was a hundred armed and mounted men at the front of the coach with another hundred at the back, and these were surrounded by 1,200 foot soldiers, paced by sixty drummers. Stone pointed to a figure commanding one of the detachments in the escort. "Look over there, that man commanding a battalion with pikes, that's John Oswald, from Edinburgh. He's one of the British Club, former officer in the army; left it in India because of the cruel treatment of enemy soldiers, and came home overland." Muir saw a tall, straight man in the green uniform of the French army, clearly an officer but wearing the knapsack of a private.

"And, there, over there, there's another of the club!" said Stone. "In the National Guard detachment by Louis's coach. That's William Maxwell, from Kirconnell in Dumfriesshire; the same William Maxwell that Edmund Burke condemned last month in parliament for raising money for arms for the republic!"

Louis suddenly emerged from his closed coach, accompanied by a priest. His coat was removed and he stood in his knee breeches and white waistcoat while the executioner's assistant cut his hair short at the back of his neck. The assistant moved to tie Louis's arms behind his back but he objected and attempted to struggle free. The priest whispered in Louis's ear and he succumbed, was secured, and walked up the wooden steps to the guillotine. He turned to the vast crowd in the square and attempted to address them. "I die innocent of all the crimes of which I have been charged. I pardon those have who brought about my death and I pray that the blood you are about to shed may never be required of France..." A nod from Santerre and a deafening roll of drums drowned out whatever else Louis wanted to say, while at the same moment he was grabbed, strapped to a plank, and pushed head-first through the "widow's window". Without a pause the executioner dropped the 12-inch blade and the head of the once mightiest autocrat in Europe was in the basket.

It was held high for all to see and the crowd chanted Robespierre's slogan, "The king is dead! Long live the revolution!" The popular journalist Louis Mercier wrote in his notebook, "His blood flowed and cries of joy from 80,000 armed men struck my ears... I saw the schoolboys of the Quatre-Nations throw their hats in the air; his blood flowed and some dipped their fingers in it, or a pen or a piece of paper... An executioner on the boards of the scaffold sold and distributed little packets of hair and the ribbon that bound them; each piece carried a little fragment of his clothes or some bloody vestige of that tragic scene. I saw people pass by, arm in arm, laughing, chatting familiarly as if they were at a fête."

Mary Wollstonecraft, whose popular book, *A Vindication of the Rights of Woman*, was published at the same time as the second part of Paine's *Rights of Man,* was in Paris and a regular at the British Club. She had watched Louis's final journey from the window of her lodgings. The streets had been empty and silent and the windows were closed, by order of the commune. "Not a voice was heard," she later wrote. The silence was made more terrible by the rising sound of the slow beating drums of the escort. She was shocked by the calm dignity of Louis and she cried. "I want to see something alive; death in so many frightful shapes has taken hold of my fancy," she wrote in her diary later that night. "I am going to bed, and, for the first time in my life, I cannot put out the candle."

CHAPTER 12

Liberty curtailed

"Tis Liberty alone that gives the flow'r
Of fleeting life, its lustre and perfume;
And we are weeds without it. All constraint,
Except what wisdom lays on evil men, is evil."

William Cowper, 'The Winter Morning Walk', 1785.

The cold bit into the bones of Alexander Wight as he turned into Parliament Close on the morning of Tuesday 8 January, the date fixed for the trial of three young printers charged with sedition. Wight was the leading defence advocate in the case. His age was telling and he was beginning to feel frail. He would much rather have been preparing for his beloved Musical Society of Edinburgh, of which he was director, than preparing briefs for the high court. But he was keenly aware of the importance of this case and others to follow. The charges against publishers and printers that Muir and others had spoken about that night in November were all now fixed in the court schedule.

The first case should have been the day before and Muir should have been conducting the defence. But the young lawyer's arrest and bail sent a clear message to James Tytler who, a month previously, had been charged with "wickedly and feloniously composing and writing a seditious libel addressed to The People and their Friends". Tytler had disagreed with the petition campaign of the reform societies and argued in his leaflet that it was useless. "The parliament has already showed itself unworthy of confidence," he wrote, "and it has usurped a power to which it has no right." The House of Commons was not democratic but "a vile junto of aristocrats" and it would make more sense to petition the king directly. "If the king hear you not," he concluded, "keep your money in your pockets and frame your own laws, and the minority must submit to the majority." Tytler decided that his chances of a fair hearing in the bullying climate of official and unofficial loyalism were negligible and he absconded. He hid for a while in a shepherd's cottage on Salisbury Crags, to the east of the town, until friends could arrange a passage to Ireland and then on to America.

Consequently, on that Monday morning, as law and tradition dictated, his name was called many times inside the court and three times from its steps, after which the lord advocate moved that a sentence of "fugitation and outlawry" be pronounced. The judges agreed and Robert McQueen, otherwise Lord Braxfield, declared Tytler "an outlaw and fugitive from his majesty's laws and ordain him to be put to his majesty's horn, and all his moveable goods and gear to be escheat and inbrought to his majesty's use."

Wight was pessimistic as he entered the courtroom. He had more, similar cases to defend before the month was out. Robert Dundas, prosecuting, knew this. He had ordered them. Writing to his Uncle Henry before the weekend, and with December's successful prosecution of Tom Paine in mind, he stated, "I hope, not without some anxiety, that an Edinburgh jury will do equal justice on our seditious gentry that a Middlesex one has done with you. Three trials of this kind come on this ensuing week."

In the high court, the prisoners John Morton, James Anderson, and Malcolm Craig were brought up; the court rose and the bench filed in. The judges were led by Lord Braxfield, and Lords Henderland, Eskdale, Swinton, and Abercromby followed. The indictment was read out by the clerk of the court, accusing the three printers of proposing the toast, "George the third and last and damnation to all crowned heads" in the presence of soldiers of the 37th regiment of foot and of "falsely and insidiously pretending that their pay was too small and holding out to them the prospect of higher pay if they would join The Friends of the People or a club for equality and freedom".

James Fergusson, Wight's junior advocate, challenged the indictment. "The crime here charged of uttering seditious speeches is one which has not occurred in this country as a subject of trial in the memory of any man living," he argued. "In former times it had often been prosecuted but those were times when the freedom of the subject was not so secure as now. The words used here are ambiguous, uttered in convivial discourse and with no wicked or seditious design." He pointed out that the prisoners only said what many people think about the pay of soldiers. "This is nothing more criminal than saying that the stipends of the clergy are too small."

He stated that none of the prisoners had any connection with any of the clubs or associations mentioned and concluded, "It is inexpedient to bring to trial a crime of this nature, of which there has been no recent example in the records of the court. It might be of dangerous consequence to introduce as a precedent the trial of a crime of such difficult proof and of so ambiguous a nature."

Braxfield nodded to the prosecution to reply and John Burnett, junior advocate in Robert Dundas's office, rose. "In this case, perhaps more than in any other," he began, "there is the greatest room for the question of intention. But the accused are printers, conversant in the meaning of words. They must know that in an established government every act to disturb that government is highly criminal at common law."

Dundas expanded the argument. "At the time when the words and speeches in this charge were uttered, the country was in a very alarming situation indeed," he claimed. "Principles had been openly and avowedly published that were hostile not only to that happy constitution under which we live, but subversive of all order and of every established government. Persons who, on such an occasion express themselves in the manner the accused did, are actuated by nothing else than a most wicked and seditious purpose, with a view to stir up that spirit of popular insurrection and to produce those scenes of riot and anarchy which have been so dismally experienced by the inhabitants of a neighbouring country." With a self-satisfied smile, the lord advocate sat down.

Throughout the rest of the long day, twenty-five witnesses were examined and cross examined, the prosecution and defence summed up, and the court was adjourned. The jury was asked to deliver its verdict the next morning at 11 o'clock, which it did, finding all of the accused guilty. The judges announced they would pronounce sentence on Friday at the same time.

On the intervening day, Thursday 10 January, another trial for sedition was to begin in the same court. John Elder, the Edinburgh bookseller mentioned to Henry Dundas by Watt, and William Stewart, a merchant from Leith, were charged with reprinting the French National Assembly's 1789 *Declaration of the Rights of Man and of Citizens*, of publishing a treatise on *Origin of Government*, and of manufacturing medals with the inscriptions referring to liberty and equality. Stewart failed to appear and was outlawed. Elder's trial was postponed three times while Stewart was being unsuccessfully hunted, and eventually the charge was quietly dropped.

Morton, Anderson, and Craig were brought from the Tollbooth on Friday morning to hear their sentences. They had sent a letter of contrition to Lord Braxfield, who had it read to the court. The three young men appealed for clemency and fair consideration; this was their first offence and they assured the bench of their future good conduct and that none of them belonged to political clubs.

Lord Henderland gave the principal judgment and began by terrifying the prisoners. "In certain circumstance I can have no doubt that even an attempt to excite mutiny or sedition among soldiers may be punishable with death," he declared, adding to the fear and tension with a long exposition of the legal history of mutiny. In descending order of terror he ruled out the gallows, transportation and flogging, settling for nine months' close confinement in the Tollbooth. "I mean that there shall be no meeting of associates," he explained, "no

gossiping or drunkenness permitted within their places of confinement, that they may be left seriously and solemnly to reflect on their
past and thereby be enabled to amend their future conduct." The
three were also bound over for good behaviour for three years. The
other judges agreed.

*

On the following Tuesday the *Gazetteer* ran a full and accurate report
of the trial. Its accuracy, even in the portrayal of Braxfield's rich
Scottish vernacular, was remarked on by many. The report began,
"The lord justice clerk, previous to the examination of the witnesses,
made many observations on the excellence of the British constitution," including, " 'The reformers talk of liberty and equality, this
they hae in everything consistent wi' their happiness, and equality
also. However low born a man may be, yet his abilities may raise
him to the highest honours of the state. He may rise to be a lord
chancellor, the head of the law; he may rise to be archbishop of
Canterbury, the head of the kirk; and tak precedence of a' ranks but
the blood-royal. What mair equality wad they hae? If they hae ability,
low birth is not against them. But that they hae a right to a representation in parliament I deny, the landed interest alone should be
represented in parliament for they only hae an interest in the country.
In God's name let them gang. I wish them not to stay; but I deny they
hae a right to representation in parliament'."

Robert Dundas read the newspaper and quietly smiled to himself.
Here, at last, was his chance. There was an old law forbidding
"murmuring" against judges. He could wound the radical paper and
one of the reformers' leading members. He set to work preparing an
indictment for contempt of court. "I consider it my duty," he wrote,
"to call to the particular attention of their lordships that the account
given of the said trial is not only partial, untrue and unjust, but by
imputing partiality and injustice to the court in the conduct of the
trial it is clearly and evidently calculated to lessen the regard which
the people of this country owe to the supreme criminal court."

William Johnston, owner and editor of the *Gazetteer*, and Simon Drummond, its printer, were ordered to appear before their lordships. Braxfield excused himself from the sitting in a show of impartiality and, in spite of learned argument by Alexander Wight, the two men were found guilty of false and slanderous representation, imprisoned in the Tollbooth for three months and bound for £500 and £100 security "for their good behaviour" for three years.

Few could believe the severity of the sentence for such an arcane offence and many, even loyalists, thought the portrait of Braxfield to be quite accurate. Years later, a senior Scottish judge wrote, "Nobody who had ever heard him speak could refuse to acknowledge that the Scotch imputed to him was rather softened than exaggerated; and everything he said during these trials shows that no injustice was done to his sentiments. In truth it was the general fidelity of the portrait, attested by its being long afterward recited, even by the Justice's friends, as an excellent imitation of the diction and manner of the original, that made it so offensive."

The assault on radical publishing in Scotland was not over yet, and Wight, Fletcher, and Erskine were shortly to appear together to defend Walter Berry and James Robertson, founders of another new reform newspaper, the *Caledonian Chronicle*. But it was not as newspaper owners they were charged. Both of them had Edinburgh bookshops and print shops and their crime was to print and sell copies of *The Bee*. This journal published in weekly parts James Thomson Callender's *Political Progress of Britain*. It argued that parliament had become "a mere out-work of the court, a phalanx of mercenaries" and "a conspiracy of the rich against the poor" which was in need of major reform. Callender thought it safer to flee to the United States than face a trial for sedition in Braxfield's court.

Fletcher, on behalf of Berry and Robertson, argued in court that the case involved the liberty of the press, and if the prosecution strikes at that, "a total darkness in political knowledge must ensue, the constitution must receive a mortal stab and may, at last, perish". He said that the author was not writing against parliament but against the influence of the crown in it, which is "a topic of discussion in the House of Commons itself". The purpose of the publication was to "correct and reform, and the same words almost have been used in other authors long ago, such as the resolution by the Duke of Richmond published in 1780."

The prosecution repeated the arguments about present dangers. "The minds of the people may be inflamed to gross enormities by publications at one time, that would have had no effect at another," answered James Montgomery, Dundas's assistant in the case. The evidence and legal argument were continued by Wight but Berry and Robertson followed their reform colleagues to the Tollbooth for three months and six months respectively, with both ordered to find £100 security for three years. Erskine took an appeal to the House of Lords but was refused a hearing.

Robert Dundas's final strike against the radical press during his January assault was on the *Glasgow Advertiser*. Owned and printed by John Mennons, it was an established newspaper that insisted on keeping its pages open to reformers. The *Advertiser* had carried a report in November of a founding meeting for reform in Partick, near Glasgow. The meeting had been held in a local inn and James Smith, a gun-maker from Gorbals, attended and proposed a resolution that was adopted by the new society. It declared that the inhabitants of the village of Partick and its neighbourhood have "formed themselves into an association under the name of the Sons of Liberty and the Friends of Man" to defend Tom Paine and his book, and to co-operate with reform associations in Scotland, England, and Ireland, for "a fair, full, free and equal representation of the people in parliament". Ten days before Paine's trial in December, Robert Dundas had guessed the outcome and ordered Sheriff Honyman to arrest both Smith and Mennons for sedition. Smith escaped to France and, in an effort to muzzle newspaper editor Mennons, the charges against him remained on file and were only dropped much, much later.

CHAPTER 13

Steady hands

"The attacks which have been made on the liberty of the press…may appeal for a moment to the minds of men, but it is in moments like these that the people can and ought to know their real friends."

Colonel Norman Macleod's open letter to Scottish reformers, *Edinburgh Gazetteer,* 18 January, 1793.

The tall figure of Basil Douglas, Lord Daer, came slowly down George Street in Edinburgh's New Town. It was a cold and damp January afternoon and he occasionally lifted a handkerchief to his mouth to help him suppress his constant cough. Daer counted off the grand doorways until he came to Norman Macleod's. He pulled the brass handle of the doorbell and the gentle ring was answered by a young serving woman who showed him into the colonel's study, where Macleod and Skirving were waiting. Macleod welcomed his fellow reformer and Skirving, who had earlier in the month arranged for the two of them to travel from London to help boost the morale of the Scottish societies, shook Daer's hand. Their speaking tour of the Scottish societies was almost at an end.

Macleod had also tried to steady the resolve of the reform societies by publishing two open letters in the Scottish papers. The first explained that he was honoured to be the first member of parliament to join the Scots association at a time when loyalists were attacking the principles of freedom and the aristocracy was intent on increasing the power of the executive, and how they both used the unfortunate events in France to oppose reform with stories of riot and massacre. "Such is the policy of the present day," he argued, "and, to the disgrace of the understanding of the public, it has been wonderfully successful in south Britain." The MP had published a second letter of support stating his belief that a just reform of parliament was possible in the not too distant future, and promising that till it is obtained, "I and my friends will not shrink from our post but freely devote ourselves to your interests".

The opposition was now formidable. Both parties in the kirk had pronounced against the reform societies; radical journeymen and schoolteachers had been dismissed, and master tradesmen and shopkeepers known for their democratic views were boycotted; lawyers of allegedly 'Jacobin' sympathies were deprived of briefs. Lord Braxfield's sister had threatened a shopkeeper with a boycott by her and her friends for having the petition lying on his counter. Posters had been torn down in various towns and soldiers at Dalkeith had stolen the local petition. Skirving had been worried that the petition campaign was just holding together in the teeth of such hostility.

A further blow was delivered in a letter Skirving received on 13 January from Charles Grey, the MP who had promised to introduce the reform petition in the Commons in May. Grey's letter claimed that supporters in England were too few to begin petitioning. He had shown the letter to Daer, who replied to Grey four days later, expressing alarm and demanding an explanation. The tone of his letter was angry. "You must tell us explicitly whether you mean to petition or not, for if you don't in England, neither (say they) will we in Scotland." He then asked Grey directly "do you think likewise of not moving in parliament for a reform? If so, many will consider it almost treachery in you and your friends." He believed it was "of great consequence to keep our leading men and societies in London high in the estimation of the supporters of freedom" and assured him that "a great body of the common people are inclined to petition". Any notion that reform leaders were lukewarm would "damp the ardour of their coming forward, if not extinguish it". Grey had asked the Scottish societies to continue petitioning on their own. "You wish us to come forward because we are more numerous," wrote Daer. "I believe that small as our numbers are, they are greater in proportion than in England, but far from enough to command protection from the executors of the forms of law." The legal and social hostility to reform would probably increase if Scotland was left on its own. The Scottish law courts were very different from those in England and had grabbed legislative power to themselves. "Since the parliaments were united," he explained, "scarcely four acts have been passed in as many score of years affecting Scots law... [Scottish judges] instead of applying to the parliament at London have taken upon themselves with a degree of audacity which can hardly be made credible to a stranger, to make...Little Laws (acts of parliament as they call them) materially affecting the liberty of the subject." He claimed that for these reasons "the Friends of Liberty in Scotland have almost universally been enemies to union with England" and that "Scotland has long groaned under the chains of England and knows that its connection there has been the cause of its greatest misfortunes". Therefore if England now deserted Scotland in the campaign for reform it would likely have "a national bad effect" and "make the Tweed appear a boundary in political sentiment or action" following which "a fatal national jealousy may arise".

The three men agreed that, nevertheless, the loyalist associations in England were more numerous and powerful than in Scotland, and were violent, overbearing and bullying. They had the unofficial support of the ministry and, they thought, some secret financial backing, too. They had heard of men of all ranks being hounded or dismissed, even losing the tenancies of their farms; Daniel Adams, secretary of the Society for Constitutional Information, had been dismissed in December from his job as a clerk in the public accounts office in London. There were even reports from parts of Northamptonshire and Sussex that house-to-house enquiries had been conducted into people's loyalty. So they could understand why Grey was defeatist.

However, Daer said he had heard from Hardy at the London Corresponding Society that Matthew Campbell Brown, editor of *The Patriot* in Sheffield, had written to him saying that although they see Scotland taking the lead, he thought constant communication was necessary between the societies, however distant, and that they all should act together. Daer was confident that Grey would come around. He thought the man was impulsive and always out of sorts unless he was sure he was on a winning horse.

Skirving pointed out that some of the Foxite Whigs in Edinburgh were now arguing for a temporary stop to the campaign. Not just Fletcher and Erskine but association members, such as John Morthland and Richard Fowler. They argued that daily attacks had caused the name of the Friends of the People to fall into disgrace, and that many who wished the cause well had been intimidated by the legal challenges, by events in France, or simply because of the lies and distortions circulated about the campaign and its members. Fowler had even suggested that they lie low until the panic blew over. He had proposed this twice at meetings and had been defeated both times but was persistent, even moving that the second national convention be deferred.

Skirving had enlisted the support of Daer and Macleod to help counteract the alarmism and the panic set up by the ministry. There were, after all, only three or four loyalist associations north of the border, the Goldsmiths Hall "lives and fortunes men", the Glasgow Constitutional Association, and a Dumfries Association for Peace and Property, for certain. That was insignificant compared to the hundreds, maybe even as high as two thousand, in England. Tom Paine had been burnt in effigy throughout England but there had been perhaps two such events in Scotland all winter.

A report in the *Edinburgh Gazetteer* that month had shown that in England loyalist threats were still being resisted. "Disappointment," it began. "On Tuesday last, a person in Sheffield, in the overflowing of his loyalty, gave his workmen three guineas to burn the effigy of that arch traitor, Paine! They took the money, and with part of it made an effigy of their employer and another of a female friend who lives with him. These they burnt before his door; and like true patriots honourably returned him the money, having only deducted the mere expence (sic) of fitting up his and the lady's strawstuffed resemblances; declaring at the same time, that unless they were permitted to think for themselves, they would not work for him any longer."

The morale-boosting tour ended at the Edinburgh committee on 23 January with Lord Daer in the chair. Macleod was congratulated for his letters, and Thomas Erskine was sent a letter of thanks for representing Tom Paine and for his defence of a free press made during the trial at the Guildhall in December. Skirving reported that the Airdrie society had written with a copy of their declaration supporting the national petitions. They dismissed "the hideous cry set forth against all reform. If the people have not a right to petition why does the constitution say so? And if they have a right, why this dreadful and terrific cry of sedition, tumult and riot when they propose exercising that right?" The Bridgeton society in Glasgow reported its opposition to war and affirmed their right to petition, saying, "To construe our designs as seditious would be worse than the sin of witchcraft. We have ground to believe that the enemies of reformation hold their allegiance only by the brittle thread of self-interest." The Glasgow Society for burgh reform noted that "reports circulated to the prejudice of reformers" painted them as "disturbers of the peace", and asked whether a war was necessary. "It astonishes us to see such formidable preparations going on, when we have not so much as heard of a foe. Let the public judge who are the disturbers of the peace."

The committee discussed the recent trials for sedition and declared them "arbitrary, inquisitorial, and unconstitutional". They sent thanks to the London society for their hospitality towards Muir and for their "affectionate attention to their brethren in Scotland on the report of their unprovoked sufferings".

But even those affirming reports could not rid them of the political chill caused by the shock of developments in Paris that week.

Reports of Louis's last hours and his final minutes on the scaffold were only now reaching them. Propaganda against reform was immediate. William Lane of the Minerva Press published a cheap, popular broadside account of the execution and pro- and anti-government newspapers agreed it provided a popular argument for war with France. The annual sermons delivered in most Anglican churches on the anniversary of the execution of Charles I on 30 January would now compare regicides in England and France. A popular pamphlet of 1792 entitled *The Confederacy of Kings Against the Freedom of the World* had argued that although France "had long groaned under despotism, [she] did not wish to annihilate monarchy; she offered Louis the most estimable present that human nature could bestow; she made him king of a free people. He abused the trust." Many reformers still agreed with that sentiment but they were about to be drowned in a tide of revulsion.

CHAPTER 14

Outlaws

"Thomas Muir is judged t'be an ootlaw and fugitive frae His Majesty's Laws."

Lord Braxfield, Edinburgh, 25 February, 1793.

Muir had clearly failed in the main objective of his visit to Paris, to affect the debate on the fate of Louis. He got there too late and soon realised that his influence was too feeble. Survival, rather than international aspirations of universal liberty, was the major concern for most leaders of the new republic. But Muir had other reasons for being in France. He wanted to be in a place of sanctuary, away from the punitive political Scottish judiciary, until he found out the charge against him. If tried for treason, the penalty would be death, in which case he might remain in France or try to make his way to America and live to fight another day. If a lesser charge was brought, then his challenge in an open courtroom might do much to strengthen and galvanise the movement for reform. He had heard nothing from his friend and solicitor, James Campbell, since he left Edinburgh on 8 January.

On the evening after the king's execution Stone took Muir along to the British Club. It was an informal meeting and the mood was mixed. Paine was tired and sombre. Mary Wollstonecraft stayed away. John Oswald, though, was jubilant. Oswald had led his battalion of pike bearers on the escort that morning. He had trained his volunteers on the Champ de Mars and thought them superbly equipped to stop any Austrian or Prussian cavalry charge. They would do well in a civil war, too, he boasted, adding that the best way of now avoiding such a calamity would be to round up every suspected royalist in France and shave off his head, just like they had done to Louis.

Paine looked up, refilled his glass with wine and narrowed his eyes at the eccentric vegetarian. "Oswald," he said with resignation, "you have lived so long without tasting flesh that you now have a most voracious appetite for blood."

Across the table, Sampson Perry laughed. "They have buried Louis's body in a double helping of lime and placed it ten feet deep in the Madeleine cemetery," he said. "The war we have to worry about is from the royal relatives who would take his place and *their* relatives on the other thrones of Europe." That afternoon Louis's body, with his head placed between his legs, had been lowered into the earth between two mass graves, that of 500 of his Swiss guards who had perished at the Tuileries in August and an older one containing the remains of 130 people crushed in the panic that broke out on the day of his marriage to Marie-Antoinette in 1770.

"Would that despotism could be abolished by so little earth," responded Paine. He added that his heart was saddened by the strife in the convention during all of the debate over Louis, and feared that it was as much to do with a struggle between Girondins and Jacobins for state power as it was to do with the fate of an insignificant individual who happened to have inherited a throne. Paine drained his glass, made his excuses and left.

Perry introduced himself to Muir. He, too, was an exile from British law who owned and edited a radical London newspaper called the *Argus*, which was closely associated with the London Corresponding Society. The government prosecuted him several times for libel and he was imprisoned twice. He edited the *Argus* from prison. In September 1792 he had received another arrest warrant for writing that the House of Commons was unrepresentative. He had decided to leave for France to avoid a third spell in Newgate jail and was found guilty in December, in his absence. He had just heard that he had now been outlawed, all of his property seized, and £100 put on his head. Muir thought to himself that he would share Perry's fate if he returned to Edinburgh to stand trial. His short time in the Tollbooth could be a taste of what might come.

The two men were joined by Helen Williams. Williams, a poet and writer, had been crossing and recrossing the Channel since the revolution began and had already published in London two volumes of her *Letters from France*. Like many others in the British Club she lamented the death of Louis and was known to be close to the leadership of the Girondins, in particular to Brissot and to Manon Roland, wife and driving force of the interior minister, Jean Marie Roland. A widely circulating rumour had it that Williams had begun a love affair with Stone shortly after meeting him at the club. Stone had moved to Paris with his wife, Rachel Coope.

Williams, too, thought that the policy of executing Louis was dangerous. She had shared her feelings with Mme Roland and remarked that she thought the king had conducted himself to the scaffold in a dignified fashion. Roland was full of scorn. She said, "Very well, he was fine enough on the scaffold; but there is no reason for giving him credit for it. Kings are reared from childhood to act a part."

Williams ran a weekly salon attended by many of the deputies as well as writers and philosophers of the Social Circle, a loose group of like-minded rationalists and republicans who had organised vast public meetings at a time when other radicals were gathering in select groups, and who also established a successful printing and publishing house producing books and newspapers for the radical bourgeoisie and *sans-culottes* alike. They were among the first republicans to declare themselves, following the flight of the king. Manon Roland wrote at the time, "The Jacobins, like the Assembly, go into convulsions at the mention of a republic."

Stone had presided at the British club's founding dinner in November, which celebrated the French victory at Jemappes. He told Muir that there had been about 100 people present. "We had business to do, preparing an address to the convention, but we mostly sang and danced and drank toasts, thirteen of them." He started to list the toasts. "We did the republic, and the convention, and the French army…"

"And the titles! Don't forget the titles," added a small, smartly dressed man who had joined the circle. Sir Robert Smyth, former MP for Colchester and currently a resident in republican Paris, had a contrary appearance in his brocade jacket and embroidered waistcoat in the old style, with the required knee-breeches. His hair was curled and powdered (but so, Muir remembered, was Robespierre's hair). "Liking neither the government nor the climate of England, I established a small bank here in the capital," Smyth explained. He told Muir how at the November dinner he and Lord Edward Fitzgerald had proposed the toast to the speedy abolition of hereditary titles and feudal distinctions in Britain and Ireland.

Helen Williams reminded them of her inclusion in the honours. They had drunk a toast to the brave women of France who had the courage to take up arms in defence of the revolution, when an additional toast was proposed to the women of Britain who had defended the revolution in print, particularly Williams and Anna Barbauld, an old friend of Muir.

A young man in the uniform of the National Guard said the most humorous toast was to Tom Paine and the new way of making good books well known, by a royal proclamation and King's Bench prosecution! This was William Maxwell, whom Muir had seen at a distance earlier that day as he led the close escort of the king into the Place de la Révolution.

Muir was aware of Maxwell's fame, or notoriety, in Britain, when in December Edmund Burke held up a dagger in the House of Commons and declared that "its murderous purposes are all we will gain by an alliance with France". Maxwell had organised the purchase of arms in Britain for the revolution through a subscription raised from individuals and clubs. About nine cases of daggers got through to France but the consignment of rifles and several thousand more of the daggers were confiscated. "Unfortunately," Maxwell

explained, "a king-and-country riot almost brought the whole enterprise to a premature end when a mob arrived at a meeting in my home
in Portland Place and threatened to destroy the house. We abandoned
our business and reassembled in the house of Horne Tooke in Soho
Square. Unfortunately we live at a period when mobs are encouraged
by those very people who are the first to clamour against sedition."
Maxwell added that there was nothing illegal in what he had done.
France and Britain were not then and were still not at war. "By what
rule of logic, then," he asked, "is it more criminal to subscribe for a
Frenchman than for a Corsican or a Pole?"

Maxwell invited Muir to join him for lunch in the Palais Royal the
following day and, as Muir was about to leave, Helen Williams invited
him to her salon on Sunday. The fine French wine had been flowing
freely throughout the evening but Muir drew his thoughts together
when he was back in his room at the Hotel de Toulon in the Temple.
He still had had no word from James Campbell in Edinburgh; maybe
letters had been delayed at Calais or opened in Dover or Edinburgh.
He sat at his desk and took up his pen to Campbell. "Write me fully
about my private affairs but about nothing else. Whenever you or
my friends judge it expedient I will immediately return; but I cannot
leave Paris without regret. I am honoured by the notice and friendship
of an amiable and distinguished circle, and to a friend of humanity
it affords much consolation to find according feelings in a foreign
land."

*

Muir arrived early for lunch on the following day. He walked once
more into central Paris until he came to the Palais Royal, a piazza
that Prince Henry of Prussia had once haughtily dismissed as being
"neither a palace nor royal". It was owned by the king's cousin, the
Duke of Orleans, who had come over to the side of the revolution,
renounced his title, and was now a deputy in the National Convention
with a new name, Phillipe Egalité. The great colonnaded oblong
plaza, nearly the size of the Tuileries gardens, had been a centre of

opposition to the *ancien régime* thanks to it being protected from official regulation or police control by its royal owner. The duke was never in favour at Versailles and the feeling was mutual.

It was here in the cafés, shops and theatres lining the pleasure gardens that a young orator, Camille Desmoulins, had electrified a crowd that spilled into the streets and gathered more and more citizens to itself until it was an unstoppable force plundering the city for arms. On the afternoon of July 14 1789, they had gathered at the gate of the Bastille prison, demanding the release of weapons and ammunition inside, and had shed the first blood of the revolution. Muir had heard that the Palais Royal was a disreputable place, with more than its share of pickpockets, gaming houses and shops selling obscene books. Maybe that was then. Now he saw an astonishing array of political books and newspapers on sale. Those dealing with matters of the flesh were still there, of course, as were the gaudily dressed young women and men offering those pleasures for sale, but Muir was struck by the number of open-air meetings and debates taking place in the gardens and at tables in the cafés. He remembered how the loyalist newspapers of London had mischievously reported that people in the Palais Royal had been seen dining on pâté made from the flesh of dead Swiss guards.

The Social Circle that had established the influential printing and publishing network had organised weekly discussion meetings here from the time that the Bastille had fallen. They were open to anyone who wanted to come along. One commentator noted at the time, "The Palais Royal has inundated France with all these brochures which have changed everybody, even the soldier, into philosophers." It was here that opposition to the National Assembly's proposal to limit the franchise to "active citizens", those who paid taxes equal to three days' wages, was organised. These massive meetings, at one point attracting 9,000 people, were held in a disused circus ring in the Palais.

Maxwell and Muir met in a café under the collonades. Maxwell explained that it was from there that the fateful demonstration to the Champ de Mars had been organised. Its purpose was as a mass signing of a petition opposing the reinstatement of Louis as a constitutional monarch, after he had attempted to flee the country. About 4,000 left from the Palais and headed first for the Jacobins club in the Rue St Honoré just outside. But the club at that time was split between republicans and constitutional monarchists and the demonstration went ahead without them. An estimated 50,000 people turned up to sign the petition and Lafayette, who was then in command of the National Guard, declared martial law, shot down demonstrators, about fifty were killed, closed the political clubs and shut down the radical newspapers. Lots of radicals were rounded up and imprisoned and many more had to go into hiding. Robespierre went to ground. Danton went to London.

They ordered a bottle of wine and filled their glasses. Maxwell had wanted to share with Muir some of the objectives and activities of the British Club, and how his own project to raise money in Britain for arms was not for personal gratification but had been done with the cooperation of Joseph Servan, the Girondist minister for war before the August insurrection, and now one of the republic's executive committee. Maxwell had not been acting alone but had been delegated to visit Paris by both the Society for Constitutional Information and the London Corresponding Society. He explained that Servan was not just any old war minister but an experienced army officer and thinker whose book, *The Citizen Soldier*, had transformed ideas of modern warfare. Maxwell had offered to equip a company of sharpshooters with rifle-bored guns and Servan promised to give him command of the company, on condition that payment for the rifles should be deferred till the end of the war. The background to the dagger incident, he went on to explain, was a discussion between the two of them that had led to the idea of groups of commando-type troops, equipped with pikes, daggers and small shields. Every tenth man would have a light gun to provide fire cover, while the daggers were for hand-to-hand combat.

They ordered food. Maxwell referred to the toast that Robert

Smythe and Lord Edward Fitzgerald had made at the founding meeting in November. Muir nodded. Maxwell explained that Fitzgerald was not in Paris simply to drink wine. He and Paine had been negotiating with the foreign minister, Charles Lebrun, for assistance for a Dublin insurrection and a possible French invasion of Ireland. He explained how another member of the Irish committee had been asked by Lebrun to travel around the continent and put together sufficient officers to command such an uprising from the Irish presently serving in European armies.

The address of the club to the National Convention, Maxwell continued, was not just bold words and personal desires. It was a reminder to the deputies that France needn't fight for liberty alone. The address had been read to the convention on 28 November and expressed the wish that liberty "will no sooner arrive than we shall see the formation of a close union between the French republic and the English, Scotch and Irish nations." This would readily happen "if public opinion were consulted, as it ought to be, in a national convention" meeting in Britain. So the activity of the reform clubs in Scotland had been followed by the British Club in France.

Maxwell was realistic, the influence of the British Club was modest but effective. Its members had plans for printing and distributing books and pamphlets in Britain to spread the ideas of egalitarian democracy; Paine was helping to write a new constitution for the Republic and cooperating with the government to supply French assistance for Ireland; Maxwell had attempted to organise a subscription for arms; and Oswald was drilling volunteers for pike companies, "Although his ideas for taking the revolution to London on the ends of those pikes is not universally shared!"

Their lunch was interrupted by a surprised voice in a familiar accent. "Thomas Muir! Mr Maxwell! Blow me down! To find fellow countrymen and like minds here in the Palais Royal is a pleasant turn of events."

Both men rose. "James!" said Muir. Maxwell extended his hand. "What has brought you here?"

"Och, I was indicted on charge of sedition for placing an article in the *Glasgow Advertiser* praising the *Rights of Man*," replied James Smith with a smile that bisected his large, round face. "I came here before they could get their hands on me and I'm now told I've been outlawed." Smith was the gunsmith from Gorbals who had proposed the founding resolution at the Sons of Liberty and Friends of Man in Partick.

"Come, sit down. Join us," said Muir. "Citizen waiter, another glass please."

Later that evening, Smith wrote to a friend in Glasgow telling of his good fortune. The letter, which was also opened and read in the Glasgow Post Office and its contents relayed to the lord provost, said, "I had the honour to dine with Mr Maxwell and Mr Muir. We met by mere accident in a coffee house in the Palais Royal. We had all the fashionable dishes, with a variety of wines, Burgundy, etc, for 3/6d. All perfectly quiet here since the death of the king...much safer than Glasgow, no robberies or pickpockets...women very well dressed."

*

On Sunday afternoon, Muir found Stone, as they had arranged, in a small wine shop in the Cordeliers district on the left bank, between the Sorbonne and the Luxembourg gardens. This was where the Cordeliers club had been formed by Georges Danton to open up radical politics to the *sans-culottes*. Only the well-off could afford the fees of the Jacobins and Danton's club charged just a few sous.

Stone poured Muir a wine. "Paine was out of sorts at the British club," he said. "He's moved out of White's to avoid the constant stream of visitors that come to see him. He has had to start making appointments and restricting visitors to two hours a day. He says he wants to move out of the city soon, into one of the suburban *faubourgs* where there is countryside around."

The two men drained their glasses and headed out of the wine shop towards the river. They turned west along the left bank heading for the Williams's apartments in the Rue de Bac. They climbed to the upper story of the building, to where Williams lived with her mother and sister. Paine was there, of course, accompanied by his close friend Nicolas Condorcet. Williams introduced Muir to Condorcet and brought the newcomers fresh glasses for wine. Muir and Condorcet found a seat by the window, with its view across the river to the Tuileries. Condorcet, a former marquis and now a member of the convention, was interested in Muir's account of the reform movement in Scotland and of all he knew about the organisations in England and Ireland.

Muir, in turn, felt he was in the presence of greatness. For the generation of revolutionaries in their twenties and thirties, Condorcet was their direct link to the thinkers of the Enlightenment. He was known to them as the "dean of the Republic of Letters", last of the great *Philosophes*. Now fifty, he showed no signs of slackening his furious pace of life. A mathematician and philosopher, Condorcet was also known for his political writing in which he advocated free and equal education for all, equal rights for women and all races, a liberal economy and a constitution based on the American republic, which he greatly admired. Along with Paine he had founded the Republican Society and its journal *The Republican*, before any of the radical assembly members had begun to talk of a constitution with no king. When Lafayette's martial law was lifted in August 1791, Condorcet, along with Brissot and others from the Social Circle, had revitalised the Jacobins club and provided its leadership. That had lasted until Robespierre, Marat and their associates took control in September the previous year, following the massacre of priests and royalists held in the Paris prisons.

Muir and Condorcet (who later described Muir as *le doux Ecossais*) joined the others. Paine, Williams, and Stone had been wondering whether the Mountain was gaining support in the convention because the Girondins had uttered scarcely a word since the execution of the king. Feeling on the streets was running high and demands for control of prices were opposed by Girondin and Jacobin alike, but Robespierre and Marat were more perceptive politicians than Brissot and were taking on board popular demands. Those, though, who opposed "the people" were now routinely denounced as traitors, counter-revolution-aries, even as aristocrats. In truth, the Jacobin leaders differed little from their Girondin opponents in social background or outlook. They were all republicans (now), idealists, humanitarians, and aware that their revolution, the war and the convention were of fundamental historical importance. Their difference was that the Jacobins had more political nous and a deeper awareness of the concerns of the common people, and they were more willing to gamble with tough political calculations.

Paine summed it up, "Brissot will declare war again, to divert attention from domestic problems." Sure enough, five days later war was declared, not on the nations of Britain and the Dutch United Provinces, but personally on George III and William of Orange. One deputy described his feelings. "I have voted for war against the cabinet of St James because I hope to see the English people spring up at last out of the stupor in which they have sunk from long habituation to their constitutional slavery." One of the more naive Jacobins said in the club on the Friday evening that war was declared, 1 February 1793, "It is in London, under the windows of George, that our troops are going to plant the tree of liberty. George, perhaps after a bit, will depart from his palace as Louis Capet has departed from the Tuileries, he will leave it to enter the Tower of London, where he will go on the same promenade as Louis Capet. Then the two peoples will embrace." Loud applause followed.

*

Shortly after the declaration of war, Maxwell broke the news that he was leaving for home. Now that the two countries were at war he felt he could no longer wear the uniform of the National Guard. To do so would cast him as a traitor and he preferred to be at home and fighting for a reform of parliament with his freedom intact and unquestioned. He was gone by the end of the month.

Paine, too, told of his unease at the bitter factionalism in the convention, with the warlike Girondins wishing to stop the revolution now they were in charge of government, and the Jacobins backing popular conspiracy theories in order to win it from them. The blood spilt from the guillotine was becoming a stain on the principles of liberty and making the task of reformers in the rest of Europe more hazardous. As for Muir, he would have to wait for the charges against him to be declared before he could plan his next move.

Later that week Stone knocked on Muir's hotel door and presented him with a bundle of letters that had been brought from London by an acquaintance to his address in the Palais Royal. A note explained that James Campbell had sent his letters from Edinburgh to a mutual friend in London, who passed them to the Frenchman who brought them to Paris. Muir thanked Stone, who added that he, too, was leaving France for Switzerland.

Muir opened the package and found a letter from Campbell, another from his father in Glasgow, and notes from Johnston and Skirving. The letter from Campbell was almost two weeks old, dated 26 January. Campbell wrote that just half an hour before he had been served with Muir's indictment. The charge was sedition, not treason, and the trial was set for 11 February, now just three days away. The decision Muir had been unable to make before had now been made for him, he would return to Scotland and stand trial. But how? There was now no normal travel between the Channel ports and both British and French navies were patrolling the waters. It might be possible to reach the free port of Hamburg and sail from there; or an American ship sailing from France might put in somewhere on the British Isles before heading out into the Atlantic.

Passports, too, were a problem. Muir would need safe passage from Paris to the coast, otherwise he might be detained as an escaping émigré or a counter-revolutionary spy. Outsiders could not travel across France without a passport from the Department of Foreign Affairs.

He called on friends and acquaintances to set the machinery in motion and it was decided his best chance would be to travel to Le

Havre and find a neutral ship, even though the local committee there was known to have impounded some that called into English ports. He would also need a certificate of residence from the commune and an additional passport for internal travel from the committee of surveillance. All this would take time.

In Edinburgh, Campbell managed to have another date set for the trial after hearing from a friend in London, "I think he is delayed due to the embargo laid on ships in French ports and so a plea to delay his trial should be entered." The new hearing was to be February 25.

The bureaucracy of government in Paris was amateur and patchy. Officials were preoccupied with problems other than obtaining a passport for a foreigner. Cold and hunger were more important and food riots broke out in the capital. Grocery stores, hardware shops and bakeries were invaded by angry crowds of armed citizens who believed that rising prices were caused by hoarders, "monopolists" and unjust traders. The Girondist government was forced to subsidise basic items, much against its beliefs. The Jacobins, too, condemned the rioters, Robespierre because the sacred nature of insurrection should not be employed to obtain "paltry merchandise"; and Marat, who typically found evidence of an aristocratic plot, because "luxury goods", coffee and sugar, were included in the rioters' shopping lists. But they recognised the power of the *sans-culottes* and this in turn strengthened their hand against Brissot and his ministers. Foreigners began to be regarded with suspicion, many of them having been identified with the Girondins, if for no other reason than their leadership was mostly fluent in English.

Muir had written to friends about his plight but he decided to make his position public and wrote to the *Edinburgh Gazetteer* on 13 February. His letter was published on 1 March. It read, "Upon the evening of the 8th I received letters from my father and my agent Mr Campbell informing me…that my trial was fixed for Monday 11th. The distance and the shortness of the time could not permit me reach Edinburgh by that day. War is declared between England and France and the formalities requisite to be gone through, before I could procure passport, would at least have consumed three days. I will return to Scotland without delay. To shrink from danger would be unbecoming of my character and your confidence."

At the same time Smith the gunsmith wrote to his society in Glasgow, "Mr Muir makes a great sacrifice in coming so soon back as he has already made a very great proficiency in the language, has made valuable and dear connections, and is enchanted with the climate." The coded language meant that he thought Muir was strengthened in his belief in the fight for liberty and democracy and was prepared to face his accusers in open court.

Rumours were circulating in Scotland that Muir was already in America, while others maintained he was serving in the French National Guard, and some scaremongers even had him preparing to come home at the head of the French army. But his difficulty in obtaining travel documents and a passage caused him to miss the postponed trial. On Monday 25 February his name was called "oft times" in Edinburgh's high court, then three times from the steps outside. The judge, Lord Braxfield, who spoke perfect English and was fluent in Latin, delivered his verdict in his favourite Lallans Scots.

"Thomas Muir is judged t'be an ootlaw and fugitive frae His Majesty's Laws," he declared. "It is ordainit that he be pit t'His Highness's horn, and aw his moveable goods and gear be escheat and inbrocht t'His Majesty's use, for his coantempt and disobedience in no appearin this day and place, t'hae underlyen the Law for the crimes o sedition and ithers specified in the said criminal letters raised against him thereanent. It is ordainit, forbye, that the bond o caution granted by William Moffat and ithers for the appearance o the said Thomas Muir be forfeit."

CHAPTER 15

Petitioners and conspirators

"The majority of your honourable House is elected by less than fifteen thousand electors, which even if the male adults in the kingdom be estimated at so low a number as three millions, is not more than the two hundredth part of the people to be represented."

From the petition to parliament of the Friends of the People, 6 May, 1793.

"I feel, in the strongest manner, how very formidable an adversary I have to encounter in the honourable gentleman opposite," announced Charles Grey as he looked across the floor of the House of Commons to the government benches and the hint of a smile on the usually impassive face of the Prime Minister, William Pitt. "Formidable from his talents," he continued, "formidable from the influence of his situation, but still more formidable from having been once friendly to the cause of reform, and becoming its determined opponent." The boos of government supporters, firm in their opposition to Grey's timid motion requesting only an inquiry into the franchise, drowned the cries of support from the rump of the old Whig party still in opposition to Pitt's Tories.

As Daer had predicted in January, the impetuous Grey had come around and renewed his support for the reform campaign. Despite reluctance by the aristocratic Friends of the People in London to provide enthusiastic leadership, the societies across the country had organised their own activities and sent thirty-six petitions to parliament, twenty-four of which came from Scotland. The *Edinburgh*

Gazetteer reported at the beginning of March that in Renfrewshire 6,000 people signed the reform petition in four days, and 12,000 had signed in Paisley. Norman Macleod had introduced the petition from Edinburgh and when it was unrolled it stretched the entire length of the House. He wrote to Skirving, "The receipt of so many petitions from Scotland gave very great satisfaction here; I distributed them among our friends in parliament to be presented and I carried up five or six myself. I unfolded the Edinburgh one to show the house the number of names, and it extended from the door to the table."

The majority in the Commons was unhappy at the insolence of ordinary people petitioning, mostly for universal suffrage and annual parliaments. They looked for trivial and technical reasons to refuse them. One petition from Sheffield, signed by 8,000 townspeople, was rejected by 108 votes to 29 as being improper. The member who moved its rejection said, "It was not worded in a manner sufficiently respectful to that House, and they could not, consistently with their own dignity, receive it." The petitioners had made the mistake of declaring themselves, "lovers of peace, of liberty, and justice" and describing themselves as "in general tradesmen and artificers, unpossessed of freehold land, and consequently have no voice in choosing members to sit in parliament". They went further and exclaimed, "though they may not be freeholders, they are men, and do not think themselves fairly used in being excluded the rights of citizens," and concluded, "They think men are the objects of representation, and not the land of a freeholder, or the houses of a borough-monger."

A printed petition from Norwich, with 3,700 signatures, was dismissed because an old standing order was discovered, dating from 1656, which forbade the printing of private petitions before they are read in the House.

Although the reform societies had joined in the campaign they were privately sceptical of the outcome. The London Friends of the People were slow to make their strategy known, in spite of repeated requests from campaigners throughout the country. In February its secretary wrote to Thomas Hardy telling him, "At present we think that to make public our views on these subjects would be to furnish arms to our enemies and to injure the cause in which we are engaged. The period, however, is probably not very far distant when these particulars will be made known to the public." Hardy wrote back, "We are sorry that you should appear to be hurt by the plain question we put to you… We can discover no advantage likely to result from its secrecy… The business we are engaged in is of too important a nature to admit of reserve or disguise."

Hardy later wrote to Sheffield, "We are unanimous in the opinion that such a petition will not produce a reform; yet from many considerations we are now persuaded that if every society in the island will send forward a petition we shall ultimately gain ground, for as much as it will force the present members of the senate to repeatedly discuss the subject, and their deliberations printed in the different newspapers will most naturally awaken the public mind towards the object of our pursuit… Let every society petition separately; let every week furnish a fresh petition and afford a fresh debate, we seek to open the eyes of the public. Petitions on our part and rejections on the part of the ministry will do it."

A committee representing the United Societies at Norwich, comprising thirty or forty in the town "and many more in country villages", wrote to the Society for Constitutional Information in London in March, "We think ourselves under that degrading necessity to state our grievances to the House of Commons with a request for redress and should they refuse to grant our reasonable petition, we have still got (no thanks to them) a formidable engine that will convey the insult to the remotest parts of the kingdom."

The threat of war and its declaration by France in February led many societies also to campaign for peace, particularly in the manufacturing districts of the west of Scotland. The *Glasgow Advertiser* recorded at least ten societies that published anti-war resolutions between January and March and this activity was partially responsible for the modest success of the second Scottish convention in April, which was attended by 117 delegates from 28 towns and villages. That was down from the 170 who came to the first convention and many of the Edinburgh lawyers, intimidated by the arrest of Muir, failed to turn up.

The convention, unlike most of the English societies, continued in its belief in petitions and elected a committee to inquire into the present state of representation in Scotland. The convention met on Tuesday 30 April, the same day that the *Gazetteer* reported a Royal Navy press gang at work on the Leith waterfront, for the first time since the war began. Another, a gang of near thirty men, was reported by the *Caledonian Chronicle* as attempting to board the ship Caledonia of Alloa, "lying at Grangemouth, for the purpose of impressing all her hands, but were repulsed by the crew and obliged to desist". However, the papers also reported that 4,000 had enlisted for the army in Glasgow, "such is the spirit of Britons, or such is the deadness of trade".

The renewed activity of the societies confounded some anti-reformers. John Wauchope, secretary of the "lives and fortune men" of Goldsmiths Hall, had written to his sponsor the Earl of Marchmont at the beginning of January that "all dread of disturbance in this country is over. But the promoters of the mischief will require to be carefully looked after." At the end of the month he was more confident. "Fortunately the tide turned almost instantly and in the course of a very short time... I cannot go so far as to say that the snake is killed but it has got a scorching from which it will not easily recover."

But the spy Robert Watt reported to Dundas that although the actions against Tytler and Muir had dented morale among the reformers, it had recovered quickly with the leadership of Skirving, and by the visits to Scotland from Daer and Macleod. Watt also began to express doubts. "I have only to add that the numerous counter associations whose declarations daily appear in the papers," he wrote, "would almost tempt me to become an enemy of those whose servility leads them to proclaim as infallibly perfect a most defective and faulty constitution. That nation, that people, surely deserve everlasting bondage who can seriously and solemnly subscribe what not one of them I'm sure believes."

*

However, on Monday 6 May in the House of Commons, the young Charles Grey, much admired in aristocratic Whig circles (and in the bed of Georgiana, Duchess of Devonshire, the leading, married, hostess of that group), was promoting a petition drawn up by his society. The petition of the Friends of the People was signed only by its members and lay on the table beside thirty or more others. On that same day, reform petitions were introduced and accepted from Westminster, Suffolk, Poole, the parish of Aldgate, Warwick, Huddersfield, Dundee, Paisley, Montrose, Kilmarnock, Kirkcaldy, Newmilns, Perth, Edinburgh, Dunfermline, Irvine, Strathaven, Galston, Roxburgh, Linlithgow, Anstruther, and Nottingham.

The Friends petition, unlike the others, made no demand or request for a new system of representation, instead simply asking for a committee to investigate its constitutional complaints. It ran to 5,600 words and took Grey three-quarters of an hour to read it out loud. Its text was published in the *Gazetteer* and took up one and a half broad-sheet pages of closely set type. It elegantly outlined all of the faults and corruptions of the constitution, including the unequal distribution of seats, the peculiar and complicated restrictive franchises that existed in different parts of England, Wales and Scotland, the unacceptable political influence of the court and nobility in allocating seats, and the use of public money to fund a patronage system that fuelled the polit-ical corruption. It asked that "your honourable House will be pleased to take such measures as your wisdom may seem to meet, to remove the evils arising from the unequal manner in which the different parts of the kingdom are admitted to participate in the representation… And finally, to shorten the duration of parliaments."

Grey concentrated on what he reckoned would be the main objec-tion from the government benches, that the timing was wrong. "I well know that the chief difficulty to be encountered will be the argument as to the danger of the times," he said. "This, indeed, is a never-failing argument in times of prosperity and adversity, in times of war and peace. If our situation happened to be prosperous it was then asked whether we could be more than happy, or more than free. In the season of adversity, on the other hand, all reform or innovation was deprecated from the pretended risk of increasing the evil and pressure of our situation. From all this it would appear that the time for reform never yet had come and never could come."

He explained that similar motions had been presented in 1733, 1745, 1758, then by Pitt in 1782, 1783 and 1785, and among the reasons for their rejection was one or other of the arguments about the inappropriateness of the time. "The business of reform appeared to have slept from 1785 to 1790," he went on, "when it was again brought forward by Mr Flood. At that time the internal convulsion in France had just begun, and it was then asked whether we would think of repairing our house in the hurricane season."

He argued all the points in the petition and, after an hour and ten minutes on his feet, concluded, "My intention is to move to refer the petition to a committee; but I had it not in contemplation to propose any particular plan, as there occurred to me many reasons against it…and would therefore adopt that which had been usually followed, namely, after having stated the grievance to move for a committee to take it into consideration and to report to the House such remedy as shall appear to them proper."

The motion was instantly, as if by a law of nature, opposed by several placemen on the government benches for being inappropriate in time of war, for being introduced by a minority when most of the population are perfectly happy, or, on the other hand, for introducing a dangerous idea of government by majority. William Windham, one of the Whigs recently recruited to the government cause (and Dundas's competitor for the affections of Lady Ann Lindsay), railed against majorities. "If twenty persons of ordinary capacity were to decide on a question by a mere majority, is it a certain rule that the majority will be right? By no means. If to these twenty as many more are added, will the certainty be greater? It will be less, for as the number is augmented the deficiency of deliberative judgment, the most essential quality, will be greater. If, therefore, the plan of these reformers who say that nothing but a mere majority ought to govern were to be carried, the nation must be undone."

Support for Grey came from his colleague Thomas Erskine, brother of the Edinburgh lawyer and borough reformer, Henry Erskine. "Had I been absent at the opening of the debate," he began, "I certainly never could have collected from the smile of approbation which covered the features of the right honourable gentleman opposite," he glanced across at Pitt, "that the motion which, to his perfect satisfaction was reprobated and ridiculed was no other than the very motion which he himself first formally introduced and made the first characteristic of his public life to originate and support. I must also bring it to the same right honourable gentleman's recollection, that the disturbances and revolutions of the world, and the progress of principles dangerous to monarchy which are now set up as reasons against all reformation, were by himself made the very basis of his own similar application to the House at the close of the American war."

Erskine argued the remainder of the case and, seeing it was now the early hours of the morning, concluded, "I will therefore recall the attention of the House to the motion before it. What is it? It is simply that you should take into your consideration the petition which my honourable friend has presented and which, upon being read, the House has received. The single question is whether the petition contains sufficient matter, if taken to be true, to render it your duty either in justice or in wise policy, to endeavour to remove what is complained of ?" It being late, the House was adjourned.

*

Debate resumed on the following afternoon and the government benches once more concentrated on the French crisis, or argued that a majority of the population was against reform.

Philip Francis, a journalist and a founding member of the Whig Friends of the People, spoke directly to those who thought the timing was wrong. "I wish them only to recollect that, when this measure was introduced last year we were at peace with all the world... The question put to us then was why are you not satisfied with the advantages you enjoy?…That argument will not do now, but the enemies of reform have another in readiness to serve their present turn, they have clothes for all seasons."

He noted that their petition had been criticised by opponents for being signed by only a few people, who complained that reform does not have the authority of numbers. What would have happened if it had been circulated among thousands? "We should immediately have been told, and I think with reason, 'You have brought us a long, laboured, intricate representation, signed by multitudes, who could not possibly have read it, or known what they were signing.' Foreseeing this reflection, we have taken a wiser course. The petition is signed by a few, but by no man who has not read it, who does not understand the contents, and is not convinced of the truth of it."

Richard Wellesley, Earl of Mornington and MP for Windsor, fumed that the motion didn't supply an alternative to the present arrangements, ignoring the fact that if it had, it would have been struck down. "No wise and prudent man would commence the demolition of an established government, under which he had lived happily and prosperously, without some knowledge of the system to be raised on its ruins," he said. Predictably and obtusely, he complained that only a small number had signed this petition, whereas the others had been subscribed to by many, which he criticised as having a "striking a resemblance to each other", all demanding universal suffrage. He pointed to one in particular, "from sundry inhabitants of London, Westminster and their vicinity". Warming to his theme, he sensationally revealed its fatal flaw, "At the head of the signatures stands the name of Thomas Hardy…secretary to the Corresponding Society." He could barely contain himself. "And can any man who has observed the proceedings of that society believe that the deluded persons who compose it will rest satisfied with any temperate reform?" To close his perfect circle of sophistry he concluded, "I contend, from all these considerations, that the plan of universal suffrage, connected with the principles of the French revolution, is that which is most likely to be substituted in place of the present system of representation." Laughter, boos, and jeers from the opposition forced him to his seat.

Samuel Whitbread, the brewer and anti-slavery campaigner, tried to steer the debate away from bombastic points scoring. "I take it for granted you will not deny the existence of a very numerous body discontented with the present state of the representation," he said. "Would it not be well to give satisfaction to those persons? If we go into committee and find on inquiry that the complaints stated in the petitions are unfounded, there will be an end to the business. But if the grievances are found to be real then a remedy ought instantly to be applied. It is a question which ought to be at rest and it can only be so after a solemn and deliberate investigation of its merits."

William Pitt rose with all the authority of the First Lord of the Treasury. "I shall beg leave to remind the House of the grounds upon which I opposed the notice of a parliamentary reform when brought forward last session… I perceived forming within the bosom of the country a small, but not contemptible party, who aspired at something more than a moderate reform, whose object was nothing less than to introduce here those French principles which, from their consequences, I could not regard but with horror… I would rather forego for ever the advantages of reform than risk for a moment the existence of the British constitution."

He insisted it was legitimate to compare them to the French. "Societies have been formed in this country, affiliated with the Jacobin clubs in France, and though they have since assumed a different shape, were then employed for the purpose of spreading Jacobin principles… Nothing less than a National Convention is held out as a sufficient remedy for the abuses which prevailed in the representation… All these petitions come either from England or from Scotland, or from places in England and Scotland that seem to have no natural connection or likelihood of communication. Yet coming from these different places they are all the same in substance and nearly the same in style… They all, it must be confessed, betray a family likeness… There is every reason to suspect that they are the work of a few individuals. They have certainly much more the appearance of the design of a few individuals than of the general expression of the sentiments of the country. If it were asked then, what weight they ought to have the answer is easy. None... The fraud is too gross and palpable, and it is evident from what quarter they come and with what views they are presented."

The playwright Richard Sheridan rose to reply to the prime minister and, using his softest Irish voice, mocked him, "The speech of the right honourable gentleman was an extraordinary effort of his splendid talents, and of his noble and vigorous mind." Pitt had objected to the motion because "the right honourable gentleman told the House that he was now convinced of the impropriety of that measure. Convinced of the impropriety? What was it that convinced him? Was he afraid that the proposal of asking for a committee to inquire into the truth of any allegation of the corruption of parliament might be attended to with success? What was he afraid of? Did he fear that he should be obliged to carry a plan for parliamentary reform? I hope the right honourable gentleman has some reasons for this change of his mind...I wish Mr Pitt would either tell the friends of parliamentary reform when he thinks he should lend his assistance or say that he never will. He has proved he was of opinion that a season of permanent prosperity was not the time. He has proved, too, that a time of war is not the time. Will we have the assistance of the right honourable gentleman after the war with France is over, or will we then be told that, the French being subdued, we should not suffer any alteration in our constitution?... I would rather hear that the right honourable gentleman had abandoned it altogether than find he abandoned it only while he was minister."

Sheridan was followed by Fox, who turned to the French question. "That dislike [of universal representation] is no reason for charging it with more mischief than is fairly imputable to it. It has not been the cause, as the right honourable gentleman alleged, of all the evils in France. The first, or constituent assembly, was not elected on this plan but on old uses and old abuses; yet that assembly had done some of the most unjustifiable things done in France, it had despoiled the clergy without regard to situation or character, and destroyed the nobility. The second, or legislative assembly, was not chosen by individual suffrage; for when the constitution was framed, wild as the French were, they had laid many restrictions on individual suffrage, and made the distinction between active and inactive citizens. It was, therefore, unjust to charge it on what was done by assemblies elected before it was brought into use. France, after doing great honour to herself by shaking off her old intolerable despotism, has since been governed by counsels generally unwise, and often wicked. But what has this to do with our reform? What have we to fear from what no man in his senses would wish to copy?

"The petition," he went on, "presents facts into which the House is bound to inquire... In the petition it is affirmed that peers nominated members to seats in the House and that we have a standing order that no peer should interfere in elections. In the petition it is asserted that bribery and corruption are openly practised at elections and that we have a standing order against bribery and corruption. Let the facts be inquired into or these idle denunciations be expunged from our journals!...It was triumphantly said by gentlemen on the other side that ninety-nine out of every hundred of the people of England are well affected to the constitution, and I believe that they are right. Where then is the danger of inquiring into the defects of the constitution with a view of correcting them. Could we hope for some golden period, in which the proportion of the ill-affected would be less than one to ninety nine? The objection to the time is therefore a fallacy, a mere pretext for putting off what the House cannot help but seeing to be necessary, but feels unwilling to begin."

Grey's motion was defeated by 282 votes to 41. It was 4.15am.

CHAPTER 16

The green bough

"What have you in your hand? A green bough.
Where did it first grow? In America.
Where did it bud? In France.
Where are you going to plant it? In the crown of Great
    Britain."

Part of a question and response to prove membership of
the United Irishmen.

In March, Muir had written again from Paris to both Skirving and
Campbell reassuring them that he would return as soon as he had
obtained a passport. At the same time he received a further letter
from his father, James, telling him he had been outlawed and advising
him to go to America. Some belongings and letters to friends had
been sent to Philadelphia for him, including a letter of introduction
to General Washington.

Paris life was deteriorating fast. Following military defeats on the
northern front and the defection of General Dumouriez and his staff
to the Austrians, an attempted insurrection failed to topple Brissot's
government but resulted in the destruction of all of the Girondin
printing presses. Pierre Vergniaud, one of Brissot's supporters and an
acclaimed orator, went to the tribune of the convention and made a
terrible prophesy. "So, citizens, it must be feared that the revolution,
like Saturn successively devouring its children, will engender, finally,
only despotism with the calamities that accompany it."

The government declared war to its south, on Spain. The combined armies and navies of monarchist Europe were now ranged against the republic. In the west of France, in a region called the Vendée, a counter-revolutionary army supported by royalists and encouraged by the British was taking control of the towns and surrounding countryside. Colonel John Oswald and his battalion of pike men paraded through the hall of the national convention on its way to fight the rebellion. He addressed the convention and asked that they be allowed to exchange their pikes for guns and march against the rebels. Oswald and his soldiers filed through the hall, he with the usual knapsack on his back, the same as a private soldier. This was to be Oswald's final appearance in Paris. He was killed in the Vendée later in the year.

In early April, Muir received his declaration of residence from the commune and later in the month managed to secure a passport from the Ministry of Foreign Affairs to travel to Philadelphia. On 4 May he received his internal travel permission from the committee of surveillance and on the same day set off for Le Havre to look for a ship. Progress was slow. Political turmoil meant that committees in every town and village wanted to know the business of travellers and so it was twelve days later that Muir arrived in the Normandy port and managed to find a berth on an American ship bound for New York. The town's surveillance committee impounded the ship. He could do nothing but sit tight and wait for another neutral vessel.

Daily he walked the wharves of Le Havre, and daily he heard terrifying news of further revolts against the revolution at Marseille, Lyon, Bordeaux, and in nearby Caen. The news from Paris was no better. A revolutionary committee of the Paris sections had rendered the convention impotent. Marat had called for a purge of the Girondins. A nine-member Committee of Public Safety was now in effective control of government and a special Revolutionary Tribunal was created to try those accused of counter-revolutionary activities.

Paine had written despondently to his friend Thomas Jefferson in April. "Had this revolution been conducted consistently with its principles there was once a good prospect of extending liberty throughout the greatest part of Europe; but now I relinquish that hope… [Jacobins] act without either prudence or morality…[and] the prospect of a general freedom is now much shortened." His mood worsened in May, when he wrote to Georges Danton about the current "spirit of denunciation". "My despair arises not from the combined foreign powers, not from the intrigues of aristocracy and priestcraft, but from the tumultuous misconduct with which the internal affairs of the present revolution are conducted."

Robespierre sensed that the time was right to expel the Girondins from the convention and set up his "republic of virtue". At the Jacobins club on 26 May he invited "the people to place themselves in insurrection against the corrupt deputies" and several times that week spoke of the need for "moral insurrection". In the early hours of 31 May the tocsin was sounded and armed *sans-culottes* surrounded and invaded the convention. In the next few days the vast crowd grew to about 80,000, mostly armed. The president of the convention sent a message outside to the commander of the National Guard, asking him to end the intimidation. The commander disdainfully replied, "Tell your fucking president that he and his assembly can go fuck themselves, and if within one hour the twenty-two [Girondin deputies] are not delivered, we will blow them all up." Cannon were moved toward the doors to reinforce his argument.

Twenty-nine deputies were taken at gunpoint and interned. Paine was one of them. Vergniaud rose and offered the remaining deputies in the convention a glass of blood to slake their thirsts. The purge was complete and the Jacobins were in control. Thus began "the horrid days of Robespierre" as Paine called them in a letter to the French people. The terror had turned its attention from champions of the *ancien regime* and had begun to devour the revolutionaries. Robespierre demanded more stringent laws against foreigners and asked for their expulsion. The committee of public safety ordered that they be rounded up and imprisoned.

In Le Havre, another American ship, the Hope, arrived. She was bound for Baltimore by way of Belfast. Muir approached the captain, George Towers, and secured a berth, hiding on board until she sailed. On the evening of Saturday 13 July, as the Hope left the mouth of the River Seine and breasted the waves of the Channel, Charlotte Corday, a young woman from Caen, walked into Marat's Paris bathroom, where he was immersed in water to relieve the pain and itching of his chronic eczema. She pulled from beneath her dress a kitchen knife with a five-inch blade and stabbed it deep between Marat's right collar bones, severing the carotid artery and draining his life on the floor.

During the four-day voyage to Belfast, Muir kept below decks. Although the Hope was a neutral ship she might still be stopped and boarded by the British looking for French contraband or Jacobin agents. He was still uncertain what to do. In the gloom of his cabin he tossed the alternatives back and forth. He had a ticket to Baltimore. He had friends and money and goods in Philadelphia, as well as letters of introduction. From there he could encourage the Scots reformers and return when it was safer. On the other hand, he remembered how some had criticised Paine for not standing his ground in London and using his trial as a rallying point for radicalism. Maybe, though, if he were found guilty in Edinburgh his punishment wouldn't be severe. After all, those convicted of sedition earlier in the year had received sentences that were bearable. Would, say, two years hardship be a mild price for illustrating the growing despotism in Scotland and England? Might it serve as a focus for a re-invigorated reform campaign?

Muir stood next to Captain Towers on the deck of the Hope. Bangor, a small town on the south bank of Belfast Lough, slid by as Carrickfergus appeared on the north shore. It was early morning on 17 July as the captain prepared to take on board a pilot who would guide them safely to Belfast dock. Near the harbour, a line was thrown to rowers in small boat to pull the ship on its final stretch. The towing rope creaked as men grunted and oars splashed. Muir was not quite home but felt a surge of exhilaration at the familiarity of the countryside.

He told the captain that he would catch the early stagecoach to Dublin, having decided to meet some of his fellow reformers in the Society of United Irishmen. They might have recent information that would guide him in his dilemma. Towers told him he had two weeks to return. He intended to sail for Baltimore on 30 July.

As the Hope scraped against the wooden jetty, Muir jumped ashore with a small bag in his hand and headed for the centre of Belfast and the departure point of the stage. When George Towers had secured his ship and completed his duties at the harbour office, he went below to check on Muir's luggage. Muir had confided in him during their crossing from France and friendship had grown between the two men. Towers decided to let Muir's family know he was safe, so far, and sent a brief, cryptic letter to James Muir at Huntershill.

*

At nine o'clock that evening the summer sky was still streaked with blue light above Dublin as the Belfast stage came to rest in Sackville Street. Muir asked for directions to nearby Dominick Street, the town home of Archibald Hamilton Rowan, secretary and founder member of the Dublin United Irishmen and, with Dr William Drennan, author of the controversial address that Muir had read to the convention. Muir had had extensive correspondence with both these men and felt he already knew them well. In January that year they had enrolled him as an honorary member of the United Irishmen. He and Paine were the only non-Irish to be given that honour. Muir wasn't worried about turning up unannounced at Hamilton Rowan's door.

Before the polished wood front door had opened Muir could hear the loud barking of a dog. The nose of a very large, shaggy Newfoundland pushed into the narrow opening. The door was swung wider to reveal a similarly large man in his forties, dressed in a green uniform and holding a great knotted club in his hand, attached to his wrist by a leather thong. Muscular arms hung either side of a broad chest, topped by a huge head with a deeply furrowed brow and enormous dark eyebrows. A small sword hung at one side of his belt and a pistol at the other.

The large man's voice was friendly as he asked the stranger how he could be of assistance. Muir identified himself and apologised for arriving unexpectedly. The Irishman was overjoyed at the sudden appearance of his fellow reformer from Scotland, who was made welcome by Hamilton Rowan and his wife, Sarah Ann. They brought him food and wine as he explained how he had come to be there and what had happened since his arrest in January.

Hamilton Rowan explained how he, too, had been arrested in December on a charge of seditious libel for distributing a leaflet written by Drennan, *An Address to the Volunteers*. He was at present on remand. The uniform he wore was that of the First National Battalion of the Volunteer Corps and the emblem on his badge was a reworking of the Irish crest – a harp with a cap of liberty at the top, where a crown usually sat. The government banned the volunteers from meeting to celebrate the victories of the French over the allied armies but many of them still defiantly walked the streets in their green uniforms and still held public meetings.

On the following evening Muir and Hamilton Rowan had dinner with William Drennan, the doctor, poet and reformer, educated, like Muir, at Glasgow and Edinburgh universities. Although said by some to have a cold and diffident manner, and described by one acquaintance as resembling "the demure minister of some remote village congregation of the Scotch kirk", Drennan welcomed Muir into his home with warmth. It was from Drennan's pen that the lofty fraternal address to the Scottish convention had come. Over the remains of a splendid dinner, the two Irishmen spoke to Muir about the similarities and differences between the movements in both countries.

"Another glass of port, gentlemen," urged Drennan. "It aids digestion in the mind as well as in the gut." He poured three large glasses. "Thomas, you know well that our political situations are not dissimilar. As we stated in our address to your convention, our rights and wrongs are the same. You have now had two conventions in Scotland and that is significant. We, as you may not be aware, have had many conventions over the years and have won significant advances from London, or we thought we had. Eleven years ago, we achieved our own parliament here in Dublin. But that was merely protestant independence."

"It was achieved by holding conventions and presenting petitions," explained Hamilton Rowan, "but our volunteers were the extra ingredient." He told Muir how the French had landed at Carrickfergus in 1760 and the volunteer militia were formed by the English government to defend its western colony. However, during the American war, when Britain faced the fleets of France and Spain, the people of Belfast requested the government to station a body of troops there.

"Government replied that they could afford only half a troop of horse and half a company of invalids," said Hamilton Rowan. "This was sufficient for the people to arm and defend themselves. Almost every parish in Ulster soon boasted its volunteer corps. The voice of liberty was heard echoing across the Atlantic; it awoke a kindred spirit in the breast of the Irish nation, and from having risen in arms to defend her shores, she grasped them more firmly to assert her rights, she felt her power, and determined to be free."

Drennan explained how he had joined the volunteers in the 1770s and although those companies were raised to defend Ireland from foreign invasion, they also agitated for free trade and legislative independence.

"I became a spokesman for catholic relief and parliamentary reform," he said. "We got legislative independence in 1782 but the campaign to widen the franchise was misplayed. Even though the reform movement and the volunteers lost momentum, I campaigned into the eighties, calling for freedom from English control and to unite Catholic and Protestant in a common cause. Then the volunteer movement revived at the outbreak of the French revolution."

Hamilton Rowan broke in. "The French revolution acted as a spell on the minds of Irishmen," he said, "rendering them more and more impatient of their grievances, and prompting them to more action.

They had seen a mighty nation rising from slumber, casting off the yoke under which she had groaned for ages, and demonstrating the impotence of despotism against the stern resolves of a people intent on their rights."

In the summer of 1791 Wolfe Tone's pamphlet, *An Argument on Behalf of the Catholics of Ireland*, was published. At just a shilling, it sold 6,000 copies by the end of the year and another 10,000 were sold in the following twelve months.

"By that time we had founded the Society of United Irishmen in Belfast and Dublin along with Tone, and I became its first president," said Drennan. "Although Tone and I don't see eye to eye on everything, he is right to argue that not only are Catholics capable of liberty but that there can be no liberty for anyone in Ireland until Irishmen of all denominations unite against what he calls the 'boobies and blockheads' that govern us. When the great Catholic nation of France destroyed despotism, many Ulster Presbyterians looked at Irish Catholics with fresh eyes."

Drennan, however, was frank about his suspicions of Catholic intentions at times, particularly their leaders' commitment to parliamentary reform. Tone, an Anglican, went to work for the Catholic Committee and organised a Catholic Convention in Dublin at the end 1792, which drew up a petition to George III. The war with France was looming and so the Catholic Relief Act, offering the county franchise on the same terms as Protestants, but not the right to stand for election, was pushed through the Irish parliament in March.

"Then in April the Catholic Committee dissolved itself, thinking its work was done!" exclaimed Drennan. "Fools! Tone, to his credit, denounced the offer as partial and illusory."

As the glasses of the three men were filled, so the port bottles were emptied and Muir absorbed much about the present state of the Irish movements and the activities of the Catholic Defenders in the countryside, their secret drilling, the manufacture of pikes by local blacksmiths, and the burning of property and harvests belonging to Protestant landowners. The Dublin government's Gunpowder Act, which prevented the movement of arms, was undermining the volunteers, who in any case had been proscribed in March. But it was the Convention Act that caused Muir most concern. The volunteers had held a giant convention in Dungannon in February. Its demands were mild, it was anti-republican and supported the constitution, but its call for a national reform convention, encompassing all strands of opinion in Ireland, was enough to prompt Dublin to enact a law banning all extra-parliamentary assemblies.

Muir learned much about Ireland from his two colleagues and it was then that he resolved his difficulties about whether to return to Scotland or to go on to America. His place was in Edinburgh. Drennan and Hamilton Rowan congratulated him for his courage.

Early the following morning, Drennan sat at his desk and, as he did most days, wrote to his sister Martha McTeir and her husband Sam in Belfast, "Mr Muir of Scotland is arrived here, and intends in a day or two to go down to Belfast in his way to Scotland, where he will stand his ground. He seems a very sensible, honest, intelligent man, and I shall give him a line of introduction to you."

That evening they attended a small meeting of the United Irishmen in Back Lane. It being summer, many members were out of Dublin. Edward Fitzgerald was away at his country place, Frascati, with his new wife, Pamela. It was rumoured she was the love child of Phillipe Egalité, the Duke of Orleans as was. Wolfe Tone's wife had delivered a new baby son in the spring and they also were spending summer in the country.

Hamilton Rowan suggested they spend some time with Sarah Ann and his children at his country place in Rathcoffey, a small town in Kildare, just eighteen miles from Dublin. Muir travelled there with the Hamilton Rowans, their eight children and their oversized Newfoundland hound, to spend a few days at their small estate, before returning to Belfast. He enjoyed the company of the family and spent time in their extensive library there. Hamilton Rowan amused Muir with experiments performed in his newly constructed chemistry laboratory, and demonstrated his lithographic skills in the print shop he had installed in his country house (and which the government had begun to take notice of as political pamphlets and handbills were printed on it throughout 1793). The friendship between the two men deepened in those calm summer days that Muir used to salve his doubts and strengthen his resolve. The political terrain on which each of them had to operate might be hugely different but their ideas were, it seemed to them, universal. Hamilton Rowan explained to Muir his "three great objects", which were, "Exclusion from the Irish House of Commons of all place hunters and pensioners, disfranchisement of depopulated boroughs, and the secret ballot, which would exempt the tenant from the too frequent tyranny of the landlord."

One evening, in the fading twilight after the eight children had been put to bed and Sarah Ann had gone to visit a friend, Hamilton Rowan and Muir sat at a table in the garden in the glow of a lamp hanging from a branch above their heads. Hamilton Rowan filled their glasses with wine. They talked about France and about the contacts between the United Irishmen and Paris. Muir knew that Edward Fitzgerald together with Tom Paine had had discussions with foreign minister Lebrun, remembering his conversation with Maxwell in the Palais Royal in January.

Hamilton Rowan told him that Fitzgerald brought a Colonel Eleazer Oswald, an American citizen acting on behalf of the French, to see him. Oswald offered French support for an Irish uprising, which the United Irishmen declined. The offer from the French convention was that they would deposit in any bank in Europe the pay for 40,000 men for six months on the condition that absolute independence was declared from England. But that offer had been refused because the number of men was based on the number of the Irish volunteers whose delegates had assembled at a convention. The offer was founded on a supposition that the opinions of the volunteers were for independence and a republic, which the convention had not agreed. Fitzgerald had told Paine that four thousand disaffected volunteers could overwhelm the understaffed garrisons in three months. Paine was impressed, and agreed to put a request for French backing to Lebrun. But, Hamilton Rowan pointed out, Fitzgerald had been at the February volunteer convention in Dungannon, they had travelled there together and he had seen with his own eyes that, although the volunteers were applauded, reform of the existing constitution was what was called for, and condemnation of the war against France was defeated. Although they had welcomed the offers of help from France, they made it clear that Ireland was not ready for rebellion.

Hamilton Rowan was somewhat suspicious of Fitzgerald, a son of Lord Leinster, Ireland's premier peer, a great grandson of Charles II, a nephew of the Duke of Richmond, and a cousin of the Whig leader, Charles Fox. But his suspicion was not from the circumstances of his birth. Fitzgerald was, after all, an outspoken member of the Irish parliament and when assemblies of volunteers were banned, he spoke out against the measure, and spoke well. His radical reputation was high and his face even appeared on Belfast jugs as 'the man of the people'. In Dublin it was said he had turned a complete Frenchman, who cropped his hair, despised his title, and walked the streets instead of riding because he felt more pride in being on a level with his fellow citizens. But Hamilton Rowan was afraid that, having just come from Paris, Fitzgerald had rejected his former belief in parliamentary reform and now thought only in military terms. He was, after all, a soldier by trade and now believed that the revived volunteers could secure democracy in an independent Ireland. There was maybe some support for this position from dispossessed Catholics in the countryside, Hamilton Rowan thought, but he preferred to believe that the United Irishmen, in trying to unite all of the factions, could still challenge the Protestant Ascendancy in Dublin and the short-sighted, obdurate politicians in Westminster through a reform of the constitution.

*

The next morning a messenger arrived from Dublin with mail for Muir. It was a note from Captain Towers reminding him of their sailing date and enclosing a confused and cautious reply from James Muir to Towers's note about Muir's whereabouts. It read, "I am at very great loss how to answer your letter, as it's not understood by me, if it's the Friend that I have, if it's he, I would be overjoyed to see his handwriting, and to know what has become of him these three months. I thought he had been at Philadelphia ere now, where letters are forwarded for him; and if you are to stay any time at Belfast be so kind as to write and I will come over and see you and him. You can write the time you mean to stay. Mr John Richardson, the son of Deacon James Richardson, I saw him this week at Greenock, where he is to sail in the Almy of New York directly, who has two packets of letters and a trunk for him; and here are many letters wrote for him to the first people of America. And once he were there, he'll get letters to General Washington. I hope, dear sir, you will shew him every civility in your power, which I hope some day to gratefully thank you for. If it's the person I mean, a cousin of his, William Muir formerly of Leith, is lying at Philadelphia. His ship is American. The loss of this young man has been a dreadful affliction to us. Please give your friend this letter. I honoured his draft in favour of Mr Masey. He'll get his letters in the post office of Philadelphia. I hope in a year or two he can return, if he doth not love America; and be so good as to cause him write me one line in your letter. You can direct it; and if he does not choose to sign it, you can put your initials to it."

Muir sat quietly for a time. He was overjoyed at hearing from his father but guilty and sad at the pain he had caused his family. He knew he would see them soon but that this might be an unwelcome surprise for them. He couldn't know under what circumstances they would meet. He scribbled a short note to Captain Towers. "This day I received yours and will be down upon Tuesday evening. I have taken my place in the coach for tomorrow. I am happy to hear my friends are well. I will write them from Belfast."

As Muir packed his bag, Hamilton Rowan came into his bedroom with a package under his arm. It comprised a number of letters and some of the United Irishmen's literature. He asked Muir to take them to Scotland and explained that the package contained a letter to Colonel Macleod telling him how the Convention bill had been hurried through the Dublin parliament "to prevent the people from acting by deputies in obtaining the redress of grievances or even applying to the king or parliament...leaving a melancholy but plain alternative; unconditional surrender or defiance." Hamilton Rowan was concerned that the political state of Ireland be fully understood in Scotland and, through his letters and documents as well as Muir's first-hand understanding, hoped for close cooperation between the national organisations through "a frank and ingenious correspondence".

On Tuesday 30 July in the early morning, Muir once again stood beside Captain Towers on the quarter deck of the Hope as it glided up Belfast Lough to the Irish Sea. His luggage was on deck, in preparation for transfer to the daily mail packet coming from Donaghdee, at the south of the lough mouth, and heading across the twenty miles to Portpatrick, on the south west tip of Scotland. He clutched Hamilton Rowan's packet to his breast. Among its contents was a letter to their mutual friend, Rev Thomas Fyshe Palmer in Dundee. Fyshe Palmer and Hamilton Rowan had been close friends since they were students together at Queens' College in Cambridge.

CHAPTER 17

Heart of Midlothian

" 'Then the Tollbooth of Edinburgh is called the Heart of Midlothian?' said I. 'So termed and reputed, I assure you.' 'I think,' said I, 'the metropolitan county may, in that case, be said to have a sad heart.' "

Sir Walter Scott, *The Heart of Midlothian.*

"Palmer! Open up! We know you're there. Open this door!" The shouts of the sheriff's officer and the loud banging on the door of Mrs Donaldson's house by his small party of enforcers, echoed round Old Assembly Close. The Rev Thomas Fyshe Palmer of Dundee kept two rooms there in the centre of the Old Town's High Street, which he used when he preached in Edinburgh, as he often did.

Mrs Donaldson opened the door and filled the space with her bulk. She folded her arms across her chest. "Come away, boys, did your mothers teach you no manners? Do you have to be so noisy?" She addressed the leader of the group. "William Middleton, I thought you'd have known better. What's your business at my door?"

Middleton looked uncomfortably diminished as he apologised to Mrs Donaldson and explained bashfully that they had come to arrest Mr Palmer.

"That's better," she said. "Mr Palmer!" she called upstairs, "it's for you."

Palmer looked bemused as he came to the door with his spectacles in his hand. He asked in his soft, polite English voice, "May I be of assistance, gentlemen?"

"We have come on the orders of the lord advocate to arrest you on suspicion of sedition," said Middleton. "Come with us please."

"May I be told why?" inquired Palmer, with a look of disbelief on his face.

"Just come with us, sir, and you'll find out."

The walk from Mrs Donaldson's to the sheriff's office in Parliament Close took only a few minutes. Palmer was shown into a room where he found Harry Davidson, the Midlothian sheriff, William Scott, the procurator fiscal, and a government solicitor, Joseph Mack. The sheriff's officer, William Middleton, remained in the room. It was Friday 2 August.

"Mr Palmer," said Davidson, "when were you last in Dundee?"

"I am sorry, sir," replied Palmer, "but I cannot answer your question until I know why I am brought here."

"Just answer the question, Palmer."

"I cannot," repeated Palmer, "because I don't know why I am arrested. I have seen no document authorising this and, although I am not well acquainted with the law of Scotland, I decline to answer this or any other question put to me without knowing the reasons they are being asked or to what purpose my answers will be put."

"Are you acquainted with William Skirving of Strathruddie, residing in Edinburgh and sometimes designated secretary to the Friends of the People?"

"Again, I cannot answer that question for the reasons I have given."

"And are you," continued Davidson, "acquainted with Alexander Morrin, grocer and spirit dealer in the Luckenbooths here in Edinburgh?

Palmer repeated his reasons for remaining silent.

Davidson went on to ask Palmer if he had ever corresponded with either of these men, and he produced two letters signed by Palmer and addressed to Skirving and Morrin, as well as the manuscript of a handbill and copies of a leaflet that had been printed in Edinburgh and distributed in Dundee. It was headed *An address to friends and fellow citizens*.

Palmer realised what was happening. He was being set up for prosecution, just as the printers, publishers, booksellers and journalists had been earlier in the year. He was determined to say nothing without legal representation, and told Davidson so. Middleton was ordered to take Palmer into another room and stand guard over him. In a little while he was taken back before the sheriff who presented him with a transcript of the interview. Davidson asked Palmer to sign it. He refused. Middleton again was told to take Palmer to another room and in a short while ordered back. This time the procurator fiscal, William Scott, produced a written warrant for Palmer's arrest. It had the previous day's date on it.

"Will you now answer Mr Davidson's questions?" asked Scott.

"No, sir, I will not," replied Palmer, "and I wish to make it clear that my refusal is not from any contempt of the court or the law. But I will not answer your questions at this time and will not sign any declaration you put before me."

"Very well, Palmer," said Davidson, "you can cool your heels in the Tollbooth tonight and we'll talk again in the morning."

The ancient prison was near, linked to Parliament Close by a narrow passage, partly covered over, and it stood in the middle of the High Street, having the cathedral on one side and tenements on the other. Palmer was delivered to its gothic entrance, minded by a sentry of the town guard in his red uniform, and handed over to the turnkey. He was locked in a dark and musty cell. Sitting alone in the evening gloom on a rough wooden chair, the clergyman was distressed. He tried to work out what to do. No one knew where he was, except the authorities. He would have to get a message out. He would try to write to his friend and lodger, James Ellis, in Dundee. He'd do that first thing in the morning when he might get access to pen and paper. The manuscript he had been shown by the sheriff was one he had corrected. It had been written by his friend George Mealmaker, a fellow member of the Friends of Liberty in Dundee. Mealmaker was a weaver, erudite but self-taught, and had asked Palmer to revise his draft. Palmer had corrected it for grammar and spelling and had also moderated some of the language in the original. What was seditious about the handbill? It had said the first petitions to reform the House of Commons had failed, but that should not deter them from further campaigning. It argued why the Commons should be reformed, and it pointed out that the present war was in no one's interest, trade had declined, unemployment had risen and taxes had gone up. "What's illegal in that?" thought Palmer. He had actually opposed publication of the handbill, arguing that it would be better presented in a newspaper. "Our meetings have the same right to hold discussions and have opinions that members of parliament have expressed," he told himself. Even the prime minister and the Duke of Richmond had held these opinions and organised meetings to support them, and they were guilty of no sedition. "Maybe," he thought, "there is no change in the law but there has been a very considerable change in the views of the disapprovers of reform."

What else had he done? He had arranged for the leaflet to be printed in Edinburgh by John Morrin, brother of the Luckenbooths grocer Alexander. He had written to Alexander asking for his assistance. He had also written to Skirving offering him copies of the leaflet for distribution in Edinburgh and the rest of Scotland. What was illegal in that? And how had the sheriff come to have these letters in his office that afternoon?

Unknown to Palmer, he had been targeted. Robert Dundas had been sure that the arrest of Muir in January and the failure of the petition campaign in May, coupled with a wartime national emergency, would end the reform societies for good. He hadn't reckoned on them drawing a second wind by campaigning against the war. "I had no idea they would have stuck so long and so well together," he wrote to his Uncle Henry's secretary, Nepean, in June. The societies saw the continuation of the war with France as one more proof that a speedy and thorough reform was necessary. By July he was alarmed. "You may rest assured," he wrote to his uncle, "from the accounts I have received from Glasgow and from Perth and Angus, that those rascals have laid a plan for exciting the country again to discontent and disorder on account of the war, and that this is the topic on which they are to dwell."

Inside his letter was enclosed a copy of the Dundee leaflet. "Palmer, the Methodist clergyman who lately went over to Dundee, is strongly suspected," he wrote. "If he is the man, I shall doubt not his being got hold of." He had put the spy Watt on the case, and soon the connection to Skirving was uncovered. Dundas penned another letter about Palmer to his uncle in Whitehall. "He is the most determined rebel in Scotland," he wrote.

Middleton and his men had also been hard at work. Morrin's shop in the Luckenbooths had been searched and his letters seized along with copies of the printed handbill. Skirving's house in Horse Wynd had been turned over and Palmer's letters taken from his writing bureau. Skirving had spent part of that Friday in the same Tollbooth but was released without charge or bail before Palmer was jailed. Sheriff's officers had also been busy in Dundee and had, without warrant but with threats of imprisonment, searched the houses of some of Palmer's friends for letters or leaflets.

"Wake up, Palmer! The sheriff wants you." The rough voice of the turnkey at the end of his night's shift startled Palmer as it roused him from a fitful sleep. The thin, cold light of dawn filtered through the prison window. Palmer rubbed the sleep from his eyes and patted down his greying hair. The turnkey took pity on him and gave him some porage to revive him and fresh water to wash his face and hands. He was handed over to Middleton at the Tollbooth door and taken once again to a waiting room near the sheriff's office.

"Mr Middleton, no one is aware of my whereabouts," Palmer said, "and I would greatly appreciate a pen and some paper to let a friend know what has happened." Middleton hesitated but conceded the point, and sat Palmer at a desk in the corner of the room, where he wrote a short note to James Ellis in Dundee. "Dear James, I was imprisoned all last night because I would not answer any questions put to me and am now in the sheriff's chamber, waiting a second attempt. I have been permitted to see no one yet. Was not allowed bail last night, I suppose I shall this morning. Yours, TFP." He handed the note to Middleton, who promised it would be in the first post.

An hour passed before the sheriff, the procurator fiscal and the government solicitor assembled once again in the room next door. Middleton seated Palmer in front of them and the sheriff read over the declaration from the previous night, including Palmer's refusal to sign it.

"Do you still adhere to that position, or will you now answer the questions that were put to you?" he asked.

"It appears to me inconsistent with justice," Palmer replied, "to desire a man to answer questions which might criminate himself. I am ignorant of Scotch law, and of the tendency of the questions, and how far I might be implicated by my answers. I mean no contempt for your authority Mr Sheriff. Those are my reasons for declining to answer your questions or to sign your declaration."

"Very well Palmer," said Scott, the procurator fiscal, "you are free to go. You will be released on bail and in due course a summons will be served upon you on a charge of sedition."

*

Around the time Palmer was arrested in Edinburgh, Thomas Muir steadied himself on the handrail of the pitching mail packet and scanned the northern hills protecting the coastal town of Portpatrick. He assessed his chances of reaching Edinburgh undetected. They were slim. He had not concealed his identity in Ireland. Government officials and informers were sure to have noted his presence there. He was, after all, an outlaw and reversing his status as a fugitive was going to be his first task in the Edinburgh court. It was public knowledge that he had been in France and it was highly likely that the dense network of customs and excise officials stationed around the Scottish coastline would have been warned keep a lookout for him.

The harbour and lighthouse of Portpatrick were drawing nearer. Muir had been warned by a fellow passenger about the porters on the busy wharf, collectively known as 'The Robbery' for their high fees and annoying persistence. "The manner in which their fees are extracted, particularly when they meet with any difficulty in the payment, is rather harsh and disagreeable," his acquaintance had cautioned.

The harbour was busy. Around a dozen ships regularly traded here, importing black cattle and horses from Ireland, and four passenger vessels carried the mails between the countries each day. They were timed to meet the coaches from Dublin and Edinburgh, and the road from Carlisle to Portpatrick passed through Stranraer, carrying a daily mail coach to London. The loud shouts from the Robbery began as soon as the mail boat docked and its gangplank was lowered. "Bags, sir! I'll take your bags, sir! Edinburgh or London coach?" Muir took the advice of his fellow passenger and fastened himself to a young porter, pointing out his luggage and paying him handsomely in advance.

"Stranraer," said Muir. "Whichever goes to Stranraer."

"Right sir, leave it to me, sir," said the porter, loading Muir's bags on his barrow. "That coach over there, sir, next to the inn."

Muir stood by the door of the inn while he paid for his seat on the stage and saw his bags loaded on the luggage platform at the back. James Carmichael, commander of the local prison hulk, sipped at his small beer inside. Looking out at the waiting coach, he recognised Muir as he climbed aboard. Carmichael had once been employed in an attorney's office in Edinburgh and had seen Muir plead at the bar. He turned to his companion and told him quietly not to do anything that would draw attention to him. As the horses strained to pull the heavy coach forward, Carmichael jumped on to one of the empty seats on its roof. Stranraer was only eight miles away. In an hour he would be in the office of the sheriff there. He was sure there was a reward on Muir's head and soon it could be his.

In Stranraer, Muir had his bags taken to a nearby inn, where he booked a room for the night, intending to begin the 20-hour journey to Edinburgh on the early morning stage. He had entered his room when he heard the sound of boots on the stairs. The Stranraer sheriff, accompanied by Carmichael, burst through his door.

"Thomas Muir, you are a fugitive from justice," declared the sheriff. "I am arresting you on the authority of the High Court of Justiciary and you will be detained in the tollbooth until you are transported to Edinburgh."

"Sir, I have come here after many difficulties to declare my presence and to apply for the fugitation to be lifted," responded Muir. "I was intending to make my way to Edinburgh tomorrow morning and present myself at the High Court."

"That's as may be, Muir," said the sheriff. "I'll tell Edinburgh you are here but you'll stay in my tollbooth until I hear from the authorities."

The sheriff wrote to Robert Dundas, "Muir was apprehended here on his way from Ireland. He seems a good deal confused re the idea of Stranraer jail till he is conveyed to Edinburgh." Dundas sent the news to his uncle. "I have little doubt, though he avow his intention of coming home to have been with a view to stand trial, that he is an emissary from France or the disaffected in Ireland."

Muir spent four nights in the Stranraer tollbooth until, on the morning of Sunday 4 August, George Williamson arrived from Edinburgh carrying a warrant from the High Court. Williamson, a well-known "thief-taker", had arrested Muir at Holytown in January. He went first to the local magistrate for a sealed package of papers taken from Muir on his arrest, before crossing to the tollbooth to collect his prisoner. Muir was bundled into the back of a coach and transported to the capital in irons. He was delivered to a cell in the Heart of Midlothian in the early hours of Monday 6 August.

*

Skirving had only recently moved house, from Horse Wynd, near the Palace of Holyrood, to a larger and more central apartment at the foot of Old Assembly Close, off the High Street. He had also only recently finished apologising to his wife, Rachel, for the distressing intrusion into their new home by the sheriff's officers. Rachel was concerned that her husband, now approaching fifty, was wading into deep water. She had supported him in his previous political activity: he had campaigned for repeal of the Test Act, so far unsuccessfully, which ensured that only those accepting the Church of Scotland's confession of faith could hold public office. Skirving belonged to a dissenting Presbyterian sect, which also led him to be active in the Association for the Abolition of Patronage, the measure allowing landowners to appoint church ministers. She agreed with the campaign for parliamentary reform but nevertheless worried for his safety, now that the law was involved.

The search of their home the previous week by the sheriff's officer, Middleton, and his men, coupled with Skirving's arrest and detention had scared them both. Nevertheless, he had been released without charge and believed no more would come of it. He had been back to the jail to visit his friend Muir, although this made him uneasy. It looked as if Muir might face a period in detention if the sedition charge was proven. However, they were also sure that the trial would advertise their cause and galvanise their supporters. During his evening visits Skirving was able to bring Muir up to date with the campaign. The failure of Grey's motion in May, and of their petitioning, had had one fortunate, unintended consequence. Far from causing widespread disillusionment it had encouraged the societies, particularly in England, to seek more effective co-operation. Meetings of the Scottish associations had fallen away for a while and just as they were wondering how to continue, a proposal came in a letter from Thomas Hardy. He suggested a closer union of all the societies to bring about a stronger organisation. It was dated 17 May and read, "The London Corresponding Society requests of your society a renewal of correspondence and a more intimate co-operation in that which both societies alike seek, a reform in the parliamentary representation. We are very sensible that no society can of itself bring about that desirable end; let us therefore unite as much as possible, not only with each other, but with every society throughout the nation. Our petitions, you will have learned, have all of them been unsuccessful. Our attention must now therefore be turned to some more effectual means. From your society we would willingly learn them, and you, on your part, may depend upon our adopting the firmest measures provided they are constitutional. And we hope the country will not be behindhand with us. This war has already opened the eyes of many; and should it continue much longer, there is no answering for its effects on the minds of the people." It was signed by Maurice Margarot, chairman, and Thomas Hardy, secretary. Skirving had started a correspondence with Hardy, who had assured him that the societies in the major English cities, such as Leeds, Sheffield and Birmingham, had written to him quite independently on "the necessity of a general union". The idea of holding a national convention was forming.

Skirving had also given Muir another small item of good news, Alexander Lockie, the chaise-driver convicted of riot and sentenced to transportation, had been pardoned thanks to the plea prepared by Muir, and had been set free in February while Muir was in Paris.

Skirving, back at home, was sitting at his desk when he was roused from his thoughts by loud banging at his door. Voices called to him to open up. Rachel, distressed, ran into the room. Skirving opened to door to their apartment to find Middleton, the sheriff's officer, accompanied by Sheriff Harry Davidson and Joseph Mack, the government solicitor. Davidson announced he had a warrant to search the house and the three men barged into the room.

Rachel kept close to Skirving as he protested that he had given them all of the Dundee papers and he had been released without charge. He was accused of concealing information, which he denied. He had told them at his arrest that he had one more letter from Palmer which he couldn't find. He described its contents, which were of no consequence. It had been agreed that if he should come across it he would hand it over. But Davidson insisted on finding the letter immediately, as Middleton and Mack began once again turning out the contents of drawers and cupboards in every room. Some time later, they presented a letter to Skirving, which they said they found in a coat pocket. Standing in the middle of a litter of clothes and paper, Davidson arrested Skirving as a party to the publication of a seditious paper.

A surge of angry helplessness overcame Rachel as her husband was taken down the stairs of the tenement and led the short distance to the Tollbooth. She knelt among the debris and wept. She felt shocked and vulnerable. Their home had been violated once more. It was ten o'clock on the night of Wednesday 7 August.

*

Muir became aware of Skirving's presence in the Tollbooth on the following morning and arranged for James Campbell, the lawyer and society member who had attended to Muir's affairs while he was gone, to visit them. But Skirving was insistent that he would not apply for bail, being an innocent man, asking Campbell instead to begin a legal investigation of the treatment he had received. "I have never acted with the smallest impropriety in relation to the Dundee leaflet," he insisted.

On the following day, Campbell had two tasks to perform in the high court. First he presented Skirving's petition for wrongful imprisonment, which the bench dismissed. After that he was to try to free Muir, who was brought from the Tollbooth with an escort of soldiers. The public drama was heightened by redcoats marching with bayonets fixed, a spectacle that suggested a desperate revolutionary or a French *agent provocateur* had been captured in a dangerous encounter.

The court was full of Muir's supporters when Campbell presented his second petition of the day, to have Muir's status as an outlaw reversed. Lord advocate Robert Dundas, stood before the bench, his head held high in an attempt to overcome his diminutive stature. At first it seemed as if he would oppose the request. "Whatever motive Mr Muir had for leaving the country was best known to himself," said Dundas, "but one thing is certain, he left it at a very critical period, and when there lay against him a very serious accusation". However, he recommended that the sentence of fugitation be erased, adding,

"That said, if Mr Muir should ultimately meet the full severity of justice, after trial by jury, he shall not have occasion to complain that unfair advantage has been taken of him."

Shouts of encouragement from the public gallery were accompanied by applause. Campbell requested that Muir be released on bail. Dundas demanded that Muir be re-arrested on the sedition charge and the mood in the courtroom turned to dismay and anger. Campbell protested that his client could not possibly prepare his defence on such a serious charge in the cramped conditions of the Tollbooth.

"Mr Muir had been bailed on a surety from his father and still failed to attend this court in February," said the judge. "He may flee the country again. We need new guarantors, unrelated to the accused."

"I will stand surety myself, your honour," said Campbell.

"Very well," replied the judge, "bring me the legal proof on Tuesday next and we will consider it."

The gallery gasped in disbelief. Campbell protested at the unnecessary delay but Muir was led away, still in shackles, and accompanied back to the Tollbooth by the armed squad of infantry.

It was a long weekend in the Heart of Midlothian for Muir and Skirving, although they were visited by family and friends and supporters each day. On Tuesday, 13 August, Muir was back in court and was granted bail until his trial on 30 August. James Campbell had to guarantee 2,000 merks (about £115) – the court still dealt in old Scots currency despite sterling being the legal tender throughout the United Kingdom. On the following day, Skirving gave up his protest and applied for bail. He was released on the even more excessive sum of 3,000 merks, around £175 sterling.

CHAPTER 18

The Trial of Thomas Muir

"I am not surprised that you have been shocked at the account you have read of Muir's trial; you would have been much more shocked if you had been present at it, as I was."

Sir Samuel Romilly, law reformer, letter to a friend, 1793.

Muir was going to be late. He was embarrassed that he had taken so long to get dressed. Most people wore the common blue or brown but on the Friday morning of his trial, Muir decided he would not only give the performance of his life but would look the part as well. His auburn hair was brushed and tied at the back in the French way, fashionable with reformers, and he wore a suit of dark green velvet, set off at the collar and cuffs by a white cambric shirt. He had been staying at the family home of his friend William Moffat, who had assisted him in preparing his defence and would act as his solicitor in court today. Moffat had left for Parliament Close before him and Muir planned to catch him in the High Street but now, fighting for breath as he hurried up the steep Canongate hill, he was astonished find a great mass of people standing in his way, waiting for his entrance to the old court.

The morning was warm and close and people had taken advantage of the late summer weather to gather outside the old parliament building in the hope of securing a place in the small courtroom or in the great hall leading to it. Some had been there since dawn. Word of Muir's trial had spread throughout the country and people had been arriving in Edinburgh for days. They came by coach, horseback and foot from every part of Scotland. A number had travelled from England, too. Muir pushed his way through the crowd as he was offered handshakes, applauded and encouraged, and he managed to reach the courtroom and his place beside Moffat only after the ten o'clock chimes of St Giles had faded and the clerks, the prosecutors, and the five judges had entered the room in procession and taken their seats.

Muir tried to apologise to the bench for his lateness but his words were brushed aside by Lord Braxfield, who told him brusquely to pay attention to the indictment, which was read by the clerk of the court. The simple charge of sedition had been expanded into four separate counts, first of "wickedly and feloniously exciting, by means of seditious speeches and harangues, a spirit of disloyalty and disaffection to the king and the established government". The other three charges were also concerned with "wicked and felonious" acts, involving the distribution of seditious publications, advising people to read or buy them, and reading aloud "a seditious and inflammatory writing, tending to produce in the minds of the people a spirit of insurrection and of opposition to the established government". The last charge referred to the Irish address to the convention.

The indictment went on to state that these offences took place between September and December 1792, that they had taken place in Kirkintilloch, Milton, Lennoxtown, Glasgow and Edinburgh, and that the seditious publications involved were Paine's *Rights of Man*, the *Paisley Declaration of Rights* and an *Address to the People*, a publication called *A Dialogue Between the Governors and the Governed*, and a number of copies of a newspaper entitled *The Patriot*. It named some of the people who had attended his meetings in the Campsie towns near Huntershill and who had bought or handled those publications, as well as individuals who had done the same in Muir's father's shop in Glasgow.

The clerk of the court drew breath and continued reading lengthy excerpts from each of the books or papers. The crowded courtroom and the mass of people in the hall beyond listened attentively. The whole of the indictment took more than half an hour to read aloud and when the final words of the charge were read, "the said Thomas Muir ought to be punished with the pains of law, to deter others from committing the like crimes in all times coming", a short silence was broken by audible hissing at the back of the hall.

Braxfield ordered Muir to stand and asked him how he pleaded. "Not guilty," said Muir, who explained that he would be conducting his own defence.

It was customary in Scotland at the time that the substance of a defence should be submitted to the court in writing, together with a list of witnesses, on the evening before the trial. Moffat and Muir had given in their statement and a list of fifty-four witnesses. The prosecution had summonsed another forty witnesses. It was also customary for all of the evidence to be presented to the court in one day's sitting.

"It's going to be a long day and night," Muir whispered to Moffat, as the clerk began to read his defence to the court. It began, "The criminal libel is false and injurious." Murmurs of agreement came from the great hall. "It can easily be proved by a numerous list of witnesses that, upon every occasion the accused exhorted them to pursue measures moderate, legal, peaceable, and constitutional." It went on to argue that there was at present a great national question concerning equal representation in the House of Commons and that information for the people was "the chief thing requisite to accomplish this great object... He uniformly advised them to read every publication, upon either side, which the important question of parliamentary reform had occasioned."

The five judges sat in a row in front of a huge fireplace, old and cracked and half full of cold ash. On each side of the mantelpiece was a panel of dingy black velvet with letters of faded gold thread, one displaying the Lord's Prayer, with the Ten Commandments on the other. The judges were required to rule on whether or not the charge was relevant in law. One by one, they looked down on the ancient, gloomy, dark brown courtroom and made their pronouncements. And one by one they strayed from their lawful duties and expressed their prejudices.

Lord Henderland was first. He remarked on how serious these charges were; he spoke of the consequences of such crimes in the history of the country; and he said that if Muir had cared to examine "a neighbouring country", France, "he would have seen that similar crimes had, like an earthquake, swallowed up her best citizens and endangered the lives and properties of all". He found that the indictment was relevant and, if found true, should "infer the pains of law, and those pains include every thing short of capital punishment".

The air in the outer hall seemed to heave with a disbelieving gasp as the news was passed back from the public gallery.

Lord Swinton followed. "I have never heard such an indictment read," he admitted, "and I do not believe that in the memory of man there ever has been a libel of a more dangerous tendency read in this court. There is hardly a line of it which, in my opinion, does not amount to high treason and which, if proven, must infer the highest punishment the law can inflict."

Muir and Moffat exchanged quizzical glances as onlookers' feet scraped and shifted.

Lords Dunsinnan and Abercromby agreed that, if proven, the highest punishment should apply. Lord Braxfield elaborated on the crime of sedition. "That crime is aggravated according to its tendency," he said. "The tendency here is plainly to overturn our present happy constitution, the happiest, the best, and the most noble constitution in the world, and I do not believe it possible to make a better! The books which this gentleman has circulated have a tendency to make the people believe that the government of this country is venal and corrupt, and thereby to excite rebellion. I therefore agree to find the libel relevant to infer the pains of law."

Braxfield began to pick, and pack, his jury. The method of choosing a jury was for officials of the town and surrounding counties to compile a list of 135 eligible jurors. This was reduced to forty-five by court officials who then passed it to the bench to pick the final fifteen. Of the first five selected, one, Captain John Inglis, felt it was inappropriate for him sit in judgment of someone accused of a crime against the government since he was in the king's navy and therefore employed by the government. His objection was dismissed.

Muir was asked if he had any objection to any of the five. Moffat had been hurriedly checking all of the names on the list with the membership of "lives-and-fortune men" in the anti-reform association. "These gentlemen," said Muir, "belong to an association which assembled in Goldsmiths Hall, calling themselves the friends of the constitution, united to support it against republicans and levellers, and expressing their zeal to suppress tumult and sedition. I belong to the Association of the Friends of the People... To the constitution, in its genuine principles, we have solemnly pledged ourselves. Never have we professed to be its enemies, yet the association in Goldsmiths Hall, by a deliberate and public act of theirs, have declared that we were the enemies of the constitution... I am accused of circulating the works of Mr Paine. That association has...offered a reward of five guineas to anyone who will discover a person who may have circulated them! If this is not prejudicating my cause, I demand to know what prejudication is. Accused this day of sedition, of an attempt to overthrow the constitution, shall those men be my jurymen, who have not merely accused me, but likewise judged and condemned me?"

The crowd heaved forward into the public gallery as the solicitor general rose. "This objection is most extraordinary!" he said. "The prisoner might as well object to your lordships being his judges as you, too, have sworn to defend the constitution." The smiles and quiet laughs from the court officials at the cleverness of this response were quickly drowned by the rising hubbub from spectators objecting to the speciousness of Robert Blair's comment.

Muir shot to his feet. "I object to these gentlemen, not because they associated in defence of the constitution, but because they have publicly accused me of being an enemy of the constitution, and have already pronounced the sentence of condemnation!" Braxfield overruled the objection. Muir made the same protest at the next two sets of five jurors and was similarly dismissed. When the jury was sworn, Muir once again rose. "I believe these to be men of truth and integrity," he began, "but never will I cease recalling to their attention the peculiarity of their situation. They have already determined my fate. They have already judged my cause, and as they value their reputation, their own internal peace …"

"Sit down Mr Muir!" interrupted Braxfield. He stared severely at Muir, gathering together his big, dark eyebrows and continued in a low growl, "Your conduct is exceedingly improper in taking up our time on an objection that has already been repelled. Sit down! Call the first witness!"

"Call Alexander Johnston!" shouted the macer, the court official charged with keeping order. Johnston, a bleacher from Kincaid's textile factory in Campsie parish, took the stand. So began a procession of witnesses, most of whom had attended reform meetings at which Muir had spoken or with whom he had been engaged in conversation in Glasgow. The amiable Robert Dundas (later judged as a lord advocate "of no professional consideration and of very moderate ability"), with the help of the solicitor general (similarly found to be "without any general knowledge, enlarged views, or any splendour of talent"), presented little in their evidence to support their allegations. Twelve witnesses were called and four who had been at one or more of Muir's meetings in the Campsie towns established nothing against him and agreed that in public and in private his conduct was constitutional, even loyal. Three delegates to the December convention were questioned about the address of the United Irishmen: Robert Forsyth, James Campbell, and James Denholm, all lawyers. Campbell said that Muir simply read the address and suggested answering it; Denholm swore that Muir had read the address and, when objections had been made about it, said "that he saw no harm in it"; Forsyth maintained that Muir not only read the address but when it was objected to, "defended the paper and proposed it should lie on the table and be answered". So far,

Dundas had only proved that Muir actually read the address, which fell short of doing so from "wicked and felonious" motives to create "a spirit of insurrection". None of the lawyers in the witness box believed the address was seditious.

That left five more witnesses, Henry Freeland from Kirkintilloch, William Muir, John Muir, Thomas Wilson and Ann Fisher, all from Glasgow, to establish whether Muir recommended or circulated Paine's book or any other of the named seditious publications. But first, an unexpected face came into the witness box: Lapslie, minister of Campsie and so-called family friend of the Muirs.

"Let this witness be removed," objected Muir. "I have many objections to state against him." Lapslie was asked to step down and leave the courtroom. "I know not what title this reverend gentleman has to act as agent for the crown," Muir continued, "but this I offer to prove, that he assisted the messengers of the law in exploring and citing witnesses against me; that he attended the sheriffs in their different visits to the parishes of Campsie and Kirkintilloch; that he conversed with witnesses of the crown; that he attended their precognition, put questions to them and took down notes; nay more, that without being cited by the prosecutor he offered himself against me."

Members of the Campsie societies had informed Muir about Lapslie's activities and Moffat had assembled the evidence and the witnesses to prove them. Braxfield asked for them to be called. The first three attested that Lapslie had been present when they were questioned by Sheriff Honyman of Glasgow. One had been offered a reward by the minister. As Muir was about to call a fourth person, Robert Dundas gave up Lapslie as a prosecution witness.

As news of the Campsie minister's treachery reached the crowd outside in the close heat of the afternoon, balladeers at once began composing rhymes and songs to take around the taverns and coffee shops later that day. Within minutes a simple ditty was being passed back inside the great hall, "My name is James Lapslie, I preach, and I pray, / And as an informer, Expect a good pay."

The prosecutor resumed his evidence. Henry Freeland, the weaver who had organised the November meeting in Kirkintilloch and had invited Muir to speak, was sworn. He was named in the indictment as the person to whom Muir had given Paine's *Rights of Man*. Freeland told the court he had asked Muir about it, had not been recommended it, in fact had been told by Muir that it was not suitable to their purposes and that it "had a tendency to mislead weak minds". He had simply taken a copy of it from Muir's greatcoat. The only book that Muir had recommended to him was *Henry's History of England*.

Dundas was not doing well. John Muir and Thomas Wilson, both of Glasgow, admitted to talking with Muir about Paine's book in the summer, but denied having bought it as a result of those conversations. William Muir, after spending some time in the Tollbooth for refusing to take the oath, which he said was contrary to his religious beliefs, simply said he saw Freeland take the Paine book from Muir's coat pocket but did not remember Muir speaking against the government or advising unconstitutional behaviour. He had got eleven copies of *The Patriot* for his society.

Everything now depended on Ann Fisher, the former scullery maid. After Muir was arrested she had left the family and had been given a post with John Carlisle, a tax collector in Glasgow. She, like Lapslie, was a voluntary witness. She had often been seen in Lapslie's company after she left the Muir household and other witnesses noticed that the two of them were in close conversation in the court. Fisher upheld the charge in the indictment that Muir had recommended and even procured seditious publications. Her evidence contradicted all of the other witnesses. "I saw a good many country people coming about Mr Muir's father's shop," she said. "Mr Muir frequently said to them that Mr Paine's *Rights of Man* was a very good book. I frequently bought the book for people in the shop. I bought the first and second parts of Paine at different times, I did that for Alexander Muir, Mr Muir's uncle. John Muir was much pressed upon to purchase the book. I bought one for Barclay, a weaver from the parish of Cadder. I know Mr Muir's hairdresser, Thomas Wilson, and I heard Mr Muir advising him to buy Paine's *Rights of Man* and to keep them in his shop to enlighten people as it confuted Mr Burke entirely. He said a barber's shop was a good place for reading in."

Her tutored and remarkably precise evidence continued in the same way, almost exactly following the indictment. She revealed that Muir had read *A Dialogue Betwixt Governors and the Governed* out loud to his mother, sister and others; she could not remember who the others were, "and that Mr Muir said it was very clever and was written by one Volney, one of the first wits in France". She told how Muir read French law books, and he said that if everybody had a vote he'd be MP for Cadder, that members of parliament would have thirty or forty shillings a day and none but honest men would be members, and that France was the most flourishing nation in the world as they had abolished tyranny. And on, and on, ending with a swipe to annoy their lordships on the bench. "He said the court of justiciary would need a thorough reform, too, that they got their money for nothing but pronouncing sentence of death upon poor creatures."

Muir rose to object and asked that the witness be removed. When she was out of the room he said, "The conduct of the lord advocate is in every respect highly reprehensible. He has put a variety of questions to witnesses with regard to crimes of which I am not accused. The indictment charges me with making seditious speeches...with distributing seditious books...and of having read in the convention the address from the Society of United Irishmen in Dublin. The indictment charges nothing more, there is not single letter within its four corners which points out to me the charge of speaking disrespectfully of courts of justice, tending, in any manner, to excite the people against the administration of the law... If the public prosecutor had evidence that I was guilty of this crime, he was deficient in his duty to the public in not making it an article of accusation... To attempt to steal it in as evidence in this way, to prove a crime which he durst not openly libel because he knew it could not be supported, merits the severest reprobation."

Dundas replied, "Mr Muir is indicted for the crime of sedition, and that crime may consist of many facts and circumstances... I am entitled to bring in evidence every word or expression which he held in his own family and every conversation with ignorant country people."

Muir once more objected, "If you accuse a man of a crime, you must tell him what that crime is in order that he may be able to defend himself."

Swinton said from the bench, "It is the general proposition of the libel that the accused went about sowing sedition and as the courts of justice are part of the constitution I am of the opinion that reflecting on them is included in the general charge." Again, the air was sucked from the room as the gallery and the great hall gasped. Dunsinnan and Abercromby agreed with Swinton and Braxfield overruled the objection.

Fisher was brought back to the stand and Dundas asked her if there was anything further she would like to tell the court about the conduct of Muir during that summer. "I was sent by Mr Muir to an organist in the street," she replied, "and he asked me to get him to play *Ça Ira*."

Muir was asked to cross-examine the witness. "I disdain to put a question to a witness of this description," he answered. For this he was reprimanded by Braxfield and told by Henderland that if he was not standing as the accused he would have been sent to prison for such behaviour. Braxfield then complimented Fisher. "I have never heard a more distinct and accurate evidence in my life," he said. As Fisher was leaving, Captain Inglis, from the jury, asked if she had had any quarrel with the Muirs before leaving their service. "Far from it," she replied. "My mistress gave me five shillings more than my wages and Miss Muir gave me a petticoat, with some other presents." This was later denied by the family but, for now, the impression of cordial relations had been created.

Fisher joined Lapslie, who had been waiting for her in a side room, and they left the court together. As they emerged into Parliament Close a universal hissing greeted them. Lapslie attempted to speak but could not be heard above the noise. By that time a ten-verse news ballad was already circulating in the crowd, who paid the balladeers to sing it over and over. Called *The Clerical Informer's Creed*, the most memorable verse was, "I shall do all I can, Dundas may be sure, To gather up falsehoods against Mr Muir; And if he's found guilty how happy I'll be; For I as informer expect a good fee, To buy black coats and cravats so white."

Evening was approaching and the heat of the day still lay over the courtroom like a blanket. Robert Dundas informed the bench that he intended to call no more witnesses.

"There is one witness whom the lord advocate has omitted," stated Muir, "William Ross, one of the justices of the peace for the county of Wigton."

"I did not think it was necessary to summon him," said Dundas.

"I am very sorry about that," said Muir, "as I had some material questions to put to Mr Ross, but seeing his name in the list of witnesses for the crown, I had not cited him in defence."

Muir now began his defence by calling his witnesses. Nineteen of them were eventually examined and they all described him as a person of constitutional views who supported the present frame of government, although not its faults. They agreed that he didn't recommend or circulate any of the books named in the indictment and it wasn't his habit to do so. Dundas could extract nothing from his cross-questioning so was reduced to telling the jury that since they were all reformers they were probably as bad as the prisoner at the bar. After Muir's sixteenth witness, the lord advocate objected. "It is unnecessary for Mr Muir to bring so many witnesses to prove the same thing," he said in a frustrated tone.

"I intend to bring witnesses from every part of the country where I attended societies for reform, that I might clearly prove my innocence," Muir said, holding the disdainful stare of the prosecutor. However, he called three more witnesses and relented. Everyone, he could see, was losing concentration and was thinking only of their evening meal. It was now 8.30pm and the retreating sun had done little to cool the close, thundery feel of the evening. Lord Braxfield called an adjournment.

An hour later, when the court reassembled, a thunderstorm broke in the darkening sky and rain fell so heavily it bounced from the streets to knee height. Torrents ran down the High Street and fed the wynds and closes with tumbling streams. The water didn't deter onlookers. The gallery and the great hall were again packed and those outside sought shelter under eaves, or wax cloth, or large hats. The court was cooler as the judges once again entered in procession, filing behind the jury box to reach the bench. On passing one of the jurors, a family friend, Braxfield whispered, "Come awa, Maister Horner, come awa, and help us to hang ane o' thae daamned scoondrels."

Dundas began his summing up. He stood and faced the jury. "Thomas Muir is a man who has been, under the specious pretext of a reform, sowing the seeds of discontent and sedition." Disapproval from the gallery charged the air. "He in everything betrays a most decided spirit against the constitution, and all under the veil of parliamentary reform. We all know the pernicious effects of the seditious writings and conduct which have lately appeared in this country. I trust that as the evidence has clearly unfolded the diabolical and mischievous conduct of this person, he will receive a guilty verdict. Who could have conceived that a man who has received a liberal education, who has practised as an advocate at this bar, should be found on every occasion among villagers and manufacturers, poor and ignorant" – growls and hisses floated in from the great hall – "for the purpose of sowing among them sedition and discontent?"

The lord advocate repeated the charges. "As to the first charge, that of making seditious speeches and harangues, the evidence I chiefly rest on here is Johnston and Freeland." Their evidence had, in fact, exonerated Muir but Dundas glossed over that, relying instead on the prejudices of the jury and asserting that talking of the success of the French armies and pointing to heavy taxation was seditious. He used the same sly technique when examining the second charge, circulating seditious books. "Freeland is again in evidence here," he told the Goldsmiths men, "and I must observe that it appears to be doubtful whether he told all he knew." He emphasised the testimony of Ann Fisher. "I dare say, gentlemen, you will agree with me that her evidence was correct, well founded, stands on the basis of truth and", here he inserted his own untruth, "is corroborated by the evidence of others."

Dundas called Muir's father's shop a "cathedral of sedition" where Muir "sat like a spider, weaving his filthy web". Muir was described as "a demon of mischief", "diabolical", "tainted from head to foot", "as unworthy to live under the protection of the law as the meanest felon", and the "most criminal" man to have ever appeared before him in court, betraying "the greatest appearance of guilt". He was, in fact, "the pest of Scotland". Having read out the Irish address at the convention was enough, in Dundas's law, to condemn Muir as "the determined ringleader in a uniform scheme of sedition". But when he asserted that Muir had had no intention of returning from France to face his accusers the gallery and the great hall erupted in angry protest and drowned the appeals of Braxfield and his macers for order with loud whistles, while the wooden floors shook as the stamp of heavy boots brought the evening's thunder inside the building.

The lord advocate capped his performance by stepping, unchallenged by the bench, across one more legal line and referring to a forthcoming trial, implying the guilt of the accused. "You may in some degree judge a man by the company he keeps," he said. "Among Mr Muir's papers we find a letter, here in my hand, addressed to the Rev T Fyshe Palmer, a man who is indicted to stand trial at Perth, in the course of a few days, and who most of you must know." Dundas demanded that the jury, "seize Muir in his career and by your verdict do justice to your country and honour to yourselves".

Renewed protests from supporters drowned out the ten o'clock chimes of St Giles as Muir rose to defend himself, reminding the jury, "All that malice could devise, all that slander could circulate, has been directed against me." He also tried to turn their attention on their own reputations. "The eyes of this country are fixed upon us both. The records of this trial will pass down to posterity. When our ashes shall be scattered by the winds of heaven, the impartial voice of future times will rejudge your verdict."

He explained to them again that his being stranded in France was unavoidable and could not be used as a means of establishing guilt. "Do not all my private letters, which have this day been read, prove my uneasiness upon account of the delay, and my anxiety to return?" He reiterated that he had returned openly to stand trial. "In the list of witnesses against me, I saw the names of Carmichael, the person who first recognised me at my landing at Portpatrick, and of Mr Ross, the magistrate at Stranraer, before whom I first appeared... I would have adduced them as witnesses to prove that, so far from concealing myself, I announced myself publicly and without disguise." He accused Dundas of deliberately not calling them as witnesses. "This was an art to prevent me citing them. It has succeeded. I am deprived of their testimony."

He turned then to the events of the previous winter. "The prosecutor has talked of the danger the people of this country were in last winter! Of deep-laid plots! And of tremendous conspiracies! I am the man whom he charges as the author of the whole, whom he represents similar in malignity to the demon of mischief, and who he honours with the title of the 'pest of Scotland'... Where has the proof of this design been found? Has it been discovered in meetings of the Friends of the People who, conscious of the purity of their intentions affected no concealment, assembled with doors open to all... Could in the crowds that were admitted to attend the deliberations of these societies, be found no ruffian who could at least give a bold and manly testimony against me? To support the accusation, the testimony of a miserable scullion girl must be brought forward with regard to words spoken under the guardianship of a paternal roof... The evidence of Ann Fisher comes forward to you with peculiar distinction, caressed by the prosecutor and complimented by the court, her wonderful accuracy extolled and her abilities admired."

He challenged her credibility and her veracity on individual points. "She swears that I used to recommend to a great many country people who came to my father's shop, to purchase and read the works of Mr Paine. She can only specify one, John Barclay, and he gives her the flattest contradiction."

He questioned her evidence of having bought parts one and two of Paine for his uncle, Alexander Muir. "Why is not Alexander Muir brought forward as a witness? Certain it is that he was closely interrogated before the inquisition held by Mr Sheriff Honyman. But the lord advocate says that his feelings would not permit him to examine the uncle against the nephew. Wonderful humanity! Goodness ever to be remembered and extolled!" He looked directly at Dundas. "But did not you, sir, advise and direct the whole proceedings against me, and will you have the effrontery to maintain that Alexander Muir was not dragged like a felon from his own home by the myrmidons of power, carried before your friend Honyman, and that every art was employed to wring from him every domestic secret?"

He ridiculed the notion that his asking Fisher to have a street organist play the French tune *Ça Ira* was sedition. "If it had been possible for me to have caused to be sung, upon the streets of Glasgow, one of the psalms of the Hebrews, in the original language, in which the triumphs of the people and the destruction of tyrants are recorded in a strain of the highest poetical inspiration, the criminality would have been the same with that of listening to *Ça Ira*."

He warned the jury against giving weight to Fisher's evidence. "Let me solemnly caution you against the dangerous precedent of giving credibility to witnesses of this kind, under accusations of this nature. The crime of sedition, if you attend to its essence, never can be committed within the walls of a private house. It supposes the highest publicity, the convocation of many. But if power shall say that words spoken in an unguarded moment within the sacred walls of a family amount to this crime, what will follow?"

Muir defended the reform campaign. "Gentlemen of the jury, let us this night throw away vain pretext, let us act fairly and candidly. I smile at the charge of sedition. You yourselves are conscious that no sedition has existed in this country. I know for what I am brought to this bar, it is for having strenuously engaged in the cause of parliamentary reform... Yes, I plead guilty. I openly, actively, and sincerely embarked in the cause of a parliamentary reform, in the vindication and in the restoration of the rights of the people... Can it ever be forgotten that in the year 1782 Mr Pitt was stained with the same guilt? ... Have you forgotten that in the same year the Duke of Richmond, the present commander of the forces, was a flaming advocate for the universal right to suffrage? Shall what was patriotism in 1782 be criminal in 1793?"

Turning to Dundas, he said, "You have honoured me this night by the title of the 'pest of Scotland'... But what term of super-eminent distinction will not you, the public prosecutor, you, the lord advocate of Scotland, appropriate to yourself? Were you, not many months ago, likewise a reformer? ... Were you not one of those men who, for that purpose, assembled lately in this city in what they called a convention, and assumed to themselves the title of delegates from the counties? Were you not yourself employed in framing a bill for the extension of the elective franchise? ... In accusing me, you charge yourself with sedition." He went on to remind them of the Bill of Rights, which guarantees the right to petition parliament.

On the question of Tom Paine's *Rights of Man*, he asked if it had been proscribed when he lent it to Freeland. "No," was the answer. "Was there a judgment in any court in England or in Scotland against this book at that time? No. Then I had no cause for alarm. But some months before, a proclamation against seditious writings had been issued. A proclamation, gentlemen, is not law. It can declare and it can enforce what the law has already enacted but it has no legislative authority. But was there any mention of Mr Paine's works in the proclamation. None."

He asked them to examine the books as a whole and not just the odd quote, taken out of context and repeated in the indictment. "Can you point me out a single sentence where he provokes insurrection? Mr Paine's writings are indisputably of a speculative nature. He investigates the first principles of society, he compares different forms of government together, and where he gives the preference he assigns his reasons for so doing."

This, Muir argued, was what liberty of the press meant. "If you destroy that liberty, you accomplish one of two things, the people will be buried in ignorance, the iron throne of despotism will be erected... If to lend the works of Thomas Paine today be sedition, to lend a translation of the Republic of Plato tomorrow will be treason... Gentlemen, I shall conclude upon the subject of Mr Paine's works by observing that all the witnesses have uniformly sworn that I refused to recommend them... Mr Paine is a republican and the spirit of republicanism breathes through all his writing. This is his darling system. The object of these societies was, by constitutional means, to procure a reformation in the constitution, not a revolution... All the witnesses who speak of my conduct in the societies tell you that I recommended none but constitutional measures and that the only book which I recommended to them was *Henry's History of England*, as the best calculated, by its accuracy and plainness, to give them insight into the nature and progress of their constitution."

He reminded them that they were the first jury in Scotland to pronounce upon the works of Paine and that it was no crime for Plato, or Cicero, Sir Thomas More, Harrington or Hume to speculate on forms of government. "These authors indulged themselves in a liberty, which if we now are to be deprived, we must be left hopeless and in despair, as the attempt at amendment and reform will be forever precluded."

Murmurings of agreement came from behind him in the public areas. He still had far to go in examining the evidence of individual witnesses. He had been speaking for nearly three hours. He was tired. He saw that everyone else was, too. "I hasten over the evidence of the remaining witnesses against me. I am overcome by the exertions of this day, and you must be greatly exhausted." More sounds of agreement came from behind, and he sped through the remaining testimony.

However, there was one more thing to do. "Gentlemen," he said, "I now come to the last charge, that of having read in the convention of delegates, the address from the society of United Irishmen in Dublin. I admit the fact and I glory in the admission. The prosecutor has represented that society as a gang of mean and nefarious conspirators, and their diploma of my admission into their number as an aggravation of my crime. Let me tell the lord advocate of Scotland, that society stands too high to be affected by his invective, or to require the aid of my defence." Muir read most of the address again and discussed its various parts. "I maintain that every line of that address is strictly constitutional," he claimed.

It was now late, approaching one o'clock in the morning. "I hasten to my conclusion," Muir said. "Much yet remains to say. But after, upon my part, the unremitted exertions of sixteen hours, I feel myself nearly exhausted." He quickly ran over the charges and gave brief summaries of his objections. He looked at every man in the jury box and said, "This is now perhaps the last time that I shall address my country... Of crimes most foul and horrible I have been accused; of attempting to rear the standard of civil war, and to plunge this land in blood, and to cover this land with desolation. At every step, as the evidence of the crown advanced, my innocence has brightened... What then has been my crime...having dared to be, according to the measure of my feeble abilities, a strenuous and active advocate for an equal representation of the people in the House of the people... It is a good cause. It shall ultimately prevail. It shall finally triumph... I am careless and indifferent to my fate. I can look danger and I can look death in the face, for I am shielded in the consciousness of my own rectitude. I may be condemned to languish in the recesses of a dungeon. I may be doomed to ascend the scaffold. Nothing can destroy my inward peace of mind, arising from the remembrance of having discharged my duty."

In the moments of complete silence that followed, Muir looked back to his mother and father and sister at the front of the public gallery. Tears filled the eyes of them all. He moved his gaze to the bench, nodded briefly towards Braxfield, and sat down.

An enormous burst of applause rang around the courtroom and the great hall. Booted feet once more stamped approval on the wooden floors. The loud acclaim continued longer than Braxfield's objections or his macers' cries for order. Three cheers were called. "Hip, hip!" and the shouts of "Hooray!" followed in the customary triple accolade. All the judges looked grim. When the ovations died away, Braxfield turned to the jury.

"There are two things which you should attend to, which require no proof," he began. "The first is, that the British constitution is the best in the world. For the truth of this, gentlemen, I need only appeal to your own feelings." He was making a direct reply to the public gallery, those people who had brought insolence into his courtroom. "Is not every man secure in his life, liberty and property? Is not happiness in the power of every man", and here he started to take revenge, "except those, perhaps, who, from disappointment in their schemes of advancement are discontented! ... The other circumstance, gentlemen, which you have to attend to, is the state of this country during last winter. There was a spirit of sedition and revolt going abroad which made every good subject seriously uneasy... I leave it for you to judge whether it was perfectly innocent or not in Mr Muir, at such a time, to go about among ignorant country people, making them leave off their work, and inducing them to believe that a reform was absolutely necessary to preserve their safety and their liberty, which, had it not been for him, they never would have suspected to have been in danger. You will keep this in remembrance, and judge whether it appears to you, as to me, to be sedition."

He made an extraordinary statement about the legality of Paine's books, saying, "A judgment of a court of law is by no means necessary to make it seditious, it is in itself most seditious, treasonable, and dangerous," before going on to praise once more the evidence given by Fisher. The Irish address he condemned as seditious and inflammatory, and declared that Muir's visit to France was evidence of guilt as well as "a species of rebellion", having made an embassy to a foreign country without proper authority. "I was never an admirer of the French," he added, "but I can now only consider them as monsters of human nature."

As to Muir's many defence witnesses, "Mr Muir might have known that no attention could be paid to such a rabble," he said, risking a riot. "What right have they to representation? He could have told them that parliament would never listen to their petition. How could they think of it? A government in every country should be just like a corporation and, in this country it is made up of the landed interest, which alone has the right to be represented. As for the rabble, who have nothing but personal property, what hold has the nation on them. What security for payment of their taxes? They may pack up all their property on their backs and leave the country in the twinkling of an eye, but landed property cannot be removed." Muir's plan was to discourage revolt "until everything was ripe for a general insurrection". He was "poisoning the minds of the common people and preparing them for rebellion". He concluded, "I leave it with you and have no doubt of your returning such a verdict as will do you honour," for all the world as if he had given an impartial summary, where he might have been expected to ask the jury to clear away their prejudices and consider only the facts presented in court.

It was after half past one on Saturday morning when the court was adjourned until midday. Half an hour later Lord Braxfield was seen setting off on foot to his town house in George Square. His manservant was in front, holding a lantern high enough for them to see their way through the steep streets. Braxfield clutched his heavy blackthorn stick. 'Wi' this thing in ma twa hauns," he told his servant, "ah believe ah'm a match for onie man in Scotland."

*

As St Giles's bell struck noon, the sky over Edinburgh was once more dark with thunder clouds and the rain washed the streets as the court resumed. Gilbert Innes, the chancellor, or chairman, of the jury was asked to stand and state their verdict. "We all, in one voice, find Thomas Muir guilty of the crimes libelled," he declared.

Muir and Moffat exchanged glances that said this was not unexpected. Muir turned to his parents and his sister and gave them a reassuring look and a thin smile. Lord Braxfield turned to the jury. It is customary for the leading judge to thank the jury for their attendance and their attentiveness. Braxfield went further. "The court highly approves of the verdict you have given," he said. He then asked the other judges what punishment should be inflicted.

Henderland spoke first. The "indecent applause" given to Muir at the adjournment at night proved to him that the spirit of sedition had not yet subsided. He outlined the choices of punishment available to the court, banishment, fine, whipping, imprisonment, and transportation. "Banishment," he decided, "would be improper, as it would only be sending a man to another country where he might have the opportunity of exciting the same spirit of discontent." A fine would only punish his parents, and they already had had to forfeit bail for him; whipping was too severe and disgraceful for a man of his rank; imprisonment is only temporary. "There remains but one punishment in our law, transportation." Fourteen years.

Swinton agreed, adding that the distinction between sedition and high treason is negligible and he sought a punishment in law adequate to the crime. It was unfortunate that torture had been abolished. Transportation. Fourteen years. Dunsinnan spoke so softly that no one could hear what he thought, but all were agreed that he seemed to concur with the first two judges. Abercromby, too, agreed, adding for good measure that Muir avoided tumults simply because "a revolution could only be effected by an insurrection of the general mass of the people; trifling tumults would not answer". Muir protested. "I deny it, my lord, it is totally false." Braxfield agreed with Henderland that the "indecent applause which was given the prisoner last night convinced me that a spirit of discontent still lurks in the minds of the people and it would be dangerous to allow him to remain in this country." Transportation. Fourteen years.

Muir rose. "Were I to be led this moment from the bar to the scaffold, I should feel the same calmness and serenity which I do now. My mind tells me that I have acted agreeably to my conscience, and that I have engaged in a good, a just, and a glorious cause, a cause which sooner or later must and will prevail, and by a timely reform, save this country from destruction." He was once again led from Parliament Close in chains and delivered to the turnkey in the Heart of Midlothian, to await a sailing for the hulks in the Thames. The crowd was silent.

CHAPTER 19

Defiance

"Scots, wha hae wi' Wallace bled,
Scots, wham Bruce has aften led,
Welcome to your gory bed, –
Or to victorie."
Robert Burns, probably 1793, first published
anonymously in the *Morning Chronicle*, May, 1794.

Muir's cell was on an upper floor of the Tollbooth. It had a barred window high in one wall, through which he could hear the calls of traders in the Luckenbooths below. Filtered light seeped through the narrow gap between the prison and the wall of St Giles cathedral. Another grilled window was cut in the heavy wooden door but this afforded no light, as it looked out on a dark corridor. Muir's furniture comprised a wooden chair, a small table and a cot bed with a mattress made from stuffed jute bags. Moffat had stayed with him all through Saturday, as they tried to come to terms with the severity of the fourteen-year sentence of transportation. Both came to the conclusion it would not be implemented. It was not a lawful sentence for sedition under Scots law. They had been shocked by the punishment, but neither now felt overawed. Moffat had promised to come back to the Tollbooth on Sunday morning. He would arrive shortly, thought Muir.

About the same time, the jury in Muir's trial was holding an unofficial meeting. They, too, had been shocked at the sentence. They had met together immediately after the court rose at the request of

Captain Inglis, who told them he was "thunderstruck" at its severity. All agreed. They had thought a few weeks' imprisonment would have been sufficient. They had brought in a unanimous guilty verdict but had believed that Muir's guilt was trivial, so Inglis suggested they petition against the sentence. The jury chancellor, Gilbert Innes, advised caution. He thought the jury should sleep on it and meet again on Sunday morning. They did, and when they met Innes produced a letter he said he had received overnight. It was a death threat, punishment for concurring in the guilty verdict. The jury decided that intimidation of this sort changed things, there were desperados among the reformers. They should not interfere with the sentence of the court.

The threat to Innes was never carried out and two days later he was elected deputy governor of the Royal Bank of Scotland. No one on the jury imagined for a moment that this was his reward for undermining their intentions. They all knew that the wheels of patronage could not turn at so rapid a pace, not even in Dundas's Scotland. But it was as well to take notice of the opinion of such a high standing leader in Edinburgh society. He might reward their acquiescence one day. In a very few years Innes became lord lieutenant of the county and was awarded the freedom of the city.

*

As promised, Moffat returned to the Tollbooth in the late morning along with his wife. They brought with them clean bed linen, a tablecloth, fresh cut flowers, candles and candlesticks, and a basket of good food and wine. They realised that Muir would probably receive many guests, and wanted to help him entertain them in some small comfort. The Moffats had agreed they would visit daily and keep Muir supplied with food and clean linen.

Moffat explained that he had spoken to Muir's parents the night before and that they would arrive shortly. Extra chairs were brought to the room by the turnkey's boy. Prison was as comfortable as you could afford to make it and the Moffats had passed a few coins to the turnkey to ensure the best possible service. Prison jobs were obtained by patronage and the mood and cooperation of jailers were determined in the same cycle of corruption. The Canongate committee agreed to send two of its members to dine with Muir each evening, as much to ensure that his privileges were safe as to provide him with company.

James and Margaret Muir looked distressed when they entered the open door of the cell. His mother did her best to suppress her anxiety while his father was angry that they had both been searched and had to empty their pockets before being admitted. Muir reassured them that he would, in all likelihood, be spending some time in this comfortable room and then freed. They talked over lunch about the challenge that could be made to the sentence, but mostly about his sister, Janet, who had gone home to her new husband. She had married David Blair, a former naval officer, while Muir was in France. They now lived in Glasgow, where Blair had a manufacturing business. Muir's parents told him they would stay in Edinburgh for as long as they could see him and, before they left the cell that Sunday afternoon, presented him with a pocket bible. They had written in the flyleaf, "To Thomas Muir from his afflicted parents." He put it in an inside coat pocket to keep it with him, as you would a talisman.

On Monday morning Moffat arrived with a sheaf of newspapers in his arms. Muir was news. He dropped the Edinburgh, Glasgow, London and Belfast papers on the table and they read through the reports: a full page in the *Edinburgh Herald*; a page and a half in the *Caledonian Mercury*; a report in the *Morning Chronicle* alongside a list of comparative punishments – "The authors of a pamphlet describing parliament as 'fit for the gallows', a few weeks imprisonment; Lindsey, who kidnapped a counsellor to stop him from voting, fined £50; a forger, seven years transportation, commuted to serving in the navy; a murderer, fourteen years transportation"; Belfast's *Northern Star* boasted a "more correct and full account of the trial than has appeared in the English or Irish papers", and so on. Later, the news would be taken up in the Paris and New York papers, too.

A knock came at the open door and a familiar face walked in. It was James Robertson, who had been jailed for six months for selling copies of *The Bee*, while Muir was away in France. His sentence was almost at an end but he thought he might be of assistance to Muir in his remaining weeks. Robertson still owned a bookshop, a printing press, and a newspaper, the *Caledonian Chronicle*. He offered to produce the authoritative version of Muir's trial from the notes taken by Muir and Moffat for the trial and from reports in his *Chronicle* and other papers. Muir agreed and the three set to work, Moffat and Robertson assembling the transcript and Muir editing his closing speech. In a little more than a week, "Robertson's edition", as it came to be known, was on the bookstalls. It was printed in Edinburgh and London and soon reprinted many times. Other versions appeared in different parts of the country, as well as two in New York, both of which sold out within a week. Muir sent copies of Robertson's edition to Hamilton Rowan and Drennan in Dublin. He told Drennan that demand for it was "altogether unexampled" and wrote to Rowan, "The cause of truth and freedom derives strength from persecution. The apathy of the public mind is fast melting away. In number and respectability our friends are daily increasing."

*

William Skirving, secretary of the national association, called the meeting of all of the Edinburgh societies to order. The room was busy. The spy Watt sat near the front. He had given up sitting at the back of meetings in case it threw unnecessary suspicion on him. He looked around and counted 160 people. He had decided not to take notes, again to avoid notice. It was Thursday evening. More people came in. Watt counted 200, and yet more came, until there was standing room only. The hall could seat 300. Watt had got to bed very late on the previous night because of his informing duties. He had been at a meeting of the Canongate society and had afterwards sat down in candlelight with pen and ink to tell the lord advocate about the new life and activity of the reformers, how Muir, he had heard, "keeps up his spirits amazingly" and how "almost every-body, even the most loyal subjects," thought his sentence too severe. The Canongate society had declared that, though the "accuser of brethren" might brand Muir as "the pest of Scotland", they hoped the time would come soon when Scotland would regard him as their hero.

Watt was brought back to the business in hand when he heard a voice from the rear of the meeting demand a membership check to avoid spies. He froze momentarily, but relaxed as another voice called out, to huge applause, "It doesn't matter if half of the room are government spies, we're doing nothing illegal!"

People spoke of their fears for the unconstitutional intentions of government. The suppression of conventions in Ireland had led many to think that Pitt would do the same. They resolved that, "so far from fainting in the day of evil…we will immediately proceed to renovate our various societies before the sitting down of parliament, to make up our minds about another application for redress of griev-ances and restoration of rights, that, with the same purpose, we will also immediately proceed to cultivate a more intimate correspon-dence with all the societies of parliamentary reform in the kingdom." The question of another convention was not aired, just yet. Skirving was trying to keep his powder dry, aware that spies would almost certainly be in the room.

"Incendiary letters, it seems, have been sent to judges and jury in Mr Muir's trial," announced a young man. "The *Gazetteer*," he said, "has reported that threatening letters have been sent to jury members and a list of their names posted on walls and lamp-posts." He held up the newspaper and read from it. "It states, 'no person but an enemy to reform could have been guilty of such improper actions', and I move that we should record similar sentiments. Only a blackguard would do such a thing."

Someone else called out, "Aye, only those who wish to hurt a good cause would be guilty of such a cowardly act!" It was agreed by all.

＊

By the end of the week the city authorities began expressing their fears to the home secretary in London and to the lord advocate, on holiday in Dunkeld. The new lord provost, Thomas Elder, wrote to both of them on Saturday, "I have the honour to write to you at the request of the magistrates and several of the gentlemen of the Goldsmiths Hall association to state to you that Muir's sentence has revived the frequency of the meetings of the society called FOP, and in considerable numbers, and that his remaining here tends very much to keep up the spirit of sedition. We therefore earnestly entreat you may get him removed from this country as soon as possible."

Elder also complained about inflammatory posters on the city's walls and a constant stream of visitors to Muir, which "induced me to order the jailers to admit no stranger into the prison without writing in a book kept for the purpose" and restricting admission to individuals to once a day and no more than two visitors to a cell at a time.

Two days later, Sheriff Pringle repeated the plea. "You will have received a letter from the provost signifying the wish of the magistrates to have Muir removed from here as soon as it can conveniently be done," he wrote. "As the minds of the lower class of people will be kept in a ferment while he remains here I take the liberty to concur with the magistrates in earnestly requesting that you will be so obliging as to take the proper measures for having him immediately removed from this country."

Watt managed to join the visitors at the Tollbooth but found nothing important to report to his masters. "I found him as usual crowded with company, ladies and gentlemen," he wrote. Among Muir's visitors was Lord Daer, Citizen Douglas, who assured him he would talk to sympathetic parliamentarians about the unusually severe sentence. He also received David Dale jnr, who had been a defence witness at his trial, and Samuel Romilly, who explained to Muir he was collecting evidence for proposals to reform the legal system and had been appalled by the conduct of the bench at his trial. He later wrote to his colleague and fellow social reformer Jeremy Bentham, "I doubt whether this would be a very safe country, just at the moment for you to be found in; for I heard the judges of the Justiciary Court, the other day declare, with great solemnity, upon the trial of Mr Muir, that to say the courts of justice needed reform was seditious, highly criminal, and betrayed a most hostile disposition towards the constitution."

*

The following Thursday, 12 September, at eight o'clock in the morning, Thomas Fyshe Palmer stepped into the dock of the circuit court in Perth, accused of sedition. Like Muir, he was said to have committed this crime "wickedly and feloniously". Unlike Muir, he was represented by an advocate. His charge concerned the leaflet written for the Friends of Liberty in Dundee. The indictment said the handbill was "calculated to produce a spirit of discontent in the minds of the people, against the present happy constitution and government of this country and to rouse them up in acts of outrage and violence." It added, for good measure, that it misrepresented the government and "vindicated the enemies of our country, with whom we are at open war".

It seemed from the start unlikely that such a mild, caring man of maturing years, he was 47, would consider advocating riot to achieve better representation in parliament. Palmer was a learned man. Born in Bedfordshire, he was educated at Ely, Eton and Cambridge. He became a fellow of Queens College and was, for a time, a Church of England curate at Leatherhead. He mixed with people such as Dr Johnson and James Boswell. Influenced by the writings of Joseph Priestley, he left the established church and became pastor to a new Unitarian congregation in Montrose. He moved to Dundee in 1785 and preached frequently in Edinburgh, Glasgow, Forfar, Arbroath and Newcastle.

Once again, as in Muir's trial, the judges, Lords Eskgrove and

Abercromby, allowed their political prejudices to influence the picked jury; both of them concluded, in considering the relevancy of the charge and in advance of the evidence, that the document was seditious. Eskgrove, who had an unfortunate and often remarked-upon look, turned his red and blue mottled face toward the jury. He had a very big bottom lip, and when it began to move underneath his equally generous nose, an inaudible mumble preceded speech. "I do, for one," he eventually made clear, "hold that the liberty of this country is doubtless closely connected with the right to petition the legislature." He reverted to a low drone once more, until, "But if any man shall think it proper to call meetings and collect together mechanics, and those whose education and circumstances do not entitle or qualify them to judge matters of legislation, people ignorant altogether of the very grievances which they are told they are loaded with, the case is exceedingly different." He spoke as if Palmer had already been convicted. He concluded that the charge was relevant and should be heard, and that the leaflet had "scarce anything in it but is seditious".

Abercromby, who had been one of the judges at Muir's trial and who had a reputation for agreeing with whatever his colleagues said, was true to form. "I agree with your lordship," he said. He had not the smallest doubt that "there is not within these walls one man of common understanding, whose mind is not warped by some strange bias, by some unaccountable prejudice, who does not concur in the opinion given by your lordship."

Once more, witnesses were called but evidence was thin. The prosecution, encouraged by the judges, planted in the minds of the jury that discontent and a desire to change the constitution was the same as sedition. In spite of a long, learned and eloquent argument against this by the defence lawyer, the impression remained. Abercromby, in summing up, repeated his belief that the leaflet was seditious, after which he gave them further benefit of his wisdom. "Gentlemen, you have been told that reform is a fair and proper object. It may be so. The right of universal suffrage is a right which the subjects of this country never enjoyed, and were they to enjoy it they would not long enjoy either liberty or a free constitution. You will therefore consider whether telling the people that they have a just right to what would unquestionably be tantamount to a total subversion of this constitution, is such a writing as any person is entitled to compose, to print, and so to publish."

On the following afternoon, Palmer was found guilty by all fifteen members of the jury. In sentencing, Abercromby said Palmer's crime was aggravated by the fact that the country was quiet when the pamphlet was published. This was the opposite of the aggravation ascribed to Muir, who had acted when the country was in a state of dangerous political frenzy. Eskgrove agreed. They both thought Palmer's education and standing in the community was another aggravation. A precedent had been set just two weeks before for the punishment of transportation and Palmer was sentenced to be outcast for seven years and sent to the tollbooth in Perth to await a ship.

Skirving had been summonsed as a witness and had travelled to Perth. He was not called. He had a charge outstanding for the same leaflet and if he had taken the stand that charge would have fallen. The lord advocate wanted Skirving in the dock at some point to come. Skirving's journey to Perth had not been wasted, though. He had employed a shorthand writer from London to record the proceedings and produced a popular pamphlet, with the help of James Robertson. It was printed in Edinburgh, London, Glasgow, Perth and Dundee, and was in bookshops within three weeks.

*

The stream of visitors continued through Muir's Edinburgh cell. The Moffats, true to their word, daily brought clean linen and fresh flowers, along with plentiful supplies of paper and ink. Muir's parents came to him each day, usually for lunch. Evening meals and company were provided by the Canongate society volunteers, and Moffat and Skirving were there at most other times. Together they planned for the national convention, which was to be held in October, and prepared legal arguments against the sentences of transportation.

Skirving reported to them that the London Corresponding Society and the Society for Constitutional Information had agreed to send delegates, but the Friends of the People in London had declined. They thought that the plan would be "very improper" at present and a disadvantage to the reform campaign.

Loud bangs drowned out the conversation. The sound became more rhythmic as a beating noise grew from other parts of the jail. Prisoners downstairs were protesting, fighting the boredom of a hung-over Sunday afternoon by drumming out a popular tune on the bars. Muir and his companions realised what was happening and did their best to ignore the din but the turnkey was alarmed. Edinburgh had been edgy for weeks. There were rumours that the French were coming, that the *sans-culottes* of Glasgow, said to amount to many thousands, were on their way to rescue Muir. There was even talk of Liza Fletcher carrying a large knife concealed beneath her cloak as she walked through the streets or, more fancifully, practising beheading chickens in her back yard with a model guillotine. It was known that Archibald Fletcher still celebrated Bastille day each year but the idea of the young Mrs Fletcher preparing for Scotland's Terror was a notion purveyed by catastrophists.

Moffat went downstairs and came across the distressed the turnkey, who said he had sent an assistant for the town guard with word that there might be a party of miners tunnelling into the Tollbooth. Moffat had to stifle a laugh but the turnkey was adamant. In a few minutes the guards came from their station in the High Street with their red uniforms and cocked hats, their muskets and double-headed axes, and surrounded the ancient building. At about three o'clock in the afternoon, the lord provost and his magistrates were sent for and they hurriedly left afternoon service in the New Greyfriars kirk. The farcical episode only strengthened the belief of the provost that Muir had to be got rid of soon.

The authorities were even more unsettled later that week to hear that James Maitland, otherwise known as Lord Lauderdale, one of Scotland's sixteen representative peers in the Westminster parliament, was visiting Muir. Moffat took him up to the cell. Lauderdale was one of the founders of the London Friends of the People and had attended Muir's meeting there. His brother, Thomas, had worked closely with Muir in building the reform campaign in Glasgow and the west. Lauderdale disliked ceremony. He wore his hair and clothes in the French reformer's fashion and frequently referred to himself as "citizen". He had recently presented a petition to the king for peace with France. More than 40,000 people had signed it in Glasgow during September. The government chose not to publish it, so Lauderdale asked the *Gazetteer* to print it.

Lauderdale explained that Daer had contacted him and that the two of them had met with Sheridan and Grey to discuss what could be done. He reported that there had been some disquiet in Westminster about the legality of the sentences passed on Muir and Palmer. Fox had said, "God help the people who have such judges!" Some of Pitt's ministers were uneasy about the sentences, too.

Muir and Moffat had been looking at precedents. Muir explained to Lauderdale that the definition of sedition was very loose but that there was no specific crime of sedition in Scotland. The judges in his case and in Palmer's considered the charges relevant, so it was important to concentrate on the legality of the sentences. There was no precedent for them in the whole record of Scottish criminal law. A new charge of sedition had been invented by the judges as a common law offence. The nearest thing existing on the statute book was the ancient charge of "leasing-making", which specifically protected the person of the king and his family. So there was no precedent for the sentence of transportation either.

The sentence of transportation on Lockie, who was pardoned, was for a common law offence. Sedition was a statutory offence in England and "leasing-making" being also a statutory crime should carry a statutory punishment. In the case of the three young printers, Anderson, Craig, and Morton, who were due to be released that week,

Henderland was the first to introduce the option of transportation for sedition, which he later rejected. Muir and Moffat had consulted Henry Erskine and Archibald Fletcher and they, too, were of the opinion that sedition was close only to the crime of leasing making, and was therefore punishable only by the sentences prescribed in the statute – by a fine, imprisonment, or banishment. And banishment was different from transportation. It was simply exclusion from a community. There had been cases in the past where people were sent from Scotland to hard labour in plantations in America or the Caribbean, but those were in particular circumstances and for particular crimes, not sedition, and they were a long time ago. Banishment could simply mean being banned form entering a specific town or area.

Lauderdale promised to talk again with Sheridan and Grey with a view to raising the question in both houses of parliament. He would also request a meeting with Henry Dundas. Moffat opened a bottle of wine and the three men toasted each other and the cause of reform.

*

That evening, Skirving returned to his home in Old Assembly Close after attending a Friends' meeting in nearby Blackfriars Wynd. The members there were angry and defiant about the slanders made on their organisation during the trials of Muir and Palmer. They resolved to place the text of a resolution in the local papers, which denied that the campaign for parliamentary reform was a cloak for rebellion, an accusation made during the "imbecile ridicule of a crown lawyer" and the "unconstitutional opinions of a judge". It recorded their thanks to Muir and Palmer for all they had done, and called upon the people of Scotland to unite with them to achieve "the inestimable blessings of peace, check an increasing and oppressive system of taxation, and prevent the baleful influence of that corruption which has proved so inimical to public virtue".

Skirving was tired but had promised himself to begin sending invitations for the third convention, which would meet on 29 October.

He sat at his writing desk and lit a candle. From a pile of corre-spondence in front him, he picked up the letter from Thomas Hardy, which approved of the idea of a new convention. He read it through once more to its final sentence, "Our freedom, as you justly observe, depends entirely on ourselves, and upon availing ourselves of this opportunity, which once lost may not so soon be recovered."

CHAPTER 20

Hackney

"O Hell born tyranny! how blest the land
Whose watchful citizens with dauntless breast
Oppose thy first approach!"

John Thelwall, 'To Tyranny', written in the Tower
of London, 14 July, 1794.

It was a mild October morning as Thomas Hardy, the Scots shoe-maker who had founded the London Corresponding Society, walked eastwards out of the City towards the green fields of Hackney. He was accompanied by the society's chairman, Maurice Margarot, and its two best orators, Joseph Gerrald and John Thelwall. They were heading for the house and paddock of Thomas Breillat, who had offered his property as a meeting place for delegates from all of the London societies, where they would elect members to represent them at the reform convention in Edinburgh. The four men turned into Hackney Road at Shoreditch and began to realise that their first general open-air meeting was causing a stir. The streets and lanes leading to Breillat's were crowded with people. Traffic had stopped on the main road.

A voice in the crowd shouted, "Has Tom Paine come to plant the tree of liberty?" Another announced that the French Jacobins were on their way. "Are you meeting to lower the price of provisions?" asked a woman as she passed by. "God bless them," cried some. "Success to you!" called out others.

They discovered a great body of parish constables, maybe as many as a hundred, stationed around Breillat's field. Some Spitalfields weavers had been recruited to stand in the field and take reports every fifteen minutes to two or three magistrates who had headquartered themselves in the Nag's Head nearby. A vast crowd had gathered, many to ridicule and shout abuse.

Margarot and Thelwall, along with John Martin, an attorney, were sent to the Nag's Head while Hardy and the others gathered in a building in the centre of the paddock to explain to the 200 or more members already assembled in the field what was happening. Richard Hodgson, a hatter, was elected chairman of the meeting and he called for a delay of fifteen minutes until the delegation at the Nag's Head had reported to them. Some of the parish constables tried to force their way into the house and had to be prevented. There was a danger that the meeting would be overwhelmed if the crowd took the lead of the constables and turned hostile.

The Nag's Head deputation returned in a few minutes and Margarot reported that there were three magistrates in the tavern along with Joseph White, a Treasury solicitor. They were to sit in judgment on any who breach the peace. They were, however, polite, and listened to the reformers, who gave them copies of the address of the society and told them that between 200 and 400 members from around London were expected and that they were meeting to choose representatives to be sent to a convention in Edinburgh. The magistrates were invited to be present at the meeting, but they declined.

Hardy, Gerrald, Thelwall, and Margarot placed themselves around the grounds, explaining to the great crowd, now estimated as much as 2,000 strong, why they were meeting.

"Malicious information sent to the justices said our meeting was to declare in favour of the French republic and a French invasion," shouted Gerrald over the heads of the constables. "That is a slander on us and an insult to you. You are being lied to. Our true purpose is to join together with as many people as we can to go back to parliament and petition for your rights, your political rights. You deserve to be able to vote for those who make the laws you must obey. More than that, you are entitled to vote for them! We are campaigning for universal suffrage and annual parliaments!"

The others delivered similar messages around the paddock fence. The mood of the mob shifted. Many who had come to ridicule started to cheer. Soon the edgy crowd was an attentive audience. Cheers and cries of "Votes for all!" undermined the designs of the Treasury solicitor.

Soon the delegates from the divisions of the Corresponding Society resumed their meeting and they voted to send Margarot and Gerrald to Edinburgh. They were instructed to argue for universal suffrage and annual parliaments. It was Thursday 24 October and the convention was to begin on the following Tuesday. They would never make it in time but nevertheless left London on the Saturday night stage.

Edinburgh-born Charles Sinclair was authorised by the Society for Constitutional Information to be its delegate at the convention, while in Sheffield nearly 2,000 people met in the open air and elected Matthew Campbell Brown, editor of *The Patriot* , to represent them. They would have elected more delegates but stated, "We have many thousands of members but a vast majority of them being working men, the war has deprived many of them of all employment, and almost every one of nearly half his earnings." For the same reason Sinclair was asked to also represent Leeds. Norwich authorised Margarot to speak for them and share the cost of his expenses with London. Birmingham's societies wrote to say they couldn't afford to send anyone, "in consequence of Mr Pitt's war having almost utterly annihilated our trade in this town, and driven a great number of our best members and mechanics across the Atlantic".

The seemingly polite reception given to Margarot and Gerrald by the Treasury solicitor and Hackney magistrates turned out to have been show. Hardy later noted, "Nevertheless, those sagacious, wise and vigilant magistrates were determined not to part without doing some business that they might have something to boast of and to relate to their employers. About an hour after the society had departed…Thomas Breillat was taken into custody…on a charge of having spoken some seditious words against the king ten months before that, and sworn to by a butcher's boy… He was tried, a jury was found that gave a verdict against him. He was imprisoned in Newgate two years, paid a fine of a hundred pounds, and when he was liberated went to America."

CHAPTER 21

The third Scottish convention

"There is a convention of the Friends of the People to be held here tomorrow. And tho' no respectable persons have as yet appeared amongst them, I am sorry to say that the exertions of the ringleader for these six weeks past have been too successful."

Robert Dundas to Henry Dundas, 18 November, 1793.

Margarot and Gerrald reached Edinburgh after the four-day-long convention had adjourned. It had agreed to meet again in April, this time sending invitations in good time for delegates in England and Ireland to be elected. Whether for reasons of security or just plain miscalculation, Skirving's letters had been sent far too late for most societies properly to elect members and find adequate funding for them. This third Scottish convention had, though, a respectable list of delegates numbering around 200. There were about 160 present at each sitting, with between twenty and fifty visitors a day. It had declared for universal suffrage and annual elections, to petition parliament, and to send an anti-war address to the king. It had also discussed and agreed a democratic structure for its affairs and pledged moral and financial support for the *Edinburgh Gazetteer*. Many of the Whig professionals had again stayed away. Norman Macleod MP disagreed with universal suffrage, while assuring the convention that he was still a staunch campaigner for reform. Citizen Douglas, Lord Daer, was there representing his own society at Wigton as well as the town of Portsburgh, and chaired a committee of organisation. But the composition of the convention was more artisan than before. From the spring of 1793 new leaders had begun to emerge, including George Mealmaker, the Dundee weaver who had written the leaflet that had convicted Palmer. Journeyman weaver was the most common occupation at the October convention.

An address sent by four of the United Irishmen societies in Belfast caused no controversy this time. Nor, strangely, did the authorities show any interest in spite of this having been the chief accusation against Muir. The address pointed out that in Ireland they had already "in humble respectful petition", sent their request to the Dublin parliament. "We are sorry to say," it went on, "that these claims were not treated with deference or decency", but they were determined to continue to make their voice heard, "not, we hope, by the awful experiment of contested revolution, may Heaven avert the dreadful necessity!, but by a voluntary, immediate and radical reform."

The success of the convention was remarkable for such difficult economic and political times. Paisley had written to say they could not afford to send delegates, "trade being so stagnate we have not nor cannot get the usual supplies". They held a county convention instead and sent £4 towards the cost of the national one. Nearby Johnstone couldn't send a delegate either, although they declared for universal suffrage. Dunfermline reported that they "universally lamented" the sentence passed on Muir and added, "Our society is at present not so very numerous as we once was." However, new members had started to come along in the wake of the trials of Muir and Palmer. Montrose apologised for not sending a delegation, the members were in a "languid frame". Dunbar reported gloomily, "you have little to expect from this part of the country as it is most terribly under clerical and aristocratical influence."

In all parts of the country, many thousands were on poor relief and many more had emigrated or joined the army or navy. Around 5,000 were estimated to have enlisted in Glasgow alone during 1793. In October, it was noted by a resident there that two ships had sailed from the Clyde "full of emigrants consisting of manufacturers and bleachers. Two persons have been sent from America on purpose to entice them". Many others had returned home to rural areas, especially to the Highlands. In a letter to Robert Dundas, Lapslie wrote approvingly, "The weavers in my parish at this moment are more sober, industrious and better behaved people when making fourteen pence per day than twelve months ago, when they made three shillings. Their wives and families share more of their wages, now the publicans share less."

Henry Dundas was worried about the potential political consequences of the disruption that war with France had caused. He was close to the Glasgow merchants and authorities, and had ensured government support for the city as part of a wider programme across Britain, which included government funds for war materials. One local merchant wrote to Dundas saying that, without help, "I do not suppose that less than 100,000 persons, men women and children, would have been deprived of the means of subsistence." As it was, he estimated that "many thousands" had already lost their jobs. In spite of the poverty and unemployment, John Russell, a Glasgow delegate to the convention, said that the trials of Muir and Palmer had caused "more firmness and courage in the friends of freedom". The various societies of Glasgow had met and instructed their delegates to press for universal suffrage and annual parliaments.

On the night before the Edinburgh conference began, the lord advocate wrote to his uncle in London, saying, "The bad consequences of Muir's remaining in prison here become every day more apparent... There is a convention of the Friends of the People to be held here tomorrow. And tho' no respectable persons have as yet appeared amongst them, I am sorry to say that the exertions of the ringleader for these six weeks past have been too successful. Almost all of the clubs of last year have been revived, have been attended by very considerable numbers, and are proceeding in the same regular and systematic plan which last year was so fortunately subdued."

He went on to say that Lauderdale had visited Muir and intended to raise the case in parliament. Even this had given "the clubs additional spirits" and he asked again that Muir be removed from Edinburgh.

*

Muir was busy in his cell, reading and writing in the afternoons and meeting with Skirving and Moffat. In the evening he would receive visitors, share a meal and some wine with them, hear reports of the convention proceedings and discuss the events of the day. His routine was now well established and friends had paid for another inmate, Margaret Beattie, to act as a housekeeper to him. The arrangement suited them both but the authorities and the turnkey were becoming more hostile. The procurator fiscal complained to the lord advocate that Muir's privileges allowed him to have influence in the convention and in the general committee of the societies. "Muir, I am told, is generally observed to be up all night or greater part of it after his friends leave him at shutting the prison in the evening and is in bed all forenoon," he reported. "It is therefore no stretch of conjecture to suppose that he is then employed in preparing matter for his friends and there is little doubt that he will be so employed so long as he remains here."

Much of the time, Muir was occupied in replying to letters from well-wishers. The daily deliveries to his cell seemed to fuel the resentment of his jailer, William Binnie. In the end, Muir had to place a general thank-you note in the *Gazetteer*. "The number of addresses I have received, expressive of attachment and approbation prevents me from returning to the particular bodies of men, who have done me this honour, an answer so soon as I could have wished," it read. "I hope this general notice will plead my excuse."

On the opening day of the convention, Moffat had brought him the daily newspapers as usual and suggested that he arranged to have two delegates from the convention to dine with Muir each evening. Muir wondered if the number could be stretched to half a dozen and Moffat sought out Binnie the turnkey to ask permission.

"No!" growled Binnie, "I have strict orders from the magistrates that only two at a time are to be allowed in."

On the following day, when the convention announced its policy of universal suffrage and annual parliaments, the turnkey became violent. Maybe he had heard the disapproving words of his superiors, maybe it was the drink, or maybe he was suffering from the corruption of serving years in a place most people did their best to stay away from. But on this night, as Citizens Bryce and Clarke approached Muir's cell, Binnie leapt on them, pushed Clarke down the stairs and dragged Bryce by the neck after him. They were bundled out of the prison by guards at the door while Binnie ran upstairs and barged into Muir's cell.

"God damn these buggers, the Friends of the People and their souls to hell. Are there any more of them here?" he demanded. In the face of his fury, Margaret Beattie, who was arranging the dinner table, answered in fear, "No, Mr Binnie, there's nobody else in here."

Binnie turned on his heels and took the stairs, two steps at a time, back to the main entrance, where the delegates were insisting they be allowed back in. He grabbed Bryce, punched him and struck him with a heavy bunch of keys. Bryce and Clarke retreated and crossed Parliament Close to the sheriff's office. Pringle ignored their pleas and told them to get a warrant from the procurator fiscal, who took the opportunity of exacting revenge by charging both men with forcibly entering the jail and refusing to leave when ordered. He decreed that the doors of the Tollbooth should now be locked at 8pm every evening.

Muir's visitors were much reduced during the convention but some managed to see him each afternoon and in the early evening. In the confined space of his cell he was beginning to lose hope. His parents tried to raise his spirits and Moffat remained optimistic, but a deep depression began to settle on him and he complained of feeling unwell. His mood brightened on Monday, 4 November, at about one o'clock in the afternoon, when his good friend from Ireland, Archibald Hamilton Rowan, strode into his cell, his massive bulk nearly filling the room. With him was a young Dublin lawyer called Simon Butler, the newly elected secretary of the Dublin United Irishmen.

Muir was overjoyed at seeing his friend so soon after his trial but was curious why he and Butler had arrived then, when the convention had adjourned on Friday. Hamilton Rowan explained that he would gladly have been in Edinburgh as a delegate had they received an invitation in time, but he was here on other business, on "a matter of honour". Muir looked quizzical, and when Hamilton Rowan announced he had come to challenge Robert Dundas to a duel, his look became disapproving.

Hamilton Rowan explained that his honour had been offended during Muir's trial when Dundas claimed that the address from the Society of United Irishmen to the first Scottish convention "was penned by infamous wretches". In a reference to Muir being delayed in France, he had further claimed that Hamilton Rowan, too, had "fled from the punishment" that awaited him. The big Irishman found the slanderous claims outrageous and had said so in letters to Dundas, to which the lord advocate had refused to reply. He was now in town, in person, to have his honour restored. Muir pointed out that duelling was illegal in Scotland and in any case he had defended the reputations of the authors of the address in court, but Hamilton Rowan was determined. He delved into his bag and showed Muir his collection of pistols.

Hamilton Rowan was concerned that Muir might be ill-treated in prison and when he was told of the behaviour of Binnie the turnkey he reached back into the bag, brought out a pair of very small pistols, and handed them to Muir. They were tiny enough to lie under his pillow without anyone ever being aware they were there and they'd make Muir feel safer in the solitary darkness of the night. Muir took the pistols and hid them in his bed.

As the three men talked on, an unwelcome figure appeared at the door of the cell. George Williamson, the thief-taker who had arrested Muir in both Holytown and Stranraer, strode into the room with two henchmen.

"Archibald Hamilton Rowan, I have a warrant for your arrest," Williamson announced.

"On what charge?"

"Sedition," said Williamson, with a half smile, as he threw a glance at Muir. He read from the warrant, "Last December with a malevolent and wicked intention you did transmit to a meeting in Edinburgh a printed paper of a most dangerous and seditious tendency entitled Address from the Society of United Irishmen in Dublin; in August last you sent more of these printed papers, with the same wicked and malicious intent with other papers or pamphlets of a seditious and dangerous tendency." Williamson looked at Muir. This referred to the package taken from him in Stranraer, "and for other seditious and dangerous purposes are just now come into this country."

Hamilton Rowan looked at the warrant. It was dated 28 October, exactly a week ago and three days before he had left Dublin. "Obviously, Mr Dundas wants me within his jurisdiction," he thought to himself. He was taken before Sheriff Pringle, Harry Davidson, the Midlothian county sheriff, and William Scott, the procurator fiscal. They refused to allow Butler into the room and Rowan declined to answer questions without legal representation. He was allowed out on bail of 3,000 merks, about £175 sterling, which was put up by Norman Macleod, who was sent for from his New Town home. He had to promise good behaviour for six months and Macleod persuaded Rowan of the foolhardiness of a duel, not least because of the scorn it would bring on the reform movement. Rowan and Butler went home, via Belfast, where they were treated to a grand dinner by United Irishmen there and drank toasts to the convention, to Muir, and to "the swine of England, the rabble of Scotland, and the wretches of Ireland". William Drennan amused the dinner table with a tale about Muir that his sister, Martha McTeir, recounted in a letter to him from Belfast. "Two strong Belfast men were a few days ago in Scotland, and fell in with a petty tidewaiter [minor customs officer] who they discovered to be an officious spy and the fellow [Carmichael] who informed on poor Muir. They invited him to supper, which he readily accepted. The toast master, with a great oaken cudgel by his side, gave Mr

Muir, the fellow looked greatly dismayed, hoped he had got into company with gentlemen, and applied to the second one to stand his friend and not see him ill used. *His* reply was a bumper to Mr Muir, which example was immediately followed by the Scotchman and proclaimed by his companions, to the great delight of the people in the town where he lives despised."

*

Margarot, Gerrald, and Sinclair had arrived from London. They attended a committee meeting of the Friends of the People in Edinburgh on Wednesday, 6 November, where it was agreed that circumstances were serious enough to recall the convention as soon as possible. Waiting until the following April was not an option. Skirving issued letters and notices for a new Edinburgh gathering, beginning on Tuesday 19 November. In the meantime the English delegates visited local societies in towns and villages throughout Scotland, a move which encouraged and enlivened many of them. Their movements were closely watched. On Saturday, Sheriff Pringle wrote to Robert Dundas informing him, "The English delegates are to go tomorrow to Glasgow. I have sent notice of their intention to Mr Honyman and to Mr Orr [sheriffs there]."

In spite of the expectation of a new convention, and even with the novel pleasure of the company of Margarot, Gerrald and Sinclair, Muir's condition deteriorated. He took to his bed and his parents engaged two doctors to look after him. He had a fever, pains in his chest, and was coughing blood. Nevertheless the order came to the prison for his transfer to a revenue cutter, the Royal George, to take him to the hulks at Woolwich, in the River Thames. The *Edinburgh Gazetteer* complained that, "his removal might be attended with dangerous consequences, perhaps death, were this to happen, which Heaven avert, we would not hesitate to assert that he had been legally murdered."

On 14 November, Muir was taken to Newhaven by coach, along with four others convicted of robbery and forgery. Middleton and another sheriff's officer kept watch on them and the fiscal, William Scott, drove out to the small port to satisfy himself that Muir was taken safely aboard the cutter, pulling against her anchor as the freezing north east winds funnelled into the Firth of Forth. Margarot and the new editor of the *Edinburgh Gazetteer*, Alex Scott, accompanied Muir's distressed parents to the jetty to see him put into a jolly boat. As the boat was rowed into the waters of the firth, Muir, red-eyed and deathly pale, looked up and pointed to the heavens, indicating to his mother and father that he would see them there one day. Standing helpless in the cold drizzle, hot tears washed the faces of Margaret and James.

Someone, somewhere, had forgotten that Palmer was to sail with Muir to London, and so the Royal George rode at anchor for a further week until the legal papers were prepared to bring the minister from the tollbooth at Perth. Papers were also prepared for another ten convicts languishing in the Glasgow jail waiting for a ship. The strain was too much for James, Muir's father, who suffered a stroke during that week, from which he never fully recovered. Margaret, however, took the opportunity presented by the delay to daily pay a boatman to row her near to the cutter. She braved the winter seas in an open boat each morning to catch a glimpse of her benighted son.

One of the prisoners on board, John Grant, had been a sheriff in Inverness until he was uncovered as a forger. He had been sentenced to fourteen years transportation but was prepared to betray his way to a pardon. Muir had on occasion provided for the now penniless forger in the Tollbooth and had confided in him. Now Grant turned on Muir and reported his pistols to the master of the ship. Captain Ogilvie confiscated the weapons but took no further action.

On Wednesday 20 November, at five o'clock in the morning, Palmer was taken from his cell and led to a post-chaise outside. Around it, a party of dragoons steadied their horses in the cold of a dark, frosty morning. The air was filled with misty breath from the horses' nostrils as they snorted and moved to and fro. The sheriff ordered Palmer to stretch out his arms to be handcuffed.

"That won't be necessary, sheriff," said the dragoon officer. "We have no need of such ungentlemanly conduct. My troop will deliver your prisoner safely with the minimum of discomfort."

Palmer thanked the officer as he climbed aboard the carriage alongside a sheriff's messenger. Three of the dragoons were detailed to accompany the coach to Kinghorn in Fife, on the north bank of the Forth, where a boat would meet them and take the prisoner to the Royal George. The sheriff returned to his office and sat at his desk. He took up his pen, opened his inkwell, and began transcribing the names of the eighty or so people who had visited Palmer during his stay in the tollbooth. He folded the paper, sealed it and placed it in the despatches for the lord advocate and the home secretary.

That night, ten prisoners from Glasgow joined Muir, Palmer, Grant and three other Edinburgh convicts aboard the excise yacht. The next day saw the crew busy in preparation for the voyage down the east coast to London. Captain Ogilvie consulted his chronometer and charts and chose the Friday morning tide for departure. Mrs Muir, as usual, was in a small rowing boat in the choppy waters, but on that morning the boatman could not get her close enough to pick out her son among those on deck, as the Royal George filled its sails with a wind that took it away from her at speed and out into the North Sea.

CHAPTER 22

The British convention

"Parties are only a succession of birds of prey, of which the people are the banquet. Confide therefore in neither. The means of your security are in your own hands."

Joseph Gerrald, *A Convention the Only Means of Saving Us from Ruin*, 1793.

The recalled convention began on Tuesday 19 November. The transfer of Muir and Palmer to Woolwich was announced but delegates were cautious. They thought that any protest on their part, which could be construed by the edgy authorities as tumultuous or violent, might lead to their meeting being forcibly stopped. They were suspicious that the timing of the transfer might have been designed to provoke such a reaction from them. The *Gazetteer* editor, Alex Scott, was given the symbolic honour of representing the members confined on the Royal George.

In its first week the conference assumed the title of the British Convention of the Delegates of the Friends of the People Associated to Obtain Universal Suffrage and Annual Parliaments; it discussed spreading political knowledge in the Highlands; uniting Scottish and English societies; the financial affairs of the *Gazetteer*; and the Irish convention bill.

Margarot and Gerrald became influential figures in the debates and committees of the convention. Margarot was very different from most of the delegates. A small, dark-haired man with dark features, he dressed in black with white metal buttons and silk stockings. He was 48 years of age. Someone described him as resembling "a puny Frenchman". His father might have been French. At any rate neither of his parents was from Devon, where he was born, nor were they English. His father was a wine merchant, operating mainly in Portugal and France and the family lived for a time in Geneva, where Margarot was educated. He entered the family business and was living in France at the outbreak of the revolution. When he moved to London in 1792 he joined the new Corresponding Society and, with Hardy, built it into a formidable organisation. Hardy and Margarot had presented the society's congratulatory address to the French republic at the National Convention in Paris.

Margarot was an optimistic and charismatic man, confident of his own abilities, if prone to some exaggeration. He told the convention that 500 constables had attended their meeting in Hackney, and that the societies in London were "very numerous, though sometime fluctuating", as were the numbers he put on them. "In some parts of England whole towns are reformers," he declared. "Sheffield and environs has 50,000." Matthew Campbell Brown, the Sheffield delegate, gave a more realistic figure of between 2,000 and 5,000 members, adding that "if proper time had been given to the Sheffield society, in place of having only one delegate at this convention I am convinced we would have had at least forty".

Margarot gave what was probably an accurate estimate from Norwich, where "there are thirty societies in one". In spelling out the tasks ahead he announced, "If we could get a convention of England and Scotland called, we might represent six or seven hundred thousand males, which is a majority of all the adults in the kingdom, and ministry would not dare refuse our rights."

He later revised his estimates of the strength of English societies to 12-13,000 in London, 10,000 in Sheffield, and 3,000 in Norwich, still respectable numbers given the severe level of repression in England.

Gerrald was the theorist of the reformers. He was to constitutionalists what Paine was to republicans. His pamphlet, *A Convention the Only Means of Saving Us from Ruin*, had been published earlier in the year and argued that democracy in the British constitution stretched back to Anglo Saxon times and had been corrupted by subsequent regimes. The reformers believed that by campaigning for a recovery of lost rights they could avoid being misrepresented as foreign revolutionaries. Nevertheless, they did adopt the French form of address, Citizen, and took the French oath to "live free or die", sang *Ça Ira* in their meetings, followed the French convention's nomenclature and committee structure, and dated some of their minutes, "first year of the British convention". None of this was seditious in itself, but to the authorities it bordered on treason.

Gerrald, at 30 years of age, was slender and sickly. He was quite tall for the times, at 5ft 8in. He was born on the island of St Kitts, to the English wife of a wealthy Irish planter. The West Indies affected his health from the beginning. His mother died when he was still an infant and he was sent to London to be schooled. His tutor, Dr Samuel Parr, became a lifelong friend. Gerrald practised law in America, and went back to St Kitts to wrap up the family business, what was left of it, after his spendthrift father died. He married in the West Indies and returned to London after his wife died following the birth of their second child. Parr thought Gerrald was a brilliant student and one contemporary observed, "His eloquence had equally the power to charm and astonish; and the brilliancy of his imagination was not inferior to the terrors of his invective... He was placable and generous to an extreme." He held the convention in his hand.

"Some doubts have been introduced respecting our rights to universal suffrage," he admitted. "We can with truth appeal to antiquity for our title to this right; and it will be found to have been exercised by our ancestors in its fullest extent." He told them of Saxon government and its regional assemblies called Folkmotes, at which the king would preside, how they were forcibly dismantled by invaders at the Norman Conquest, "or rather robbery", and that the revolution of 1688 established the right of the people to alter the line of succession to the throne. The power of the monarch was from that point held in trust from the people.

"If the members who compose a government abuse their trust,

may they not be resisted?" he asked. "Let us then endeavour to instruct the people in their rights, and to inform them of our views and intentions, they will come and sign our petitions, and we shall be enabled to send them up [to parliament] subscribed by a majority of the people. The voice of the people will be heard whenever it is spoken in the language of truth, and by a number so respectable as to command attention."

He urged the convention to trust only itself. "Let [your delegates] be plain men, such as I see here, none who have ever breathed the pestilential air of a court, or bowed the knee to aristocracy. Let us renounce all attachment to parties and be no more deceived by the pretended patriotism of the great... Depend upon it, whenever leaders of parties see that the people are determined upon having their rights, they will not only endeavour to swim along the stream, but will strive to direct its course. Trust them not."

In the second week Lord Daer, who had been active from the beginning of the convention, had to leave, weakened by his tuberculosis. In that week delegates voted for closer ties with the United Irishmen; the Irish Convention Act, banning political gatherings, worried them. They agreed to appoint a secret committee of four which would call an emergency convention if a similar bill was passed in Britain. The committee could also summon members if habeas corpus was suspended, or if the country was invaded or foreign troops brought in. There was a fear that the ferocious Hessians from Hanover and other German principalities, who had spread terror during the American revolution, would be brought into Britain by King George. There was already a detachment in the Isle of Wight.

Alex Scott faithfully published the proceedings of the convention in the *Gazetteer* and Lord Advocate Dundas and Solicitor General Blair read them with great interest, alongside the daily reports from Watt, who didn't bother taking notes any more. He borrowed the minutes after they were approved each day and copied them in his fine longhand.

In the third week of the convention, Margarot announced, "I am informed there are many men who are desirous of dispersing us by force. We ought, therefore, to prepare against such dispersion." He proposed that any attempt to close down their meeting should be a signal for the secret committee to call an emergency convention in another place, and all the delegates agreed.

*

Gerrald twisted in his bed. He turned his face to the wall and pulled a blanket over his head. It was a bitter winter in Edinburgh. He was half awake and thought that either the seeping cold or Margarot's snoring had disturbed him again. The two men shared a room in the Black Bull Inn at Leith Street. As his semi-consciousness resolved into clarity he realised that they were not alone. Someone had entered the room. His eyes focused on a stranger. There were others behind the man. His ears found their range.

"Joseph Gerrald?" demanded a voice too loud for the quiet hour. "Are you Joseph Gerrald or Maurice Margarot?"

"I... What... Who are you? What are you doing here?"

Margarot was now awake. "Damn! It's not yet seven o'clock in the morning. Why are you in our room?" he demanded.

"I have a warrant for your arrest," rasped Williamson, the thief-taker. The four men behind him were carrying clubs. "Where's Sinclair?"

"He's next door," replied Gerrald, "but he's ill. Leave him be. He's been suffering a fever all week and is confined to bed."

Williamson turned to an accomplice. "Go next door. See what state Sinclair's in. If he really is ill then leave him for now. We'll come back for him later. But gather up all the papers you can find."

"I must protest, sir!" objected Margarot. "You have shown us no warrant nor stated the charge against us."

"Don't worry," replied Williamson, waving a paper in his hand, "this is the warrant. You'll hear the charge from the fiscal." He turned to the two men behind him. "Put irons on them and help me gather up these papers."

Margarot and Gerrald were handcuffed and told to sit on their beds while the room was searched. There were too many papers for the men to carry.

"Can we use that small trunk there?" asked Williamson.

"It's mine," said Margarot, "and you can. I have a key."

The papers were placed in the trunk and Margarot turned the key in the lock. He put the key in his pocket.

"Give me the key," demanded Williamson.

"No."

"Give me the key!"

"Show me a warrant. It is my property," challenged Margarot.

"We'll soon get a warrant in the sheriff's office," threatened Williamson, as he and his men bundled Gerrald and Margarot downstairs to a waiting chaise. Sinclair was left in his sick bed.

*

Members of the convention met each morning in committee. They noticed that Skirving, Margarot and Gerrald had been absent that day but thought nothing more of it. When the whole convention gathered at five o'clock in the afternoon there would, no doubt, be some explanation.

"I was apprehended this morning by warrant of the sheriff," Skirving told them when they had taken their seats. "By the same warrant all my papers were seized. Citizens Margarot, Gerrald, [Alexander] Callender, Scott, and the Ross brothers William and George have also been arrested and are still in confinement." He suggested that they arrange bail and two members should be sent to the sheriff's office at once. There was no need. The sheriff, accompanied by the provost and magistrates of the city, backed by a force of armed assistants, came to them.

"Is this meeting now assembled the British convention?" asked Thomas Elder, the lord provost. The chairman, John Patterson, replied that it was. "Then I order you to leave the chair and dissolve the meeting."

Skirving intervened. "We will not give up our right of assembling, nor be dismissed, till constrained," he insisted. The provost repeated his order and backed it with a threat of force. "You might be the chief magistrate," said Skirving, "but you have no authority but by law. Your authority can only be exercised in a legal way, lodge a complaint and follow judicial procedure."

"I am determined," said the provost, looking round to the sheriff and his constables with their flaming torches and bludgeons at the ready. "This is an illegal and unconstitutional meeting."

Brown, from Sheffield, shouted. "Our meeting is strictly legal and constitutional. Our doors have always been open to everyone. We have even admitted people who were known to be spies. Had we met to hatch sedition, or to promote anything unlawful, we would have acted secretly."

"I have no further time to argue!" insisted the provost. "I must insist upon your dispersing! Immediately! Otherwise I shall use force."

"We are neither willing nor prepared to oppose your violence," Skirving called out over the protesting voices. "If the provost offers to take the president from the chair we'll accept that as a token." The provost stepped up and pulled Patterson from the chair. He offered no resistance. Skirving called on the members to reassemble in Canongate, later in the evening.

*

The other arrested men had been kept under lock and key for the whole of Thursday. The room in which they were detained had no furniture, not even a chair. They were given no food or drink until five o'clock in the evening and then at seven o'clock they were separated for questioning.

Margarot was taken before the sheriff.

"Are you a member of the British convention?" asked Pringle.

"I do not acknowledge the legality of private interrogation," replied Margarot. He refused to answer any of the questions put to him and denied the sheriff the key to his box unless he produced

226 The Liberty Tree

a warrant. Margarot was released on bail of 2,000 merks (£115 sterling).

He found Skirving in Parliament Close and together they waited until the others were released. The party walked down the hill of the High Street to Canongate where, in the Masons' lodge, they resumed their meeting. Matthew Campbell Brown chaired the session and the members quickly agreed that the convention should now sit permanently, with a committee appointed to report on developments. Brown addressed the delegates on the "aristocratic influence" at work, spreading alarm about reformers. "The proceedings of this night, fellow citizens," he went on, "ought to convince you that it particularly behoves us not to sleep upon our posts."

He called on Gerrald to report on the arrests that morning. Gerrald had barely begun when a sheriff's messenger came into the room. "If government sends spies amongst us," he said pointedly, "they are acting superfluously, for we say nothing of which we have reason to be either afraid or ashamed." He pointed to the stream of officials now entering the hall. "Let these men be the objects of our pity and instruction. Though they are sent to disturb us, not one of them, I will affirm, has ever been informed of the supposed offence which we are now committing. Forgive them, for they know not what they do."

Davidson, the county sheriff, led procurator fiscal Scott and the rest of the magistrates to the front of the hall. Their henchmen again carried clubs and flaming brands.

"Behold the funeral torches of liberty!" cried Gerrald. "The rights of Britons are violated by this illegal interruption of our peaceful meeting. It is force, not reason, with which our enemies assail us. I defy them to assign one reason against the lawfulness of our meeting."

Margarot looked directly into the eyes of the sheriff. "The British convention is a legal and constitutional meeting," he said. "It is composed of delegates of the people associated to obtain universal suffrage and an annual election of their representatives. The question in the order of the day, to which we were about to proceed, was about petitioning parliament. By dispersing this peaceable and orderly meeting you will violate the constitutional rights of the people!"

"I have orders to disperse you by force!" shouted Davidson above the cries of protest. "I insist that the meeting be immediately dissolved!"

"You must show me some mark of force before I will vacate this chair," said Margarot. The sheriff grabbed him by the arm and pulled him from his seat.

"We never close without a prayer!" a member shouted.

"O thou governor of the universe!" intoned Gerrald above the pandemonium, "we rejoice that at all times and in all circumstances we have liberty to approach thy throne and we are assured that no sacrifice is more acceptable to thee than that which is made for the relief of the oppressed. O be thou a pillar of fire to us as thou wast to our fathers of old, to enlighten and direct us; and to our enemies a pillar of cloud, of darkness and confusion."

"Amen," the delegates called. At that, the British convention was once again adjourned.

*

The committee wasn't cowed. It called another meeting on the Friday evening at a carpenter's workshop in Lady Lawson's Yard, some way off the Canongate. Despite being large, the workshop was crammed with delegates. As Margarot told them of his interrogation and how he had been called back to the sheriff that morning but still refused to open his trunk, they were again harried by the arrival of Davidson and the provost and magistrates, who once more used their body-guard to force entry.

"I consider this meeting illegal," said Davidson to Margarot, "and I order you to disperse."

"We told you last night we are a peaceable and constitutional meeting," objected Margarot. "If you would only listen to what is going on you will be satisfied that we are what we say we are, we are meeting about a petition to parliament. Look," he urged, pointing to a paper lying on the table, "it has the words 'petition to parliament' written on it."

"I have come to disperse you," countered Davidson, "and I am determined to remain here till you go."

"Then show me some force," demanded Margarot, and the delegates cheered.

"I hoped force would not be necessary," shouted Davidson. "I have force with me but should be sorry to use it."

"Then show me some mark of force," said Margarot. The sheriff gripped his shoulder, after which the convention was once more broken up.

Margarot was again brought before the sheriff on the following morning, and this time a warrant for the contents of his trunk was shown to him. He gave Pringle the key and the papers belonging to him and Gerrald were confiscated. Sinclair was taken in for questioning that same Saturday and his papers were also confiscated. That afternoon, the lord provost and the sheriff issued a proclamation banning further meetings of the convention and prohibiting anyone from allowing the society to meet on their premises.

A notice appeared in the *Gazetteer* on Tuesday, announcing a meeting of the committee of the Friends of the People, to be held in Skirving's house on Thursday at noon. Skirving met Brown in the street before the meeting. As they approached Old Assembly Close they found it blocked with armed town guards and soldiers. People were gathering to see what would happen. Skirving and Brown went into the Grassmarket, intending to find a back way to his house, but people were gathering there in great numbers as well.

In Grassmarket, Skirving read out an announcement he and Brown had hastily scribbled. "Members of the committee of the Friends of the People, the magistrates of the city, having forbid your legal and constitutional meeting, have caused a great concourse of people, which may result in riot. Our meeting is adjourned. Give way to the violence used against you and you will convince the public that you did not deserve such treatment. Our business will be sent to each society by printed bulletins."

One of the sheriff's men grabbed the paper from Skirving's hand. Skirving turned to Brown. "People are assembling quickly," he said. "In a few minutes they might riot. We should go." The town guard grabbed Skirving and Brown before they had gone a few yards, and bundled them into the guard house near the Tollbooth. They were later released without charge.

Ten people had been arrested during the convention, Moffat, Callender, Skirving, Scott, and the two Ross brothers, all from Edinburgh; Brown from Sheffield; Margarot, Gerrald, and Sinclair from London. Robert Dundas assured his uncle at the home office, "No time shall be lost in bringing on their trials." In the same letter he recorded with some glee, "One of their presidents, a shopkeeper named Hart, of Glasgow, returned there on Tuesday last. Wednesday evening he appeared in the public coffee room, to which he is a subscriber, and after receiving a hiss from the whole company was, with rather too much violence, kicked out of the room."

The society of United Irishmen of Dublin, at a meeting that month, noted "the oppressive attempt in Edinburgh to stifle the voice of the people through the British convention, and the truly patriotic resistance to that attempt." It resolved "that all, or any of the members of the British convention and the patriotic societies which delegated members to that convention, should be received as brothers and members of our society."

CHAPTER 23

The hulks

"All former friendships are dissolved, and a man here will rob his best benefactor, or even messmate, of an article worth one halfpenny."

James Hardy Vaux, transported thief.

It took six days for the Royal George to sail from the Forth to the Thames. Despite heavy going against winter weather, the voyage was comfortable enough for Muir, who was still unwell, and Palmer and Grant. Captain Ogilvie extended the privileges he was taught were due to gentlemen, so his three respectable prisoners were invited to use his cabin and to dine with the other officers. Grant saw this as right and proper, as he boasted to Ogilvie of his attachment to "the honourable Mr Dundas", and of his personal correspondence with the minister's two under-secretaries, Nepean and King. He failed to mention that he had had no replies from either of them to his many obsequious pleas for clemency.

Grant continued to be a pest. Not only had he revealed the existence of Muir's two small pistols, but cravenly sought out Ogilvie and other officers to inform them in low, conspiratorial tones that Muir and Palmer intended to murder them and take the ship to France. Ogilvie dismissed the fantasy for what it was, but nevertheless, as an added safety precaution gave his crew orders that neither of the reformers should be allowed on deck after dark. There was a nagging possibility that a French ship could be waiting in the cover of night. Grant was a master at sowing doubt.

Fog hung, grey and opaque along the Thames estuary, its long skirts sticking to the water's surface. The Royal George rounded Shoebury Ness on the morning of Saturday, 30 November and made steady progress through the midday gloom, up the river to Woolwich. This was the home of the hulks, a "temporary expedient" agreed by parliament in 1775 after the transportation system was interrupted by the revolt of the American colonies. Convicts could no longer be despatched across the Atlantic but instead were housed in decommissioned ships and set to hard labour, cleansing the river of its debris and reclaiming good soil, gravel and ballast from its bed. The hulks were first anchored at Woolwich to supply labour for building the wharves at the Royal Arsenal.

Although America was no longer open for the unwanted of England, magistrates continued to pass sentence of transportation on those convicted of the several hundred offences for which it was specified in English law. Most capital offences, of which there were around two hundred, could be reduced to transportation. Some seven hundred prisoners had been sent to the furthest, little-known part of the empire, to New South Wales, six years previously to Muir's incarceration, but that made hardly any difference. A further two fleets had gone since, and a few solo ships as well, but still the steady supply of the condemned and the banished came from all parts of England and Wales. Additional hulks were moored in coastal waters to meet the demand. They were not just full, they were filthy and pestilential as well.

Muir and Palmer looked at each other in disbelief. The smell reached them before the dark shape of a rotting ship's hull could be made out in the mist. Slop buckets emptied over its side left foul stains and layered crusts that overlapped the moss green on the wooden walls at the rear of the Stanislaus hulk. The tide was insufficient to wash it all away. The Royal George edged upriver from the Stanislaus and docked at a barred and guarded jetty.

"Right now, you convicts!" roared an overseer from the wharf. "Down this plank and line up there."

As sixteen prisoners from the Royal George descended to the quay-side and waited beside a mound of iron chains, the superintendent of the Stanislaus went on board to collect the prisoner's papers from Ogilvie. He introduced himself as Captain Erskine.

Muir felt ill and looked distressed and confused. Palmer understood what was about to happen to them but was calmly observing the whole scene. He overheard part of Ogilvie's conversation with Erskine.

"I beg of you, Mr Erskine," said Ogilvie, glancing at Muir and Palmer, "treat those two prisoners like gentlemen. I did and they behaved as such."

"I'm afraid I have my orders, sir," replied Erskine, "and I am under strict instructions that all felons be treated the same."

"But these men are not felons, Mr Erskine," pressed Ogilvie. "They have committed no crime for personal gain and have used no violence."

"Those are my instructions Mr Ogilvie," Erskine repeated, "and until they change I cannot disobey them."

"Of course," said Ogilvie, distracted by the clank of chains as the legs and arms of his discharged cargo were clamped and locked, and they began to shuffle, one by one, up the gangplank of the hulk.

The new prisoners were carefully watched by inmates of the Stanislaus as they came below decks and were shown to sleeping platforms around the hull and bulkheads. A damp coldness clung to the walls and oozed into all parts of the cabin. The thin blanket issued to each prisoner only made the cold seem worse. Palmer was worried about Muir's ability to survive such conditions. He made sure the two of them found a space together. Muir lay down and arranged his chains around him. Palmer covered him with a prison blanket and sat beside him. Muir's breathing was laboured.

It was late afternoon and darkness had fallen. Candles were lit around the lower deck. Muir had recovered enough to share with Palmer the shock at the unfamiliar base language of many prisoners. They were approached by one after another from among the three hundred or so of the wretched who shared the deck and were asked for money, clothes, and favours. They were offered illicit gin or rum or tobacco for sale. In the dim glow of the candles they were also offered pleasures of the flesh in the darker corners.

"I have much to learn in this school," said Muir. "We are hurled in a moment from polite society into this, where every mouth is opened to blaspheme God and every hand stretched out to injure a neighbour. I cannot stop myself from feeling defeated."

"We'll have to fight this, Thomas," said Palmer. "There are other dangers lurking here. The dirt and foul air carries gaol fever."

There had been an unending ebb and flow of the fever ever since the hulks opened for business. On top of the ever present respiratory and venereal diseases that were spat out and scratched at, there were vermin that carried lice, and lice carried typhus. The typhus, in turn, carried off one in every three of the convicts sent on board. Regulation had been called for and granted; physicians had been demanded and appointed; hygiene had been marginally improved by lime-washing the quarters; but lice kept coming and brought death in their trail.

Loud shouts and the bang of a ladle on a metal cooking pot announced supper. Muir and Palmer left it untouched. They would soon learn to appreciate it. They had refused meat, which was dished up on only two days of the week.

At nine o'clock the candles were extinguished and Muir and Palmer lay close in the unfamiliar dark. Shuffling and murmuring, coughing and wheezing, and the background drag and clank of chains penetrated every moment of their light sleep, and, too soon, the cold dawn brought new trials.

"Everybody up! C'mon. Shake a leg! All those who can walk get in the boats!"

All those capable of walking were loaded in boats and taken to muddy, slimy beaches where, chained together in gangs, and watched by club-carrying guards, they scavenged and dug, dragged and carried for seven hours. It was winter and it was cold but, thankfully, the working day was shorter. Ten hours was the summer stretch ashore.

Muir and Palmer arrived back late that afternoon aching, hungry and barely able to stand. One of the crew called for Muir and took him to the superintendent's cabin.

"Mr Muir," said Erskine, "I have received orders this afternoon from the under-secretary at the Home Office that you are to be moved to another hulk."

"What? You can't separate Mr Palmer and I!" cried Muir. "We depend on each other!"

"Mr Muir…"

"We are a mutual solace!" Muir added, anxiously. He couldn't believe that Dundas or his underlings would be so callous and vindictive. "This is unnecessary cruelty," he said, in a softer voice, trying to cover his desperation and defeat.

"I'm sorry, Mr Muir, but I have no more control of this than you have," said Erskine. "I'll have your belongings brought to you and inform Mr Palmer. One of my crew will escort you to the Prudentia, about two miles upriver. There is a chaise waiting outside the jetty."

Down on the prison deck, Palmer was as upset as Muir, and afraid for himself and his friend. That night was difficult for him. He ate the poor barley-thickened mess that the previous day's beef had been boiled in. He needed to. He slipped into a sleep that was worried and fitful, bearing unwelcome dreams and feelings of constant danger, but he didn't wake until the overseer called the convicts to their work gangs. Amid the clatter of leg-irons, he felt for his pocket watch. It was gone.

*

Public outrage changed minds at the Home Office. From the moment the Royal George had docked at Woolwich, supporters great and small had been waiting to visit Muir and Palmer: local reform society members; liberal reformer, theologian and scientist Joseph Priestley, later to become known for his discovery of oxygen; leading opposition MP and playwright Richard Sheridan; Lord Lauderdale; radical journalists John Rutt and James Macintosh; political philosopher William Godwin. Around £600 had been raised and given to a committee of seven to administer for the political prisoners; and, crucially, newspapers had reported their hard labour on the banks of the Thames and their detention among felons, something even government supporters thought disproportionate and excessive.

Robert Dundas sent the complaints of the Edinburgh burghers to his uncle on 11 December, "I understand from several quarters that the general opinion of the inhabitants here is that Muir and Palmer ought only to have been confined till the opportunity of transporting them offered, and that their being handcuffed or obliged to work like other felons is made the handle of much clamour, and which may have a bad effect." Dundas's objection was purely practical. "If the juries here take it in their heads that more is done to these gentry than is absolutely necessary, they may acquit where they would otherwise have convicted."

Under-secretary Nepean replied to the lord advocate on behalf of the home secretary, telling him that there was "a devil of a stir in London" about the two prisoners and that Secretary Dundas had conceded they should not be kept in irons nor compelled to work. The *Morning Post* could report on 6 January, "Messrs Muir and Palmer are treated with every attention on board the hulks at Woolwich. They are not kept in irons and during the day they have a cabin to themselves. At night, though, they sleep on the same deck with the convicts, yet their beds are partitioned off and a sentinel placed on the outside to prevent their being disturbed. Their friends are permitted to visit them."

The journalist John Rutt, who wrote for the *Monthly Repository*, a Unitarian newspaper, visited both men often. They had had their privileges restored by the time of his first visit and he dined with Palmer, Captain Erskine and the disgraced Inverness sheriff, John Grant on the Stanislaus. Palmer told Rutt privately that he appreciated the hospitality but, "not unreasonably, considered Erskine as a spy on his conduct and his associations, though the captain seemed to me to overact his part by expressing the most unqualified democratic sentiments." Grant rose to the occasion by deliberate provocation. He enthusiastically proposed toasts to democratic and republican causes, which both Rutt and Palmer refused to acknowledge.

Rutt also reported that, "Mr Muir was, I believe, under the same specious surveillance." On his first visit to Muir, he found him in the company of the Prudentia captain, George Reid, along with William Godwin, who had given Muir a copy of his new book, *Political Justice*. The book cost three guineas, a sum so great that few could afford it, and that alone saved Godwin from prosecution for sedition. Pitt even declared that no book could be dangerous at that price. "The captain of that hulk complimented the author in my hearing," wrote Rutt, "by telling him that the mate of the vessel so admired the work that he would scarcely suffer it to go out of his possession. A man must have known little of the world not to have set a guard on the door of his lips in such company."

Rutt could see that even a short time in the damp and cold of the hulks was weakening Muir. "Almost as soon as he arrived on the Prudentia," he reported, "Muir had complained of chest pains… he was also very scrofulous" – he had glandular swelling. Nathaniel Hornsby, physician to the hulks, reported on 6 January, "Mr Muir has been very ill for some days with an acute rheumatism from which he appears at this time to be on recovery… An exposure to the keenness of the river air at this time of the year has probably produced this disease. He has almost ever since he has been on board the Prudentia complained more or less of a pain in his breast, which seems to indicate the latent seeds of consumption… Mr Muir sleeps in the hospital of the Prudentia, which he prefers to any other part of the ship on account of the few necessarily kept there. In the day he is permitted to walk the quarter deck, in the evening he has the privilege of sitting in the captain's cabin."

The *Morning Post* told a different story. "Mr Muir," it announced, "is so extremely ill the physician who attends him has not the least hope of his recovery. In such a situation no unfortunate man can present stronger claims to the royal clemency." Worried friends arranged for an independent physician from the London Infirmary to examine Muir. "Muir's state of mind," he reported to them, "is tranquil and he is content to stay where he is. He is of a relaxed disposition, inclined to indulge himself in bed and this renders him susceptible to cold from every air that blows. Yesterday he got up at one o'clock, sat up longer than he has done for some days past, and is this morning better. He has no symptoms of immediate danger, but a change of weather would hasten his recovery."

On Wednesday 8 January, the Home Office wrote to Duncan Campbell, transportation contractor and owner of the hulks, advising a further visit from the surgeon to consider whether Muir would be better off in some other place of confinement.

Muir was periodically lifted from his sadness and depression by the number of concerned visitors he received. On Boxing Day he sat with Lord Lauderdale, Charles Grey and the journalist and campaigner James McIntosh, in discussion about the sentences, when an unexpected visitor climbed aboard the hulk and came into the cabin. It was William Moffatt, to whom Palmer had written informing him of Muir's poor state of health. Muir was delighted and relieved that Moffat had been released without charge after having been arrested with the other convention members in Edinburgh. But he was also thankful at seeing his good friend once more. He had taken his leave of Moffat and his family in a hurried letter from the Edinburgh Tollbooth before he was driven to the Royal George. "My dear and valued friend," he wrote, "in the remotest corner of the world your remembrance and that of Mrs Moffat shall soothe me in my affliction, but my tears shall flow over the remembrance. I am really unwell. I cannot write much, nor have I time, but neither of you shall be wiped away from my heart. I am bidding you a long goodnight."

Moffat announced his intention to stay in London as long as was necessary and Lauderdale and the others pressed him to meet them in town to give them the fullest briefing about the Edinburgh trials.

In his quarters on the Stanislaus, Palmer received similar good news. James Ellis, the young man who had lodged with him in

Dundee, travelled nearly 600 miles on winter roads to be with his friend and benefactor. Palmer had educated Ellis and had hoped to patronise him until he was suitably qualified. There was a strong bond between the two men and they fell into each other's arms on meeting once again. Ellis had brought him a letter from his congregation in Dundee, a long address which ended, "Farewell, dear sir, remember us, we shall ever feelingly remember you." Then Ellis announced that he was coming to New South Wales with him, as a free settler. Tears rolled from Palmer's eyes. He sniffed. He smiled. They hugged.

*

Henry Dundas looked from the window of his study in Warren House, beyond his landscaped gardens to Wimbledon Common. It was early morning and the bright dawn drew countless sparkles from a thick frost covering the lawns and branches all around. It was the week before Christmas and Dundas had a problem. It caused him to lose sleep. He had slipped quietly out of bed and left the new Mrs Dundas to her dreams.

The severity of the Scottish sentences had caused a great many raised eyebrows in Whitehall and Westminster. Some legal advisers had warned that the punishment of transportation might actually have been unlawful and that a dangerous legal challenge could result. This could be avoided by granting a reprieve or by mitigating the sentences, but when Dundas raised this possibility with his nephew, the lord advocate insisted that any leniency shown had to be as a result of the prisoners petitioning for mercy. This, he knew, they would not do, it would amount to their admission of guilt. If the sentences were reduced without a petition, Westminster would be seen as criticising the Scottish judges and the chances of success in the remaining sedition trials would be negligible. Henry, like Robert, was determined to kill the reform movement.

Dundas was aware that Palmer was willing to petition, but not for mercy. He knew Palmer had engaged a Soho solicitor to prepare a petition to the king, and that he was planning another to the House of Commons. Both petitions addressed the constitutional rights and liberties of the subject. He had also been told that Palmer had written to Charles Grey from the Perth prison as far back as October, sounding out the possibility of presenting a bill to parliament to alter Scottish rules of evidence and appointment of juries. He knew that Lauderdale had visited Muir in the Tollbooth. Then, to top it off, only a week before, Dundas had been visited by Grey, Sheridan and Lauderdale, who voiced their concerns about the legality of the sentences and told him they intended to raise the matter in parliament. They had left him a note in which they argued that the Scottish judges had misinterpreted the legislation and had gone beyond their powers. They asked for the transportations to be postponed until parliament had had time to consider them.

His coffee had gone cold. Dundas called for a hot cup and added sugar to sustain him. He weighed up the risks from a public spat in both houses of parliament and made up his mind. For Dundas, this was no moral or legal issue; it was a practical, political problem. He had earlier written to his nephew in Edinburgh, "I had a visit from Lord Lauderdale, Mr Grey, and Mr Sheridan, on the subject of Mr Palmer and Mr Muir. As the great object is to make the business a subject of parliamentary discussion, it must be attended to in that view. I therefore trust the judges will make their report with their first convenience. At the same time, for their own sakes, and for the sake of the law of the country, which must be upheld, I hope the report will be ably and scientifically drawn up. You may communicate this letter privately to the judges. In the representation presented to me by Messrs Lauderdale, Grey, and Sheridan, they state their intention to bring the business before parliament. It is not, however, my intention to gratify them in that respect, for if the judges' report expresses no doubt upon the subject, I will carry the sentence immediately into execution, and meet their clamour in parliament without any kind of dismay."

Before signing off, he added this assurance, "There is no foundation for the report you have heard of any particular severity to Muir and Palmer."

"Darling Henry," said Mrs Dundas, rubbing her eyes with her knuckles as she entered the study. "I woke and found you gone."

"Oh, I just had a little work to do that had been bothering me, dear," he replied. "I'll be back up in a minute or two."

The new Mrs Dundas was Lady Jane Hope, daughter of the Earl of Hopetoun, and twenty years his junior. They had married earlier that year after a very short engagement. It was reported that Dundas had suddenly and unexpectedly proposed to her one winter's night, after rather too much claret. He had become tired of chasing Lady Anne Lindsay in a threesome with William Windham and saw a useful political alliance with the Hopetoun dynasty; there were seven of them currently sitting in parliament. He was still very fond of Lady Anne and they corresponded regularly.

Dundas turned his attention to the problem that had caused him to lose sleep. Lady Anne had been upset at being rebuffed by Dundas and had thrown over Windham in protest. This did not achieve its desired effect and she married on the rebound. Her choice was Andrew Barnard, a dozen years her junior, and a son of the Bishop of Limerick. Barnard, though, had limited prospects and much of Lady Anne's correspondence with her beloved Henry was aimed at elevating them. She knew that somewhere in Dundas's vast arena of patronage – as well as being home secretary, he was still treasurer of the navy and president of the India Board – there must be a living for her husband that would secure a future for herself.

Dundas picked up his pen and dipped it in the inkwell on his desk. He scribbled a note to Nepean, asking him to find out if the post of colonial secretary at Cape Town was still vacant.

CHAPTER 24

Exemplary punishments

"Martyrs of freedom! ye who, firmly good,
Stept forth the champions in her glorious cause;
Ye, who against Corruption nobly stood
For Justice, Liberty and equal laws."

Robert Southey, 'To the Exiled Patriots', 1794.

William Skirving stepped into the dock of the High Court of Justiciary in Edinburgh at ten o'clock on the morning of Monday 6 January, 1794. He had left his wife caring for their eight children in Old Assembly Close and walked into the High Street to meet a vast crowd of supporters who greeted him with loud cheers. The city had been tense with expectation since indictments for sedition had been served on Skirving, Margarot, Gerrald, Callender, Scott and Sinclair in the days before Christmas. Small children, enjoying the large gathering, ran round the outside of the crowd, sometimes daring to dodge fast-moving feet to plunge further inside the forest of legs and swirling greatcoats. Supporters accompanied Skirving the short distance uphill to Parliament Close and onlookers cheered from tenement windows. The calls and whistles were still ringing in his ears as he sat down in the same court his friend Muir had occupied just a few short, packed months before. No sooner had their lordships entered the room in a swirl of crimson gowns than the cheers and laughter turned to hisses and boos.

"Order! Order! There will be quiet for their lordships!" barked the macer, who, when the public gallery was settled, announced that he had served the relevant papers on the accused.

"What do you say to this Mr Skirving," asked Lord Braxfield, "are you guilty or not?"

"I am conscious of no guilt, my lord," answered Skirving, who chose to represent himself against charges of sedition in distributing Palmer's handbill; in distributing a handbill in October calling a seditious meeting; in taking part in a seditious gathering called the British convention; and in defying the magistrates by calling another convention meeting in the Grassmarket on 12 December.

"The very name of British convention carries sedition along with it," asserted Solicitor General Robert Blair. "It is assuming a title which none but the members of the established government have a right to assume. And the British convention associated for what? For the purpose of obtaining universal suffrage; in other words for the purpose of subverting the government of Great Britain."

Skirving replied calmly. "That the British convention is a seditious and unconstitutional meeting remains to be proved, and cannot be proved till the legislature declares them such; or until they shall be cited, tried, and condemned by law." He took up part of the legal argument that had gone back and forth in official despatches between London and Edinburgh. "In my indictment the crime laid is sedition," he said. "Neither the crime itself, nor the law defining it and declaring its penalty are stated in my indictment... If his lordship has no law by which to try my conduct, except his own opinions, and has raised this process against me, trusting that a jury in his sentiments will have the same opinion of my conduct, I will protest solemnly that I cannot be tried but by the laws of my country."

One by one, the judges dismissed the objection. Eskgrove slowly raised his oversized face to declare, "This crime, under the name of sedition, is as well understood by everyone in this assembly, as by any one of your lordships." That was as accurate a definition as the court would hear that day. Swinton ignorantly declared that the crimes were greater than sedition; for Dunsinnan they were "most aggravated"; and Braxfield, confident in the knowledge that Henry Dundas had accepted his version of Scotland's law and its penalties, thought it "unnecessary for me to use words to satisfy your lordships that sedition is a crime by the law of Scotland". As if to reinforce his presumption of guilt, he added, quite wrongly, "I think the crime might have been laid as high as treason."

Sixteen witnesses were called, none of whom offered evidence of sedition. No argument was given to show that the convention or any of its subsequent meetings was illegal. It was late evening before the crown rested its case and Skirving was invited to call his defence witnesses. He refused. "The day is already so far spent, my lord," he said, "and it appears to me so unnecessary to bring forward any exculpatory evidence, the public prosecutor having proved nothing criminal against me."

Braxfield steadied the jury. "Gentlemen, the crime here charged is that of sedition; by the penal law of Scotland, it is a crime very different from the law of England; for it is not necessary to have any act of parliament for it." He told them that in Skirving's case very little more would have made it high treason, especially "during the time when this nation is engaged in a bloody war with a neighbouring nation, consisting of millions of the most profligate monsters that ever disgraced humanity." He handed them their verdict. "Skirving is equally guilty of the pains of law with Palmer."

Skirving spent the night in the Tollbooth before returning to court at two o'clock the next afternoon to hear the jury unanimously declare him guilty. "Gentlemen," said Braxfield, with a smile, "you have returned a very proper verdict." Skirving was sentenced to fourteen years' transportation and returned to the Tollbooth.

*

There was sullen mood in the city. Once more, the severity of the judges caused public anxiety. Alexander Callender, who had moved the motion in the convention for an emergency meeting if an anti-convention bill was introduced in parliament, had guessed that leniency was scarce and had fled the country before he could be served with an indictment. *Gazetteer* editor Alex Scott was not so

244 The Liberty Tree

fast. Papers were served on him before he had booked his passage to America. He went, nevertheless. He would shortly be outlawed on the steps of the court, as was the custom. The Ross brothers, George and William, being the employees of the *Gazetteer* who had taken notes for the published account of the convention in the newspaper, were called as witnesses against Skirving and the others, and could not subsequently be charged with the same offence. No charge was brought against Moffat or Campbell Brown. But everyone was waiting for the next parade of Scottish justice in two days time, the trial of Maurice Margarot.

A reporter for the *Morning Chronicle* was standing in the chill wind at the head of Leith Street, outside Margarot's lodgings, on Thursday morning, 9 January. This is what he reported. "This morning at about ten o'clock, a vast crowd assembled in front of the Black Bull Inn, where M Margarot lodged. He shortly came out, attended by three friends. When he got the length of the Register Office the mob forced all the four into a chaise, which they had provided, and from which they had previously taken the horses. This done, they immediately drew the carriage to the Parliamentary Close, where Maurice Margarot and his friends alighted." He went on to report that the lord advocate was "indisposed" and the case was adjourned until Monday. Margarot was bailed, after which the crowd put him and five friends once more into the chaise and pulled it back to the Black Bull at Leith Street.

On Sunday afternoon, Robert Dundas was feeling better. The cold winter had sent its share of colds and flu around Edinburgh. He sat at his desk at home in George Square and thought about the insolence Margarot and his supporters had shown to the court. He wrote a note to his uncle in time to catch the evening mail and explained what had happened, in his absence. He promised it would not happen again. The lord provost and the sheriffs of the city and county had already issued a proclamation banning such behaviour by "idle and disorderly persons". They had noted that at the time of Skirving's trial many handbills had appeared on the walls of the town urging people to show their support during his appearance. They banned those as well. They ordered all hackney coaches off the streets on Monday morning. The lord provost and magistrates had a plan. "Margarot," he added, "is the most daring and impudent villain of the whole gang."

Early on Monday, the lord provost, the magistrates, deacons of the different incorporated companies, a great number of constables, and a cohort of the most respectable inhabitants of Edinburgh, met at Merchants' Hall. They were joined there by the officers and men of HMS Hinde, brought up from Leith. They agreed to requisition the Post Office and adjoining shops and apartments at the junction of High Street and North Bridge, where a likely procession of Margarot's supporters would pass on their way from the Black Bull to the high court. They would hide there and ambush the democrats.

A little before ten o'clock, a mass of people again assembled outside the Black Bull. They were all on foot, and ranged in rank and file order. Many carried flags and banners inscribed with various combinations of the words Law, Liberty, Reason, Justice and Truth. At the head of the procession was a large tree of liberty assembled in the shape of the letter M. It was about twenty feet high and ten feet wide, with a circular placard hanging from its centre proclaiming liberty and equality. Margarot walked underneath. The crowd carried no weapons and marched in silence under a blue sky filled with winter sunshine.

Provost Elder and his magistrates waited in the Tron kirk, from where they had a clear view along the deserted North Bridge. They spotted the tree turning into the bridge and the provost and magistrates emerged from the church and walked toward the march, dressed with authority in official robes and insignia. They formed a line across the roadway of the bridge, with the provost in the centre, the city officers behind them, and a hundred or so loyal gentlemen in the rear. The two sides came slowly toward each other, still in silence, until the provost stepped forward from his line, pointed his ceremonial stick at the leaders of the procession and ordered them to stop. This was a prearranged signal for the club-waving sailors from the Hinde to rush from houses on each side of the protesters and break up the demonstration. The liberty tree was torn down and thrown over the bridge. Supporters were beaten with the heavy clubs normally used by press gangs, and many ran away fearing they would be forced into service on the gun deck of a warship. Margarot was dragged from his bruised and bleeding supporters through lines of jeering loyalists and frogmarched into the high court.

Margarot had his revenge, of sorts. He conducted his own defence and used the time to confound the court with administrative complaints. He demanded to know why the titular head of the judiciary, the lord justice general, was not at his place on the bench. That position had for decades been a noble's lucrative sinecure and not occupied by a working judge. He demanded that his list of witnesses be read out before the trial began and that fresh summonses be served on any not present. He had listed William Pitt, Henry Dundas and the Duke of Richmond for his defence. "I do not ask it as a favour, I demand it; you are on the seat of justice and take heed how you administer that justice." He, rightly, enquired why the doors of the court were closed with the doorkeepers charging admission. All of these objections were rejected by the bench and Braxfield testily commanded, "Mr Margarot, stand up and hear the criminal libel read against you."

The main charges against him were substantially the same as those against Skirving: that the convention was criminal and that the prisoner was criminally responsible for what it did. The charge was found relevant once more on the belief of the judges that universal suffrage was seditious and that the adoption of French forms of address signalled regicide and republicanism.

Margarot argued the case used by Skirving. "I beseech your lordship to point out the law which makes sedition a crime," he asked, "and also, that which shows the punishment that is due to it." He was similarly unsuccessful. Margarot's list of witnesses was called out and he objected that Richmond, Dundas and Pitt were not in the room. Braxfield and the other judges argued that they had no power to compel witnesses in another country to appear.

Turning to the gallery, Margarot declared, "If the first man in England is not as amenable to the laws of his country as the meanest of you, you are slaves."

Braxfield was furious. "You come here to speak to the court and not to harangue the mob!"

"Do you call this audience a mob, my lord?" questioned Margarot, in an exaggerated tone of incredulity, keeping his eyes on the gallery and shaking his head.

"You are not to harangue the *multitude*," said Braxfield, in an unusually apologetic gesture.

The evidence submitted was much the same as that against Skirving. Five witnesses confirmed the seizure of the papers, the declarations and the dispersal of meetings, six attested to proceedings in the convention, and Margarot cross-examined them to no seeming purpose except to annoy the court.

Cross-examining Thomas Cockburn, a member of the convention, he asked, "You have seen me act as *preses*?"

"Yes," replied Cockburn.

"That word is Latin, is it not?"

"I am very little acquainted with Latin, I meant president."

"You are sufficiently acquainted with it to know that at present Rome is the seat of the Pope, are you not?"

"We have no doubt of that."

"Consequently, if there is any criminality in adopting a French word, do you think there is not an equal criminality in using a Latin one?"

Margarot took aim at Braxfield himself. "Now my lord, comes a very delicate matter indeed," he said. "I mean to call upon my lord justice clerk, and I hope that the questions and the answers will be given in the most solemn manner. I have received a piece of information which I shall lay before the court in the course of my questions. First, my lord, are you upon oath?"

"State your questions," said Braxfield, warily, "and I will tell you whether I will answer them or not; if they are proper questions I will answer them."

"Did you dine at Mr Rochead's at Inverleith in the course of last week?" asked Margarot.

Braxfield looked offended. "And what have you to do with that, sir?"

Margarot persisted. "Did any conversation take place with regard to my trial?"

Braxfield paused. "Go on, sir," he said, with suspicion.

"Did you use these words, 'What should you think of giving him an hundred lashes, together with Botany Bay?', or words to that purpose?"

"Go on," repeated the judge, "put your questions if you have more."

Margarot obliged. "Did any person, did a lady, say to you that the mob would not allow you to whip him? And, my lord, did you not say that the mob would be better for losing a little blood? These are the questions, my lord, that I wish to put to you at present in the presence of the court. Deny them or acknowledge them."

Braxfield turned to his colleagues on the bench. "Do you think I should answer questions of that sort, my lord Henderland?"

"No my lord, they do not relate to the trial."

Eskgrove agreed, "What may have been said in private company cannot in any way affect this case." "Not one of them are proper," added Swinton, "not one of them are competent, and ought not to be allowed to be put." Dunsinnan was adamant, "No answer to those questions could in any degree tend to exculpate or alleviate the charges against him."

Robert Dundas spent two hours and twenty minutes telling the jury that Margarot had used "a set of the lowest and most ignorant of the people" in an attempt to subvert government, "by aping and imitating the example, the language, and the forms of the French convention" and "following its footsteps in revolution and in blood".

Margarot outdid Dundas and spent four hours in reply. "If there is a better mode of electing members of parliament it is not only our right, but our duty to do it," he told the jury. He lectured them on the national debt, the jury system, the history and constitution of the country, the convention, and the London Corresponding Society. They jury were hungry and distracted. They shared food and wine like weary spectators at a bad play.

At one point in his summing up, Margarot ostentatiously drank down a glass of wine. "I beg pardon, gentlemen, for this interruption," he said, raising his voice to regain their attention. "I should not have done it if the example had not been set me. We have no such thing in England, gentlemen, as a jury eating and drinking in court." And he then continued, "Give me leave now to call to your lordships' attention your particular duty…"

"I will not receive any instruction from you, sir!" roared Braxfield.

"I shall take the liberty of checking your lordships, if you do not go on properly!" insisted Margarot.

"You have gone on for four hours and I would not allow you to be interrupted," Braxfield growled, increasing his volume as he spoke. "If you had not been a stranger I would not have heard one third of what you have said in four hours, which was all sedition from beginning to end!"

The court adjourned in the early hours of the morning and reconvened at half past one the next afternoon, when Margarot was pronounced guilty and sentenced to fourteen years transportation to New South Wales. Margarot said simply, "My lords, I thank you", before being escorted to the Tollbooth to join Skirving.

Robert Dundas wrote to his uncle in London on the day after the verdict, "The conduct and behaviour of Margarot during his trial was a scene of insolence, effrontery, and petulance unparalleled."

Margarot wrote to the society in Norwich, "I am confined along with Skirving and two other gentlemen, all four in a room twelve feet square without being allowed the range of the prison as is usual in all other cases but strictly padlocked all day as well as all night by particular order from the magistrate, and only two visitors admitted at a time from whom they even take their stick previous to admission."

Provost Elder, while pleased at the conviction of yet another democrat, was unhappy at the prisoners remaining in his jail. He complained to Henry Dundas of the burden on the council of paying for extra jailers while the city was so tense. "They are constantly employed in hatching mischief, writing seditious paragraphs for their newspaper...resolutions for their societies, handbills, etc... I hope therefore you will as soon as possible send down a warrant for their removal hence."

The tension was not confined to Edinburgh. The *Glasgow Advertiser* reported, "There was a kind of conventional meeting at Sheffield last week, for the purpose of taking into consideration the conduct of the Scots courts in respect to the convention at Edinburgh. This meeting had just time to vote the illegality of the proceedings of the Edinburgh magistrates, when a report of the approach of two constables dispersed them." In the same issue it recorded unease in the west of Scotland. "Handbills have, of late, been industriously circulated through Paisley, calling general meetings of the Friends of Liberty and Reform on business of importance. The magistrates of that town and the sheriff of the county of Renfrew have issued a proclamation prohibiting all such meetings within their jurisdiction."

CHAPTER 25

Newgate

"The gaol was a vile place, in which most kinds of debauchery and villainy were practised, and where dire diseases were bred, that came into court with the prisoners and sometimes rushed straight from the dock at my Lord Chief Justice himself."

Charles Dickens, *A Tale of Two Cities.*

William Moffat tapped his feet anxiously on the floor of the carriage taking him from Woolwich back to London. He had gone to Muir at the Prudentia with news of Margarot's conviction and found him missing. "Taken to Newgate early this morning, sir," Captain Reid told him. "Express instructions of the home secretary." The carriage made slow progress along the roads on the south of the Thames and Moffat was relieved when he caught sight of Blackfriars bridge in the distance. Soon the tired horse and its driver were pulling him over the river and onward for a short distance to the towering, blank, windowless walls of the notorious prison. Moffat found out from a jailer's assistant at the gate that Muir was inside and, for a small consideration, would be allowed visitors any time from eight o'clock in the morning until nine at night. Moffat paid the man and was shown to a cell where Muir, looking ill and feeble, was held in irons.

The jailer explained that Muir's situation was only temporary, and that more comfortable rooms could be had on the first floor with other gentlemen, "none of 'em ironed, sir". The rate for this "privilege" was a guinea admittance, and rental of seven shillings a week, "all approved by the head jailer, sir".

Moffat paid the rogue and had him help move Muir to his new quarters, which were larger and airier, with a decent cot, fireplace, table and chair. Moffat unpacked Muir's few belongings and hung on the chimney breast a picture of his friend's early mentor, the scientist and philosopher Richard Price.

Newgate was better for Muir than the damp hulks but it was not a place of safety. The infamous jail that had housed Captain Kidd, Rob Roy and Casanova, was also known as a "tomb for the living". It had inspired Gay's *Beggars' Opera* and Defoe's *Moll Flanders*. Its dark, dank corridors and cells incubated gaol fever as readily as the hulks, and the livid rash would climb the stairs to the gentlemen's quarters as easily as it would attack the convicts in the squalid felons' side. The last outbreak had been two months previously, in November, and it had carried off the eccentric inmate Lord George Gordon, chief of the Protestant Association and the man held responsible for anti-Catholic riots that had laid waste much of London in 1780. The prison was in three sections, the debtors' side, the felons' side and the state side. Muir was in the state side, which housed the most comfortable quarters and was reserved for those who had committed mere misdemeanours and, as its name suggested, crimes against the state. In reality, those fraudsters, psychopaths, and professional criminals with means on the felons' side could buy themselves a room on the state side, and many did.

Moffat sat with Muir throughout the afternoon and evening. He bought beer, wine, food and coal from the prison shop, also franchised by the jailer and his assistants. He lit a fire in the grate and warmed the room. He gave Muir the news of Skirving's and Margarot's convictions and told him that Gerrald and Sinclair had been given leave to return to London to settle their affairs before returning to stand trial in Edinburgh later in the month. Muir was looking brighter and better when Moffat left in the late evening, promising to return the following day with newspapers and books.

Moffat let Muir's supporters know he had been moved and Rochemont Barbauld, husband of Muir's old friend, the poet Anna

Barbauld, was the first to greet him at Newgate next morning. It was Friday 17 January, and Barbauld was only one of a number of visitors who knocked on the door of Muir's cell that day. He was brought the good news that John Thelwall was organising a series of lectures to raise money for the support of the Edinburgh "martyrs". Thelwall was a gifted working man who had become a central figure in the London reform movement. He was a propagandist and lecturer who could attract large numbers of people to his meetings.

Moffat left Muir early that evening to attend a meeting of the Society for Constitutional Information, where he met up with Gerrald and Sinclair. Gerrald was elected as honorary chairman and a defiant meeting issued a resolution saying "with regret" but "without fear" that "the period is fast approaching when the liberties of Britons must depend not upon reason, to which they have long appealed, nor on their powers of expressing it, but on their firm and undaunted resolution to oppose tyranny by the same means by which it is exercised".

Three days later the London Corresponding Society held a packed meeting in the Globe Tavern on the Strand, where they agreed to publish an *Address to the People of Great Britain and Ireland*. It would state that the erosion of civil rights, along with the Irish convention bill and the Edinburgh sentences, had dissolved the social contract. "We are at issue. We must now choose at once either liberty or slavery for ourselves and our posterity. Will you wait till barracks are erected in every village, and till subsidised Hessians and Hanoverians are upon us...? [The people] are bound to seek redress of their grievances from the laws as long as any redress can be obtained by the laws. But our common Master whom we serve...has taught us not to expect to gather grapes from thorns, nor figs from thistles. We must have a redress from our own laws and not from the laws of our plunderers, enemies, and oppressors. There is no redress for a nation circumstanced as we are, but in a fair, free, and full representation of the people."

The meeting was so full and the reception given to the proposal so enthusiastic that the floor gave way. The wood cracked, dust swirled and people were thrown against one another, but no one was hurt. They recovered from the shock to complete their vote. They agreed that a new British convention should be held, this time on English soil. The Society for Constitutional Information ordered 40,000 copies of the Address to be printed and circulated, which had the effect of rallying the provincial societies.

John Martin, who chaired the Globe meeting, wrote to Margarot afterwards and informed him, "The Society is increasing rapidly both in spirit and in numbers, and the rich now begin to come among us and sit down with pleasure among the honest men with leathern aprons."

*

Gerrald was due to leave London at the end of the week to appear in court on Monday 27 January. Many friends and fellow reformers advised him to leave the country and offered to pay his bail. It had become apparent to them that his sentence was already decided and many of them feared his poor health meant transportation was a death sentence. His old schoolmaster and surrogate father, Samuel Parr, came from his Warwickshire parsonage at Hatton to visit Gerrald in his Bloomsbury home. His was the final attempt to persuade Gerrald to avoid Edinburgh, both for his own good and for the sake of his motherless son and daughter, who were looked after by relatives and friends. Parr, like others, offered to pay his bail if he would escape, and assured him that reformers, and those convicted, would think no less of him if he did not surrender himself to those who would destroy him. Gerrald, though, was firm in his belief that having eloquently encouraged others to join the convention, he was honour-bound to answer the false charge laid against him in Scotland.

"In any ordinary case," he insisted to Dr Parr, "I should, without the smallest hesitation, and with the warmest gratitude, avail myself of your offer. I readily admit that my associates will not suffer more that I suffer less. I am inclined to believe with you, that the sense of their own sufferings will be alleviated by their knowledge of my escape. But my honour is pledged, and no opportunity for flight, however favourable, no expectation of danger, however alarming, no excuse for consulting my own safety, however plausible, shall induce me to violate that pledge. I gave it to men whom I esteem, and respect, and pity; to men who, by avowing similar principles, have been brought into similar peril, by the influence of my own arguments, my own persuasions, and my own example. Under these circumstances, they become partakers of my own responsibility to the law; and therefore, under no circumstances will I shrink from participating with them in the rigours of any punishment which the law, as likely to be administered in Scotland, may ordain for us."

Parr realised he could not win the argument with a pupil he had taught so well. He later told a friend, "Finding him fixedly determined to return that night to Scotland, I did not harass his mind by any further remonstrance. He was very calm before we parted; and I left him under the strongest impressions of compassion for his sufferings, admiration of his courage, and moral approbation of his delicacy, and his fidelity."

Gerrald had agreed to meet Sinclair to travel together on the Friday night mail coach. Before he left his house a messenger delivered a letter from William Godwin who, having heard that Gerrald would not be persuaded to flee, offered him words of encouragement for the days to come. "Your trial," wrote Godwin, "may be the means of converting thousands, and progressively of millions, to the cause of reason and public justice." He went on to advise him, "Never forget that juries are men, and that men are made of penetrable stuff... What an event would it be for England and mankind, if you could gain an acquittal? ... Depend upon it, that if you can establish to their full conviction the one great point, the lawfulness of your meeting, you will obtain a verdict. Above all, let me entreat you to abstain from all harsh epithets and bitter invective. Show that you are not terrible, but kind, and anxious for the good of all... You represent us all!"

The Royal Charlotte mail coach made good time out of London, in spite of muddy roads made difficult by winter rains. But as it progressed north the rain turned to sleet and then to snow. All day Saturday it made slow progress and by Sunday the horses held their heads low into a driving blizzard. The Great North Road became progressively snowbound and in the Northumberland town of Belford the coach came to a stop. The driver, near frozen even under his greatcoat, hat and scarf, gauntlets and layers of protective leather, reported to the passengers that they were going no further that evening. The road was impassable and they would not reach Edinburgh on time. The mail, however, would be taken on by a lone rider, if anyone wanted to send a note to relatives or friends.

Gerrald found a table near the fireplace of the inn, where he scribbled a note to the advocate John Millar. "Belford, Sunday, 10 o'clock at night. Mr Sinclair and myself set out in the mail on Friday night last from London, though both in a very bad state of health. There has been since we quitted town an immense fall of snow, and we have already travelled through Northumberland at the risk of our lives. We are now at Belford, and have offered any sum to get on to Edinburgh... But we learn, to our great grief, that no road is cut through the snow between this and Edinburgh, consequently it is impassable by any carriage. The mail goes on horseback, and forwards this letter. We trust, therefore, that you will be kind enough, for our personal honour, to state immediately to the court the cause of our absence, but that we shall be at Edinburgh as soon as ever the road is opened. Feeble and sick as we both are, we should be inevitably frozen to death if we attempted to ride."

It was Wednesday before they reached Edinburgh, the same day that Skirving and Margarot were sent south to join Muir in Newgate. The *Glasgow Advertiser* recorded the event. "Wednesday at half past two o'clock, William Skirving and M Margarot, both lately convicted of sedition, were taken from Edinburgh jail and sent off in two coaches for London, attended by two of the king's messengers and two sheriff's officers of Edinburgh. The magistrates have given each of them a good greatcoat and two pair of stockings. At the same hour yesterday Joseph Gerrald and Charles Sinclair arrived in the Royal Charlotte coach at the Black Bull Inn, from London. They were both outlawed on Monday last by the high court of justiciary, but yesterday, shortly after their arrival in town, they surrendered themselves at the Canongate jail, where they requested to be detained but were not allowed to remain. This day, however, they were both apprehended in consequence of a regular warrant and committed to the city jail."

*

The parliamentary campaign in support of the "Scotch martyrs", as they were now being called, was opened on Friday 31 January in the House of Lords by Earl Stanhope. Lauderdale had pleaded with him to withdraw his emergency motion until they could present all the relevant court documents to the house, but Stanhope was an enthusiastic loner as well as a consistent radical. He had opposed the American and French wars, supported their revolutions, stood for the rights of dissenting religious sects and for Catholic emancipation, and assisted the campaigns of the London Corresponding Society. He signed himself Citizen Stanhope and even had the coronets removed from the gates of his country seat at Chevening. To his peers he was an eccentric. Nevertheless, he raised the Edinburgh prosecutions from the floor of the house, arguing that there were precedents for the Lords intervening in cases "where Magna Charta was abused or the laws stretched to a degree unjustifiable". He challenged the proceedings of the court on the looseness of the indictments, the introduction of new charges during the trial, and the rejection of challenges to the jurors. "If all this is the law of Scotland, I would only observe that Scotland has no more liberty than it had under the race of the Stuarts." He asked that execution of the sentences be postponed until the house had time to inquire properly into the trial, and that an address be presented to the king to secure this. The judges were defended and even praised by other peers and Stanhope's motion was defeated by 49 votes to one.

On the following Tuesday, William Adam, MP for Ross-shire, presented a motion in the Commons on the criminal law of Scotland, asking that the sentences be set aside until parliament reviewed the absence of a right of appeal from the court of justiciary, the highest court in Scotland, arguing that "the court in which a case originates shall not be the ultimate court to decide". He was supported by the opposition, opposed by the government, and defeated by 126 votes to 31.

Skirving and Margarot had arrived in London. They were committed to Newgate early on Sunday morning, 2 February, and soon had supporters around them in their state-side rooms, near Muir and other jailed reformers. The bitter cold of the journey had weakened them both, but the mood of the radicals was mildly optimistic, despite parliamentary defeats. News of grass-roots organisation in their cause from around the country kept them buoyed.

Henry Dundas, though, was even more optimistic. The legal arguments sent to him by Braxfield justified the procedures of the Scottish courts and the power of judges to apply arbitrary punishment in cases of sedition. This had released his organisational flair to counter parliamentary challenges. He had seen off the first two and, even though he knew there were more debates to come, he had already sent to the palace the order for the transportation of Muir and Palmer, which the king had dutifully signed. Stanhope had been crushed on Friday, Adam had been soundly defeated on Tuesday, and by Saturday Dundas felt he was in a strong enough position to sign the order for the removal of Muir, Skirving and Margarot from Newgate to the transport ship Surprize, anchored in the Thames.

It was dark and cold when Muir was shaken from his sleep by two strangers, king's messengers who told him he was off to Botany Bay. Presently he heard the complaints of Margarot and Skirving as they were handcuffed and bundled towards him. They complained that it was not yet dawn, that they had been given no notice of their removal, and that they had not had time to pack their belongings. The two messengers bundled the three prisoners aboard a waiting coach and set off on that cold Monday morning for Woolwich. It was still not light when they reached the wharf where the Surprize was berthed. The messengers took Muir, Skirving and Margarot on board and handed them over to the officer of the watch, who ordered them below decks and locked in leg irons. They were the first prisoners aboard and remained chained until Captain Patrick Campbell reported for duty later that morning. He gave the order for them to be unlocked.

Palmer was still aboard the Stanislaus and his companion Ellis had lodgings nearby. They were informed in good time that the Surprize had arrived in the river and would be sailing soon. Palmer wrote to the journalist John Rutt on that Monday, 10 February, "Muir, Skirving and Margarot, and sheriff's officers, handcuffed, two-and-two, were put on the Surprize last night. I go tomorrow."

In a note to Moffat he gave thanks for all the support he had received. "Where I expected the ruggedness of sailors, I have met with the philanthropy of friends; my health, spirits and sleep are as good as in any part of my life; I snore so loud I disturb all the rogues. The hope of having contributed to the good of my country by stemming the torrent of despotism, in becoming its willing victim, the kindness of the Friends of Liberty, and the hope of a higher approbation than theirs, support me in all my trials."

Palmer and Ellis, along with the forger Grant, boarded the Surprize on Tuesday, in a more dignified fashion than their friends had been allowed. They were joined by sixty women who had also been sentenced to the far shores of New South Wales, and as soon as they were settled below decks Captain Campbell gave the order to cast off. The Surprize set sail for Portsmouth, where additional prisoners and a complement of the New South Wales Corps would join them for the voyage.

CHAPTER 26

In the balance

"Ah! why, forgetful of her ancient fame,
Does Britain in lethargic fetters lie?
Why from the burning cheek, and kindling eye,
Burst no keen flashes of that sacred flame…?"

John Thelwall, 'The Source of Slavery', written in
the Tower of London, 17 July, 1794.

Charles Sinclair stood by Gerrald's bedside and handed him a cup of
mulled wine to ease his chest pains. The two had been released on
bail from Edinburgh's Tollbooth after one night and were once again
in rooms at the Black Bull Inn. Sinclair had recovered his health but
Gerrald was poorly. It was more than two weeks since their perilous
journey through the snow and Gerrald showed no signs of improvement. However, that day, 17 February, he had roused himself from his
sick bed to support Sinclair at his appearance in court.

Sinclair had employed the two greatest Whig lawyers in Edinburgh
to argue his case. Henry Erskine and Archibald Fletcher agreed to
take on the case only if they were allowed complete control of the
defence. Erskine had offered to represent Muir on that basis but
Muir had preferred to fight his case on political grounds rather than
legal arguments.

Both Erskine and Fletcher made eloquent presentations to the
bench, drawing on precedents from Scots law that challenged the
judges' previous interpretations, and protesting at the vagueness of
the charge and the uncertain authority for the punishment of transportation. Erskine reminded the court, "I and the lord advocate

have both attended county meetings, called for the express purpose of obtaining a reform in the laws for electing members of parliament, and yet no such interpretation was given to our meetings." The charge, they said, should be dismissed.

Their beautifully crafted legal discourse made no impression on the bench. Eskgrove repeated his belief that sedition was a common law offence. Grasping for higher authority, he claimed that the offence was "mentioned even in scriptures". Abercromby argued that "the supreme criminal court here has always been understood to be possessed of an inherent and radical jurisdiction to punish every offence that can be denominated a crime upon the sound principle of reason and morality." In plain English, the judges had the power to create new crimes. Braxfield went further. He said the court possessed the power "of inflicting any punishment…less than death, for every crime the punishment of which is not specifically defined by statute." The charges against Sinclair were declared relevant and the case was adjourned for a week.

Back in the warmth of the Black Bull Inn, Gerrald sipped hot wine from his cup. The journey to court and back had exhausted him. But the doctrine argued by the judges – that unless a statute prevented them the punishment for a crime was entirely in their hands – alarmed him. The two men were fearful of laws that hide from the people the consequences of a criminal act. They were not alone in their opinion. Prominent lawyers in England thought the proposition preposterous. The *Morning Chronicle* paraphrased their opinions: "The discretion of a judge is the law of tyrants; it is always unknown; it is different in different men; it is casual, and depends upon constitution, temper, and passion; in the best, it is oftentimes caprice; in the worst, it is every vice, folly and passion to which human nature is liable."

The fear and resignation of both Sinclair and Gerrald to their fate was magnified by the news that the transport ship carrying their compatriots had sailed before parliament had the opportunity to examine their cases. The ministry was determined and audacious in its behaviour.

Others shared their disbelief. Muir had been in Newgate for three weeks and Skirving and Margarot for one. In that time they had had more than three hundred and fifty visits, about fourteen a day, many of them from influential parliamentarians, reformers and churchmen. It seemed, briefly, as if the ministry would not dare to defy such a body of opinion. The Rev Theophilus Lindsey, a prominent Unitarian who campaigned on their behalf, wrote to a friend, "The sentence against Mr Muir and Mr Palmer is so unjust that I can hardly persuade myself still that it will be executed, at least till their case has undergone the intended parliamentary discussion."

Gerrald and Sinclair learned from reports that the Surprize had reached Portsmouth, having been delayed by bad weather and a damaged hull at Deal. It could take up to six weeks before repairs were completed. That offered a glimmer of hope. At least the prisoners might be still in the country while parliament reviewed their cases. The next parliamentary debate was timetabled for the following Monday, 24 February, the same day as Sinclair and Gerrald were due to appear together in the high court.

*

When Richard Sheridan spoke in the Commons, he was listened to. His fame as a dramatist went before him and his concise and unassuming style often entertained, even if it failed to move votes on the government benches. He rose to introduce Palmer's petition to the house, asking members to recognise that the sentence was "illegal, unjust, oppressive, and unconstitutional". He was seconded by Fox, who pointed out, "In the present case it is to be observed that it had been decided that no appeal lay to any superior court of law, consequently no alternative remained for a man complaining of the illegality of a sentence but a petition for its reversal to the legislature."

Pitt and Dundas led the government supporters in opposition to the petition and, although they allowed it to be read to the House, suspension of Palmer's sentence was defeated by 104 votes to 34.

*

Gerrald had been too ill to attend his hearing on 24 February so his and Sinclair's cases were again adjourned for a week, when the two men sat together in the dock at ten o'clock in the morning of Monday 3 March. Sinclair's advocates, Erskine and Fletcher, were at their table but Gerrald had no representation. He had been so ill he could not visit enough lawyers to find one prepared to take his case. One brave advocate, Malcolm Laing, allowed his reason for refusing to represent Gerrald to be made public; he and others had refused the sedition brief to avoid giving the impression that a fair trial was possible. Gerrald asked the court to appoint counsel for him and Braxfield obliged. With characteristic mischief, he appointed Laing. Fletcher and a third lawyer, Adam Gillies, agreed to join in the defence, after which the cases of both Gerrald and Sinclair were again adjourned for a week, much to the annoyance of Robert Dundas, who conceded, "Although, perhaps in a few hours, I must leave this country to attend to my public duty in London, that can be no objection."

Dundas had to be in parliament for the next major discussion on the legality of the sentences on the day appointed for Gerrald's trial, Monday 10 March. William Adam was once again proposing that they postpone execution of the sentences until parliament had time to properly review the legality of the prosecutions. He got to his feet at five o'clock in the afternoon and spoke until half past eight in the evening. "There are doubts in regard to the legality of the sentences," he said. "There is an excess in the exercise of judicial discretion, in both cases, and there are in Mr Muir's case specialities, which go to show a mistrial, by an improper admission of jurymen, and an improper admission and rejection of evidence."

Robert Dundas led the government case. He defended the procedure of the Edinburgh court and concluded, "The objection to the legality of the sentences in question, and to the proceedings on the trials, are altogether unfounded; and the conduct of the court is free even from suspicion."

Sheridan asked, "What is the crime charged? Is it to out a person on the suspicion of being a disaffected subject? Is it to assume a right to prove against him general disaffection? Good God sir, is it possible that this can be the law of Scotland? If it be, it ought not to continue one hour longer."

Samuel Whitbread added, "If the law of Scotland is such as represented by the learned lord, it is a law of tyranny and oppression, and it is absurd to speak of personal liberty in that country."

Fox pointed to "the tyrannies perpetrated in the latter years of the Stuarts and which are now attempted to be revived in Scotland", and accused Braxfield of acting "with ignorance, levity and hypocrisy". "God help people who have such judges!" he declared. "Were I to live in Scotland I should consider my life, my property, and my liberty to be insecure... I would instantly prepare to leave that land of tyranny and despotism."

Pitt rose to his feet purposefully. His sharp features were easily recognisable by all in the house. He turned to look at his own benches then, holding Adam's gaze with his own, said, "In my opinion an inquiry into this business would lead to the conclusion that no doubt could be entertained, either of the legality of the trials under review or of the propriety of the manner in which the lords of justiciary have exercised their discretion."

The back benches had been given the line. Pitt elaborated for a time on Scots law to show he had a full grasp of his brief, and concluded, "I think that the judges would have been highly culpable if, vested as they are with discretionary powers, they had not employed them for the present punishment of such daring delinquents..."

"Disgrace!" cried the opposition. "Outrage!" "Retract that statement!"

Pitt raised his voice above the noise. "... punishment of such...of such daring delinquents," then even louder, "and the suppression of doctrines so dangerous to the country!"

The opposition's protests were drowned by cheering and foot stamping from the ministry's supporters. It was a quarter past three in the morning and a vote was called for. Adam's motion was defeated by 171 votes to 32. Norman Macleod was the only other Scottish MP to support his motion.

*

Gerrald sat at breakfast in the house of Archibald and Liza Fletcher. He sipped tea but had no appetite for food. In an hour he would leave the house and go with Fletcher to the high court. He felt like a condemned man and this was his final hour of freedom. Liza Fletcher pleaded with him to abscond. She argued that there was still time to get away from Edinburgh to safety. Her husband had spent the previous evening, "almost on his knees", appealing to Gerrald to escape. But he was adamant. He repeated the arguments he had given to his friends in London and, especially, to his tutor, Dr Parr – he was bound by what he had encouraged others to do – and, Liza Fletcher later told an acquaintance, "he took leave of [us] with the calm and affectionate demeanour of a good and firm man going to meet his death". Gerrald and Fletcher gathered their papers and left in a chaise, heading up the Mound to Parliament Close.

Gerrald stepped from the chaise in the High Street and was greeted by a large, enthusiastic crowd. They approved of his appearance. He wore the French costume of the day, a simple jacket, a shirt with a large collar, doubled over, his neck almost bare, and his unpowdered hair hanging loose. The heads of loyalists were invariably powdered with white dust, while modernists cropped their hair or allowed it to hang naturally. His dress was a symbol of reform, the opposite of disguising wigs and the fussy silk and brocade of privilege. Fletcher left him with Gillies and Laing, who would present to the court the case he helped them prepare. Gillies was a powerful advocate with seven years' experience at the bar, and had a plain, direct way of speaking. Laing had a reputation for integrity and intellect.

The public gallery in the court and the outer hall were packed tight as Gerrald stood and said, "My lords, I feel myself under the painful necessity of objecting to the lord justice clerk sitting upon that bench." He renewed the complaint raised by Margarot, that at a private dinner party in the house of James Rochead of Inverleith, Braxfield had prejudged his case by telling the company that the members of the British convention deserved transportation for fourteen years and even a public whipping. Unlike Margarot, Gerrald had introduced the objection at the proper time and offered to call witnesses. Braxfield left the room and Henderland assumed the chair but the judges quickly rejected Gerrald's objection as insolence. A low murmur of disapproval came from the gallery.

Braxfield resumed the bench and the indictment was read. It was almost identical to the charges brought against Skirving and Margarot, except for the mention of speeches made by Gerrald on universal suffrage and the Irish convention bill in an "illegal and seditious meeting". Gerrald pled not guilty. Gillies and Laing argued that the charges were irrelevant, that meeting in a convention was not in itself illegal; that holding opinions favouring universal suffrage and annual parliaments was not illegal; that using French phrases was perfectly legal; and that deciding to meet to consider how to oppose a parliamentary bill was perfectly constitutional. Gillies concluded, "My lord, in going through the whole of this indictment, I can perceive nothing relevant in it to infer the crime of sedition, or any other crime."

The crown repeated its familiar argument, that the convention was a conspiracy to overturn the constitution, and the judges ruled that the indictment was relevant. They left the jury with the clear impression that the convention and its proceedings, as well as Gerrald's speeches, were seditious. The bench sent Gerrald to trial with a presumption of guilt. The court was adjourned until Thursday and Gerrald was sent to the Tollbooth in the meantime.

A large number of supporters reassembled on Thursday and they once more filled the gallery and the hall. They muttered disapproval as Gerrald's objection to two jurors was refused. Witnesses for the crown, as in previous cases, did no more than establish the existence of papers and minutes. Solicitor General Blair, in his summing up, recognised this and told the jury, "The most material part of the proof you have not yet heard; it lies not so much in the spoken evidence that has been given as in the written evidence lying on the table." This comprised the minutes of the convention, the papers that had been seized, and three copies of the *Gazetteer* containing reports of the proceedings. He repeated the by now accepted official view that the assemblies had been illegal and that universal suffrage was subversive.

The defence called no witnesses. Gerrald addressed the jury. "The present legal process too much resembles those instituted in the last century," he cautioned, "when prosecutions upon prosecutions were instituted for the purpose of destroying the freedom of our country." That, though, had not prevented him from coming to stand trial, even though it would have been easy for him to forfeit his bail to flee to safety. "Can there exist a stronger proof of the consciousness of the purity of my own intentions?" he asked. "It is rather remark-able that on last Monday, marked for the first day of my trial, our representatives in parliament were in fact sitting in judgment upon these very judges; nor do I think it would have degraded the dignity of their functions if they had acted with less heat and more delibera-tion, and had patiently waited until the result of the proceedings of the high court of parliament had been known upon their conduct."

He answered the charge of using French terms as "ridiculous" and "fallacious", pointing out that all the old law proceedings were in French, and even now the king gave royal assent to laws in French. Only malevolence had included that charge in the indictment. He went on to claim that the convention, far from being illegal, was "congenial to the spirit of the British constitution itself". Their only object was to peacefully campaign for annual parliaments and universal suffrage. "Had we met as the united delegates of all Britain we should have arrogated a title to which we had no right. But we did no such thing, we met only as the representatives of some thousands who delegated us for a purpose which we knew to be constitutional."

Answering the prosecution argument that universal suffrage was impossible or impracticable he said, "I myself resided during four years in a country where every man who paid taxes had a right to vote. I mean the commonwealth of Pennsylvania." He accused the solicitor general of denying people the right to change the constitution, meaning that "our ancestors had a privilege which we have not a right to exercise". The constitution had never been stationary, "Do we not know that acts of parliament are frequently set aside and others directly contrary passed in their stead? After all, the most useful discoveries in philosophy, the most important changes in the moral history of man, have been innovations. The revolution was an innovation. The reformation was an innovation. Christianity itself was an innovation." He then added, "All great men have been reformers, even our saviour himself."

Braxfield chuckled and said in a loud whisper that could be heard in the well of the court, "Muckle he made o' that, he was hanget!" He then turned to the dock and admonished Gerrald. "All that you have been saying is sedition; and now, my lords he is attacking Christianity."

Henderland exclaimed, "I cannot sit here as a judge, and as a man, without saying that is a most indecent defence!"

Gerrald protested, "I solemnly disclaim all intention of attacking Christianity. I was merely stating the facts."

"Go on in your own way," said Braxfield with a sly smile.

"I should have been going on if your lordship had not interrupted me," replied Gerrald. And he did go on to defend good government and democracy and the right of people to resist infringements to the constitution. Throughout his address, Gerrald had struggled with a consuming cough, deep in his chest. His ill health weakened him. He was unsteady on his feet. "Gentlemen, my feelings, my exertions, and my state of health have exhausted me." He was allowed to sit for a while to rest before continuing.

He rose once more and surrendered himself to the jury. "Gentlemen, my cause is in your hands," he said. "You are Britons. You are freemen. Nothing more therefore is necessary to be said. You have heard the charge; you have heard the evidence; and you know the punishment which follows upon conviction. Weigh well, then, whether the charge itself involves guilt; whether the evidence produced affixes that charge upon me; and above all, whether, in case of conviction the punishment which I am to suffer is not more than proportionate to the offence."

A 16-year-old youth called Thomas Campbell had walked all the way from Glasgow to be present at this momentous event. In time Campbell became a popular poet and years later he recalled, "I witnessed Joseph Gerrald's trial and it was an era in my life. Hitherto I had never known what public eloquence was; and I am sure the justiciary lords did not help me to a conception of it, speaking as they did bad arguments in broad Scotch...Gerrald's speech annihilated the remembrance of all the eloquence that had ever been heard within the walls of that house. He quieted the judges, in spite of their indecent interruptions of him, and produced a silence in which you might have heard a pin fall to the ground. At the close of his defence he said, 'And now, gentlemen of the jury, now that I take leave of you forever, let me remind you that mercy is no small part of the duty of jurymen; that the man who shuts his heart on the claims of the unfortunate, on him the gates of mercy will be shut; and for him the saviour of the world shall have died in vain.' At this finish I was much moved, and turning to a stranger beside me, apparently a tradesman, I said to him, 'By heavens, sir, that is a great man'. 'Yes, sir,' he answered, 'he is not only a great man himself, but he makes every other man feel great who listens to him'."

Braxfield, though, was in vindictive mood. He was angry at his conduct having been discussed in parliament. Power and prestige was his to display. He turned to the jury and told them, "When you see Mr Gerrald taking a very active part, and making speeches such as you have heard today, I look upon him as a very dangerous member of society, for I dare say he has eloquence enough to persuade the people to rise in arms."

"Oh my lord! My lord!" objected Gerrald, raising his voice above the uproar in the public gallery. "This is a very improper way of addressing a jury! It is descending into personal abuse. God forbid that my eloquence should ever be made use of for such a purpose!"

"I do not say that you did so but that you had abilities to do it," Braxfield said peevishly, then resumed the abuse. "Gentlemen, he has no relation, nor the least property in the country but he comes here to disturb the peace of the country, as a delegate from a society in England, to raise sedition in this country. I say he appears to me to be much more criminal than Muir or Palmer or Skirving, because they were all natives of this country. Gentlemen, if you are satisfied that this meeting is a seditious meeting, I do not see how it is possible to avoid the consequence of finding this panel guilty, art and part, of the crime charged. " He had to bang his gavel repeatedly to restore order. The macer shouted at the public to be quiet. In the midst of a din of protest, of whistles and boos and loud objections, the court was adjourned until eleven of clock the following morning.

Gerrald took his place in the courtroom next morning as a tense and expectant crowd once more filed in to the gallery. The jury took their places and the judges emerged from the room behind the bench. Without any fuss, Braxfield asked the jury to retire and consider their verdict. The court fell silent and the judges withdrew.

Adam Gillies turned to Gerrald and remarked that they were in for a long wait, the written evidence being so vast it would take most of the day to examine it. The solicitor general had admitted as much in his summing up. But after just twenty minutes the jury came back with a unanimous guilty verdict. The courtroom was astonished. Gillies shot to his feet. He appealed to the bench. "This written evidence consisted of several hundred pages," he protested. "It could not have been read in less that six or seven hours… They were enclosed only twenty minutes, a space of time in which it is impossible for any human being to consider it."

Braxfield and his colleagues refused to entertain the objection, confirmed the verdict and imposed the by now predictable sentence of transportation for fourteen years.

As Gerrald was led away to the Tollbooth, Charles Sinclair was ordered to stand. The solicitor general, Robert Blair, rose and informed the judges that the prosecution would no longer pursue this case. He asked that the prisoner be released. The bench agreed. There was relief and some celebration in the gallery. Some suspected that Sinclair had been a spy but no one ever provided evidence to show how this could have been. He was accepted back into the radical movement in London without suspicion. In fact the evidence against him was tainted. After his papers were seized in the Black Bull, they had been left lying unattended in the sheriff's office for two days. A technical challenge could have had them ruled inadmissible. In any case, Blair, Braxfield and the two powerful Dundases knew they had already lopped the head from the Scottish reform movement. Sinclair was no longer of importance to them.

*

William Adam MP continued to worry at the heels of the Dundases in Westminster. On 25 March, ten days after Gerrald was convicted, he rose once more in the House of Commons and asked that a select committee be appointed to examine the crime of sedition in Scotland, the right to appeal, the appointment of juries, and the rules of evidence. Henry and Robert Dundas vigorously defended their legal system against intrusive inquiry and Fox once again swung his weight and reputation behind Adam. "This, sir, is a new case, for which there is no punishment prescribed by statute, no precedent to support it, nothing which can warrant it," he argued. "I am fully satisfied that something ought immediately to be done to correct this abuse of law in Scotland, and to put an end to the tyranny practised under the pretext of administering justice in that part of the kingdom."

Once again, the motion was defeated, this time by 77 votes to 24.

CHAPTER 27

Chalk Farm

"The critical moment has arrived and Britons must assert with zeal and firmness their claims to liberty, or yield without resistance to the chains that ministerial usurpation is forging for them... Let us form, then, another British Convention."

Thomas Hardy, March 1794, in a circular letter to all reform societies.

Thomas Hardy was easily picked out in the crowd moving through the narrow main street of Camden Town. He was just over six feet in height and broad shouldered. He walked with John Lovett, a London hairdresser, and they, like the others, made their way up the hill to Chalk Farm, where the London Corresponding Society and the Society for Constitutional Information had called an open air meeting to discuss the crisis. Lovett was to chair the meeting.

They hoped that a good attendance might help Lauderdale, who was to raise the question of the sentences in the House of Lords on the following day. But they expected little more than some useful publicity, Adam and Sheridan having been soundly beaten four times in the Commons and Stanhope ridiculed in the Lords. Having to rely on their own strength, Hardy, on behalf of the London Corresponding Society, had sent a circular to all the reform clubs in the country calling for another national convention.

A huge open-air demonstration in Halifax had approved plans for a general meeting in Bristol to plan another national convention. Bristol, Norwich and Newcastle had met and agreed, and in Sheffield a meeting of six or seven thousand was held to protest against the Scottish sentences. Henry Yorke, who should have been at the Edinburgh convention but was too ill to go, addressed the meeting and looked forward to the time when "the commanding voice of the whole people shall recommend the 558 Gentlemen in St Stephen's Chapel to go about their business."

The more cautious London Friends of the People were less enthusiastic. They had written to Hardy saying that a convention would "furnish the enemies of reform with the means of calumniating its advocates". Hardy and Lovett agreed that in plain English it meant that they and their great families would run a mile if power got anywhere near the hands of honest labourers. The Society for Constitutional Information had agreed to merge their organisation and activities with the Corresponding Society.

The swell of the crowd increased as the two men approached the assembly room facing the bowling green. They climbed the stairs to face the people, still streaming north from the city. Lovett guessed there were two or three thousand already there. In a short while the vast assembly was settled under a hot spring sun and Lovett called them to order.

"Welcome, citizens, to this meeting called by the united reform clubs of London," he called out. "Before we begin, let me say that we have been blessed with a remarkably fine day and many of you will be in need of refreshment. Well, the magistrates have denied you that pleasure. The landlord of the tavern over there, where the magistrates are sitting, has been ordered to lock his cellar door. They will not suffer him to draw a drop of beer or liquor of any kind for any that are here, except for themselves and their creatures that are in the ale house now!" The crowd laughed and jeered. "As you might imagine, they supposed this would irritate us and provoke some outrage, so they have stationed the military at a little distance from here. Please don't succumb to the insults and provocations from the Bow Street runners and police officers, the government spies and informers among you. You are thinking and reasoning men and women."

The audience gave a great cheer and Lovett introduced Hardy.

"The conduct of Scotland's judges, particularly the jeering, abrasive Braxfield, led to embarrassment and political difficulty for Dundas and the authorities in London," he told them. "The legality of the sentences handed down to Muir and Palmer were the subject of four debates in parliament initiated in the Commons by Richard Sheridan and William Adam, MP for Ross-shire, and in the Lords by the earls of Stanhope and, tomorrow, Lauderdale. In public, ministers have defended, even praised, Braxfield and the Scottish courts but in private there is irritation about his conduct. While it may have been soundly defeated, Adam's motion received great attention in the Scottish and English press."

He went on to tell the meeting how he had visited the prisoners in their crowded ship at Portsmouth, how Palmer was ill with the flux, Muir was quiet and reserved and had continuing chest problems, and had the near constant companionship of his dear friend William Moffat. Margarot had arranged for his wife to accompany him to New South Wales as a free settler. Skirving was well. But poor Gerrald was still in Edinburgh jail and was suffering from consumption.

"When the Surprize transport was lying off Portsmouth," he went on, "I was on board her and saw Mr Banks, who is an eminent sculptor, take a cast from Mr Muir's face, from which he will make a bust, and from which engravings will be made. It is a good likeness." He proposed resolutions of support for "the persecuted patriots" and argued that if they couldn't stop their transportation now then the sooner they achieved democratic representation, the sooner they would be returned to friends and families.

Lovett proposed that the meeting send thanks to the parliamentary campaigners for all their efforts, and then introduced the popular speaker John Thelwall.

"Citizens!" Thelwall began. "Under the auspices of apostate reformers we have lately beheld serious and alarming encroachments on the liberties of the people. We have seen with indignation and

horror men, legally and peaceably assembled, dispersed by unconstitutional powers and their papers seized. We have seen some of our
most virtuous brethren, whose only crime has been an imitation of
Mr Pitt and his associates, sentenced to fourteen years transportation, without the sanction of law or even of precedent. Along with
the insidious attempts to introduce foreign troops into this country
without the consent of parliament, these are measures calculated to
awaken our fears for the existence, even of the name of liberty."

He went on to congratulate "Citizen Stanhope" for his speech in
the Lords denouncing the Hessian landings on the Isle of Wight. He
pointed out that in the previous week the Commons debated a bill
to arm French émigrés resident in Britain. He warned that, "arming
one part of the people against the other, brought Charles I to the
block, and drove James II and his posterity from the throne, and,
consequently ministers in advising such measures, ought to consider
whether or not they are guilty of high treason." He congratulated
English juries horrified by the Scottish trials for acquitting two
reformers in London and Manchester who had been charged with
similar offences. He asked the meeting to consider, "That any attempt
to violate those yet remaining laws which were intended for the security of Englishmen against tyranny of courts and ministers…ought
to be considered as dissolving entirely the social compact between
the English nation and their governors." And he concluded, "As the
circular, sent by your secretary to all reform societies in the country,
says, 'Let us form, then, another British convention'."

The meeting erupted in cheers and applause. Before dispersing,
Lovett proposed sending a letter of support to the Society of United
Irishmen and to Archibald Hamilton Rowan, now in Dublin jail on
a charge of sedition.

*

On the following day in the Palace of Westminster, Lauderdale stood
in the Lords and for three hours detailed the shortcomings in the
Scottish trials. "Not one case in the whole history of the Scotch

criminal law stands upon record either to justify or even to countenance the proceedings," he said, "nor is there a statute existing by which they could be maintained." He had hoped that the matter would have been satisfactorily resolved in the Commons but that hadn't happened, so, "I propose to move an address to the crown, in favour of those unfortunate persons, whose cases I think not merely most severe as to their personal suffering, but most injurious to the country at large."

His motion was rejected without a vote.

CHAPTER 28

The Motherbank

"This gift, this little gift with heart sincere,
An exile, wafted from his native land,
To friendship tried, bequeaths with many a tear,
Whilst the dire bark still lingers on the strand."

Thomas Muir, 'To Mr Moffat, with a Watch
and Chain', Surprize transport, Portsmouth,
March 12, 1794.

James Ellis and William Moffat were on and off the Surprize at Portsmouth more times each day than they cared to remember. They brought letters, supplies and gifts to Palmer, Muir and Skirving. Margarot had his own fetcher and carrier. His wife, Mary, was on board with him and was sailing to New South Wales as a voluntary emigrant, a free settler. Moffat returned to his lodgings in Portsmouth each night while Ellis, also a free settler, took his berth on the ship. There were other emigrants on board, John Boston, his wife and three children, and Matthew Pearce with his pregnant wife.

Among the supplies Ellis and Moffat brought aboard for the prisoners was a complete set of *Encyclopedia Britannica*, sent by one of the reform societies to enrich the life of their fellow citizens in exile. Some of the belongings Ellis stowed for Palmer were more immediately useful, and some exotic: a gun; swords and pistols; and a case of tamarinds. He helped a nephew of Palmer's coax up the gangplank a hunting dog, a lurcher that had been trained to the gun. The nephew thought it might help catch kangaroos, which he supposed was the only source of meat in the antipodes.

"Shush, Maurice," said Mary Margarot, struggling to stay on the narrow bed. Another rasping snore filled the small cabin. "Maurice!" she hissed in the dark. "There are children sleeping in here." Margarot turned from his back to his side without waking. This relieved the pressure on his nasal passages and gave Mrs Margarot a few more precious inches of bed. The children in the room were not theirs. They were the three Boston siblings.

At first the Margarots had had their own cabin. As a free settler Mrs Margarot deserved that. But when the Surprize put in at Portsmouth she was joined by James Thomson, on his way to become assistant colonial surgeon at Port Jackson; William Baker who was to be the new superintendent of prisoners at Sydney Cove, and his wife; and Ensign and Mrs William Pattullo. The young officer from Dundee whose wife came from Edinburgh, was in charge of the military detachment being sent out on the ship. They all had a problem. They had to pass through the Margarots' cabin to get to their own. So they complained to under-secretary King at the Home Office. "This is extremely irksome to us, and we have disputed much that a person suffering a sentence of the laws of the country should be in the same place with officers of the government. You know, sir, having the liberty of coming into the cabin will create intimacy, and intimacy begets words. Their sentiments are specially adverse to ours."

There was a spare berth in the cabin allocated to the Boston children and, to avoid radical contagion of his majesty's officers, Mary Margarot was moved there and Maurice was allowed to crush into the bunk beside her.

Uncomfortable as it was, their small rectangular booth was luxurious compared to the accommodation below decks in the wooden dungeon. All four political prisoners had been housed in the hold alongside the felons when they first went on board in the Thames. The captain, Patrick Campbell, insisted he had received orders from the secretary of state to treat them the same as other criminals. They objected.

"Mr Campbell," Palmer had explained in the roundhouse, the

captain's quarters at the rear of the ship, "the government at first intended to send us out in the Canada with Captain Moorhead. In this ship Mr Muir and I had cabins appointed to us, and it seems to have been the original intention of the ministry to have sent us out in the characters of gentlemen. For reasons best known to themselves, the scheme was laid aside."

"Canada was unseaworthy," said Campbell. He spat the words.

"Nevertheless, we paid £50 each," replied Palmer.

"Not my problem, Mr Palmer. A cabin on this ship is £40."

"Very well," conceded Palmer, "I'll consult with my friends."

Palmer was taken below. Skirving and Muir agreed that they should pay but Margarot said he already had the privilege of sleeping in his wife's cabin at night and didn't want to pay more. Palmer requested another meeting and assured Campbell that cash would be paid as soon as they reached Portsmouth.

Campbell turned to his first mate, Hugh McPherson. "Put 'em with the soldiers," he ordered.

"But we are paying for cabins!" protested Palmer.

"When I see the money," snorted Campbell.

They were moved up a deck alongside soldiers of the New South Wales Corps. "Seventeen of us sleep in this hole, the grating of which is locked at night," Palmer wrote to a friend. "The ship is so exceptionally crowded that all conceive it impossible."

More than a week before reaching Portsmouth the Surprize had emerged from the Thames estuary into huge seas and a howling blast. Campbell got her around the point at Margate and headed south as close to the coast as he could risk. By Deal he could go no further. All of the passengers felt unwell. The stink of piss and vomit from the lower deck seeped into the ship's timbers and although Muir, Palmer, and Skirving gave thanks that they were one deck above, they were heaving nevertheless. Margarot moaned in his bunk, as did Mary. Some of the sixty women and the several men in the felons' deck prayed to their god. Most just cursed.

A deafening report of one of the ship's guns bounced off the stone walls of Deal harbour, sending a signal to the pilot that she wanted to come in. The calm waters of the harbour brought a few days' relief to all.

Sitting cross-legged on his upper bunk, Muir took the opportunity to write some letters. "In the most remote region of the earth I shall doubtless, from time to time, hear of the exertions of my friends in the cause of mankind," he wrote to Benjamin Flower, editor of the *Cambridge Intelligencer*. "Mixed with feelings of a more tender kind, I shall indulge the proud idea, that I too once associated with them and that I too once had a claim to their regard." He informed a friend in London, "I am now upon the eve of leaving Europe and civilised life, perhaps for ever. But the memory of those whom I could call my friends shall live in my recollection, and support and solace me in the remotest regions of this earth. I believe I have completely recovered from that disorder, whose consequences excited some apprehension when I was on board the hulk. I am perfectly resigned to my situation."

Muir looked across to the bunk occupied by Palmer, who mumbled for help in a low, weak voice. He asked for a bucket. Muir placed his writing materials in the corner of his bunk, swung his legs over the wooden board to drop to the deck below, found an empty slop bucket and brought it to Palmer. He cradled the preacher's head as the poor man retched. He could feel the heat from Palmer's flushed forehead and cheeks. The preacher complained of having chills, sweats and terrible dreams.

Muir and Skirving nursed Palmer in turns as the Surprize battled back into the Strait of Dover and round to the south coast of England. When she berthed in Portsmouth five days later Palmer's red rash had developed and spread. His muscle pains and headaches remained. His fever was reduced but the relief was negligible. Muir fetched James Thomson, the new assistant colonial surgeon, who was to serve as ship's doctor during the voyage. Thomson diagnosed a recurrence of Palmer's gaol fever. He had all the symptoms of the flux and Muir was asked to ensure that his patient had plenty of fresh water to drink.

The first mate, McPherson, came below and found Muir and Skirving by Palmer's bunk. He told them that repairs to the hull would mean a delay of around six weeks. They were glad of the reprieve and the precious extra time they could have with friends and supporters. But they exploded with indignation when McPherson broke the second part of his news – Captain Campbell had ordered them back down in the hold with the felons to make room for eighteen more soldiers coming aboard that afternoon. They made strenuous objection on Palmer's behalf because of his illness, but also complained that they had agreed to pay £40 each for cabins.

Later that day, Muir and Skirving, waiting on deck for an interview with Campbell, were greeted by Ensign Pattullo, who asked about Palmer's health; the minister had been a family friend of his parents in Dundee. Just then the first squad of a detachment of eighteen men from Chatham barracks climbed the gangway in pairs and soon the soldiers, wearing the familiar British red coat with white facings of the Marine Corps, formed on deck. The last half dozen to appear were in irons on hands and feet, and led by a sergeant with a bayonet attached to his musket. Ensign Pattullo took the salute and received the men's papers from the sergeant, who gave his name as Reddish.

Campbell came on deck and Muir and Skirving took the opportunity to protest about their being moved. Campbell's short temper was kept in check by a well-timed intervention by Pattullo, who pointed out the danger of moving Palmer. Campbell relented and allowed them to remain with the soldiers but turned to the newly arrived Sergeant Reddish and charged him to guarantee the safe custody of the prisoners while at liberty on the Surprize. He explained that he could not offer them cabins just then but would look into it, and because they had paid their fares they would be entitled to eat from the officers' kitchen and not with the prisoners. However, they would have to share their privilege with Grant.

"Grant!" exploded Muir. "Grant is no friend to us, sir!"

"He will eat and sleep with you," insisted Campbell.

"He is a fraudster, a thief, a liar, and as you know full well, Captain Campbell, he made unfounded accusations against Mr Palmer and me on the voyage from Edinburgh," protested Muir.

"He, like you, is a gentleman. You will treat him as such." Campbell turned on his heel and returned to his cabin without waiting for a response.

Reddish and Grant were moved into the bunkroom along with Muir, Palmer and Skirving. Corporal Timothy Ryan took one of the lower bunks. Sergeant Reddish wanted the corporal by him not only to ensure the security of the political prisoners but also to keep a close eye on some of the soldiers who had come aboard in irons. Most of the New South Wales Corps were volunteers and some saw the opportunity of a new life after discharge, while some were deserters who took the punishment option of serving in the colony. Among them was Private Draper, who was allocated a bunk under the prisoners from Scotland.

Reddish was invited by the reformers to mess from the officers' kitchen at their expense. Over dinner that evening, the sergeant explained why he wanted to keep Draper close to him. The soldier was a mutineer and was attached to the New South Wales Corps only to escape death. He had led a conspiracy in Quebec to raise an insurrection which involved an attempt to assassinate his commanding officer, Prince Edward. Draper had been condemned to death but was reprieved on condition that he serve in the newly-formed New South Wales Corps.

Each evening Sergeant Reddish displayed unexpected sympathy and even agreement with Muir and Skirving. He told them how he opposed the French war and had volunteered for Botany Bay to avoid it. He expressed concern for their sufferings in a great cause. He claimed he was the illegitimate brother of George Canning, the young Tory MP for the Isle of Wight, of whose politics he disapproved. In any case, he could see no future in this benighted country for someone of his standing. He thanked them often for their generosity and assured them he wished to serve them to the best of his ability.

Muir confided to Skirving one afternoon that he thought Reddish was a spy. Skirving agreed. He didn't trust the sergeant's pretended sympathy with reform and thought he was too close to Grant. They also noticed that Grant was making copious notes in a diary. And why, they wondered, had they put Draper so close to them? Something wasn't right.

Draper had been a tailor before becoming a soldier. He worked at his trade on board ship for those who could afford to pay for his skills. He made some shirts for Palmer, whom he asked for an advance to help him set up business at Botany Bay. Palmer refused. Ellis, however, was persuaded to buy Draper goods worth about eighteen shillings at Portsmouth. He didn't tell Palmer but, having doubts about Draper's honesty, made sure he had two witnesses to the loan and a promise of repayment. Skirving's compassion led him to lend Draper forty shillings.

*

In the weeks they had been tied up in Portsmouth, repairs to the hull were completed. All of the convicts, soldiers and settlers were now on board. Provisions for the first part of the voyage were loaded, they would restock in Brazil, at Rio de Janeiro, and much needed supplies for the struggling colony were the final cargo to be stowed. There were 480 barrels of flour and 120 of pease, 564 eight-pound pieces of beef and 2,146 four-pound pieces of pork. The ship moved out of the harbour to ride at anchor at the Motherbank, an important anchorage on the shallow sandbar in the Solent, northeast of the Isle of Wight.

Dr Thomson had been fearful Palmer would end his days before the ship sailed, but he was slowly recovering. However, he could manage less than an hour a day on deck, even with assistance. Moffat had been in constant attendance, even after the Surprize left Portsmouth and lay at the Motherbank. He hired a wherry each day to visit his friends, carrying letters and addresses, gifts and tokens back and forth. The Surprize was waiting for a fleet of merchant

ships of the East India Company to assemble along with an escort of
two warships, the Suffolk and the Swift. Surprize was to join them
for protection for part of her voyage. Each day from mid-March they
expected to sail and so each visit Moffat made he thought would be
his last.

On Wednesday 12 March, Muir, standing on deck beside Moffat
pointed to the ships' flags flying in readiness. As they wondered if they
would ever meet again, Muir handed his friend a parcel. It contained
Muir's gold pocket-watch and a poem expressing his gratitude for
the friendship Moffat had given and the assistance he had organised.
Moffat was speechless. Muir then handed him a sealed letter. He
explained it was a letter of recommendation he was to take to the
Rev Jeremiah Joyce, who was tutor to the children of Lord Stanhope.
It asked Joyce to bring Moffat to the notice of the earl and Muir
suggested to Moffat that he settle his affairs in Scotland because, as
he noted in the letter, "I know most certainly that those who rule the
courts in Scotland have determined to prevent our excellent friend
Mr Moffat from rising in his profession."

*

The Surprize rode at anchor on the Motherbank throughout March
and April, waiting for the lumbering Indiamen to assemble, and
the prisoners continued to receive visitors. As well as Moffat, other
reformers came to wish their compatriots well. Some were local and
others made the journey from London. Some were ordinary working
people, like Hardy, and some were distinguished, such as Sheridan,
Lauderdale and others from the parliamentary opposition who had
supported their cause. The presence of dignitaries on his ship obliged
Captain Campbell to dine with them and, reluctantly, he found small
cabins for Palmer, Skirving and Muir. When Ellis discovered that
other free settlers were given a cabin at government expense, he asked
Campbell for the same treatment. Campbell demanded payment and
threatened to refuse Palmer the use of his personal stores during the
whole voyage if he didn't pay for Ellis.

"By God, Ellis shall not have a cabin the whole voyage," threatened Campbell. "I will not be bullied out of anything. Mr Palmer, you may find a different treatment before the voyage is out." On 20 April Palmer agreed to pay another £40 for his friend.

It was not only friends and sympathisers who approached the Surprize. Many loyalists came to gawp at the "Jacobins" and taunt them about the Terror in France. The failure of the parliamentary campaign to free them brought groups of gloating political tourists. When news of the defeat of William Adam's Commons motion reached the naval base, a warship pulled alongside the Surprize. The officers assembled the crew on deck, issued them with brandy and ordered them to give three cheers. Campbell was losing patience. His final exasperation came when a naval officer pulled alongside in a longboat and climbed aboard, demanding to see "the incendiaries".

'Sir,' replied Campbell, "I have no incendiaries on my ship, but I suppose you mean Messrs Muir and Palmer. While these gentlemen are aboard this vessel they shall not be made a show of."

"God's truth, Mr Campbell, do not you know who I am?" demanded the offended officer.

"By your dress I should suppose you a gentleman and a commander of a man of war," growled Campbell, "but by your language I suspect I am mistaken. Now please leave my ship!"

Margarot had all this time managed to escape the captain's ire. In fact he had become friendly with Campbell in an effort to make his wife's voyage as comfortable as he could. He avoided confrontation and controversy. He stood back from the disputes about cabins. And even when Grant was shown to be a thief, he refused to intervene for fear of losing his favoured position. Grant had been seen by three witnesses stealing money from Muir's pocket and breaking open one of Palmer's boxes. The ship's carpenter, the steward and his wife told Muir and Palmer what they had seen. They reported that Grant had called himself Muir's steward, and said he had his authority to take a purse from the pocket of a pair of Muir's trousers and remove two guineas and five shillings and put them into his own. He then lifted the carpenter's chisel and broke open Mr Palmer's box. The incident was reported to Campbell, who noted the event and feigned concern, but he took no action.

Grant and Reddish were upset at losing their benefactors. When the reformers left the bunkhouse for their new cabins, the forger and the sergeant lost their food from the captain's kitchen. Grant was reduced to prison fare and Reddish to soldiers' rations. Grant resorted to what he did best. He started rumours. He put the word about that some of the soldiers were planning a mutiny and intended to take the ship to the French. His story spread quickly. Ellis heard the rumour and told Grant to hold his tongue, but the odious forger from Inverness persisted, telling poor convicts not to fear, "Something might happen that will prevent the ship from getting to Botany Bay."

On the night of 14 April, Grant squatted in the corner of his bunk with his diary, "Last night," he wrote, "Boston, Palmer, Skirving and McPherson had supper and began drinking seditious toasts, 'Damnation to the king, his family and all crowned heads', 'until we follow the example of France we must consider ourselves in a state of slavery'. Tonight they did the same. Boston stated that the present war is a king's war, and 'must be terminated by the intervention of the people', and that in Birmingham he could raise 30,000 people in arms in under fourteen days." The conversation and the record of it were both lies.

During the last two weeks of April, tension was high on all decks. The convoy was assembled and only an adverse wind kept it at anchor. Even so, Moffat rowed out every day that conditions allowed. As late as 30 April the ships stood at the Motherbank. Moffat had been invited to attend an anniversary meeting of the Society for Constitutional Information in London on Friday 2 May and to speak on behalf of the "martyrs". He wrote to the secretary apologising for not being able to attend. He explained that the fleet was wind-bound and likely to be there for a few days more. His wish was to stay with his friends on the Surprize but "you may be sure that members of the Constitutional Society will not be forgotten".

On that Friday the signal to weigh anchors was raised and the convoy moved slowly into position and round the Isle of Wight into the open sea. One constant visitor had been the Rev Russell Scott of Portsmouth. On Saturday, he explained to a friend in a letter that he had witnessed the departure, "the whole fleet being at length out of sight yesterday morning with a very fair wind down the channel".

Not long before they left, the prisoners received an address from the London Corresponding Society. A similar one was sent to Joseph Gerrald, who had been transferred from Edinburgh to Newgate in London. It conveyed their deep thanks for his work on their behalf and finished with a challenge to the government. "We are animated by the same sentiments and are daily repeating the same words, and committing the same actions for which you are thus infamously sentenced; and we will repeat them and commit them until we have obtained redress, yet we are unpunished!" The ministry took the challenge seriously.

CHAPTER 29

Treason and plot

"And there's room enough to prove our rulers mighty wise, Sirs,
For they can things discover ne'er perceiv'd by other eyes, Sirs;
Nay deem it wondrous as you will, but facts will prove it true, Sirs,
They've found it is high treason to cry cock a doodle doo, Sirs."

John Thelwall, 'Britain's Glory, or the Blessings of a Good
Constitution', 1794.

Lydia Hardy woke with a jolt at the first loud knock. "Tom, there's someone at the door." She took a deep breath and put protective hands across her swollen belly. The knocking grew louder and raised voices joined in the din outside the door of the shoemaker's shop at number 9 Piccadilly.

"What? In the name ..." objected Hardy. "It's Monday morning. What time is it?" he asked as he pulled himself from a deep sleep. The dim dawn light had already filled the room and he saw from the clock on the wall that it was just gone six. More heavy thuds were delivered to the shop door and Hardy heard his name being called.

"You stay here please, Lydia, I'll see what's wrong," he said to his wife, who was six months pregnant. He pulled on a shirt and trousers and went from the back parlour, which they used as a bedroom, into the front shop. As he unbolted the door, a group of men rushed in.

"You Hardy?" asked one of them.

"I am, and you are?"

"Lawzun, king's messenger," replied the leader.

"And these men?" demanded Hardy.

"Gurnel, king's messenger," growled Lawzun. "Constables

Macmanus and Townshend of Bow Street, and the gentleman behind is Mr John King, under-secretary of state at the Home department." The Bow Street runners had pistols in their hands. There were two or three more men outside on the pavement. "I've a warrant for your arrest," Lawzun shouted in Hardy's face, "for treason!"

"That's impossible, it's unthinkable," said Hardy as he heard his wife's call of distress from the parlour. She was sitting up in bed. He went through to comfort her and the five intruders followed him into the room.

"Please leave," said Lydia, "and at least give me the opportunity to dress. This is highly improper."

"Improper or not, missus, you stay right where you are while we search this place," ordered Lawzun.

"Show me your warrant, sir," demanded Hardy. Lawzun took a paper from his pocket and showed Hardy the signature of Henry Dundas. He quickly folded it and returned it to his coat.

"May I read it?" asked Hardy.

"No time for that now," insisted Lawzun. "It gives me the authority to arrest you and to search your house." In fact, the charge on the warrant was not treason, but suspicion of treasonable practices. "Now, give me the keys to your bureau and chests."

Hardy was sitting on the bed with his arms around his wife, his big frame protecting her vulnerability. "No, you can't have my keys," he said. "I haven't read your warrant."

Lawzun lifted a poker from the fireplace and brandished it at the couple. "Then I'll soon have them open with this!" he said menacingly.

"No, no, Mr Lawzun!" the under-secretary called out. "Send for the smith, please." A locksmith, one of those waiting in the street, came into the parlour with a large basket of tools. In minutes Hardy's bureau and two chests were opened and hundreds of papers belonging to the London Corresponding Society were bundled into sacks, along with many private letters.

One of the Bow Street men chuckled. "There's enough to send

him abroad if not to hang him." The second runner eyed Lydia with a leering smile. She was furious and embarrassed and jerked the bedclothes higher around her neck. He pointed to Hardy with his pistol and looked at Lydia. "I hope you will have the pleasure of seeing him hanged before your door," he hissed.

The party raided the shelves and cupboard in the room, filling another corn sack with books and pamphlets. When they went back to search the shop, Lydia quickly rose and pulled on a day dress.

"No doubt you'll find treason hatching among the boots and shoes!" Hardy shouted.

"We'll be back to search that bed now that Mrs Hardy's up," called Lawzun. After they had turned over the shop they ignored Lydia's objections and stripped the sheets and blankets from the bed, turned the mattress and peered underneath the bedstead.

Hardy was taken outside to a hackney coach. He controlled the rising anger and frustration coursing through him as he was driven across town with Gurnel and Townshend. Lydia was kept inside by the others to prevent her seeing in which direction they had taken her husband. The carriage took him to King Street in Westminster, Gurnel's family home.

Lydia Hardy stood alone among the wreckage of her home. Her fists were clenched. "Robbers!" she shouted, to no one in particular. "Despots!"

Hardy remained a prisoner in Gurnel's while preparations were made to have him interviewed by the Privy Council later that day. At 11am he was shown into the home secretary's office before a panel of interrogators that included Pitt, Dundas, Lords Montrose, Stafford, Grenville, Hawkesbury and Salisbury, along with the lord chancellor and the solicitor general, plus Joseph White, the solicitor to the Treasury who had been at the Hackney open-air meeting, and, much to Hardy's annoyance, John Reeves, leader of the anti-republican loyalist organisation that had done so much to intimidate free thinkers and break up reform meetings.

*

Gerrald lay in his bunk and stared at the ceiling of his Newgate cell. He glanced at a calendar on the wall. It was 12 May and he had been in London for more than a month. He thought about his friends, now at sea for ten days, and wondered where they might be and how they were enduring the voyage. He expected to be sent after them any day and could not understand why he was kept in Newgate. He was still very ill but that, he thought, would not be an important consideration for the home secretary. He looked around at his cell mates. They were all reformers and they shared a large room with a window and a fireplace. There was a table in the middle, where they held dinners and discussions, most often with friends and fellow radicals who visited every day. He had been able to secure a place in the state side of the prison thanks to the Corresponding Society, who had voted him a guinea a week. He could pay his seven shillings rent to the turnkey out of that and still have enough to contribute for food and coal for the cell.

Gerrald had been depressed and ill in the Edinburgh jail and in the early days at Newgate. He had shown little interest in companionship and some visitors described his appearance as "slovenly". But in a short time he recovered his sociability, thanks to the company in his cell and in adjacent rooms. The jail was packed with reformers who attracted streams of like-minded visitors, and formed a popular dining and discussion club. The *Morning Post* reported that the state side of Newgate was so full "that there is not room for another prisoner. Should government persevere in prosecuting booksellers and poor devils for selling such stuff as *Pig's Meat*, it would be well if they directed some clever architect to build a new wing to the prison." *Pig's Meat* was a popular penny weekly that took its name from Edmund Burke's reference to the people as the "swinish multitude". That phrase bred the most popular metaphors of the time. One of Gerrald's cell-mates, William Hodgson, had been sentenced to two years for calling the king "a German hog-butcher". *Hog's Wash* was a magazine published by Daniel Eaton, publisher of

Gerrald's pamphlets. Eaton, who was indicted and acquitted several times in 1793 and 1794, was a constant visitor to the Newgate democrats, along with the radical philosopher William Godwin, the poets Robert Southey and Samuel Taylor Coleridge, and James Parkinson, a leading London activist and pamphleteer. Parkinson, a doctor who later became famous for his pioneering medical classification of a condition that became known as Parkinson's disease, was a frequent contributor to Eaton's *Hog's Wash* under the pseudonym Old Hubert. He wrote political satire, the best known being *An Address to the Hon Edmund Burke from the Swinish Multitude.*

Gerrald was thankful for the stimulating company. Also sharing his room were the attorney John Frost, found guilty of uttering seditious words, and a baptist minister, William Winterbotham, sentenced to four years for seditious preaching. Winterbotham used his time writing a series of works on China and America, published by fellow cell-mates Henry Symonds and James Ridgeway, each serving sentences for publishing seditious libel, including works by Paine. Symonds and Ridgeway established a successful radical publishing business from their Newgate cell. A third publisher, Daniel Holt, also convicted of seditious libel, shared the room. Holt and Winterbotham employed a servant, selected from the female prisoners, to wait on the company. The painter Richard Newton had been in and out of the state-side cells in recent weeks, sketching the radicals and their visitors for a painting, showing all of them together around a grand dinner table. He would call it *Comfort in Prison* and intended to raise funds by selling engravings of the finished work.

The sound of the cell door being unlocked for the day roused Gerrald from his thoughts. John Smith from the Corresponding Society ran in as soon as the turnkey had opened the door. He could barely conceal his agitation. Smith, a bookseller and one of the Corresponding Society's general committee members, was the person nominated to look after Gerrald's finances. He had a look in his eyes that told Gerrald this visit was not about money.

"Citizens!" Smith shouted urgently. The whole cell was drawn out of slumber and daydream. "Hardy has been arrested on suspicion of treason. It happened early this morning. Daniel Adams of the Constitutional Society was arrested shortly after. All of their papers are seized."

There was consternation in the room and someone wondered if they had been brought to Newgate. Smith's latest information was that they were being held by king's messengers. He had just come from Piccadilly, where a distraught Lydia had told him Hardy had been taken away in a hackney coach. Smith had come through Soho to get to Newgate and had seen Bow Street runners busy at doors in Compton Street. The arrest of Hardy has caused a panic.

*

That evening Pitt and Dundas smiled as they left the king's private residence, Buckingham House, and climbed aboard a closed coach. They had come from an interview with George III and had got what they wanted. Dundas called to the driver to head for parliament. He had on the seat beside him a large package containing the papers seized from Hardy and Adams that morning. They had been shown to the king, their relevance had been explained, and he had agreed to the wording of a royal message to the house. The papers had been tied and sealed with wax in his presence.

Pitt and Dundas agreed that the home secretary would deliver the king's message to the parliament and ask for it to be debated the next day. Pitt would open the debate and propose what to do next. The two men hopped from the carriage in the coach yard of the Palace of Westminster and walked to the Commons chamber. A porter carried the great parcel behind them. They took their places on the front bench and Dundas signalled to Henry Addington, the speaker of the house.

"Mr Secretary Dundas," he called.

"Mr Speaker, honourable members," Dundas began in his soft Scottish accent. "Mr Pitt and I have come directly from the king, and I have here", he waved a piece of paper, "a message from his majesty respecting the present seditious practices in the country." He held the paper before him and read, "His majesty, having received information that the seditious practices which have been for some time carried on by certain societies in London, in correspondence with societies in different parts of the country, have lately been pursued with increased activity and boldness, and have been avowedly directed to the object of assembling a pretended general convention of the people, in contempt and defiance of the authority of parliament, and on principles subversive of the existing laws and constitution, and directly tending to the introduction of that system of anarchy and confusion which has fatally prevailed in France, has given direction for seizing the books and papers of the said societies in London, which have been seized accordingly."

To add drama to the surprise announcement, Dundas motioned to have the large, sealed package placed on the speaker's table. He continued reading the king's message, telling the shocked members that the parcel contained "matter of great importance to the public interest" and that the king had ordered it to be considered by them and trusted they would take measures to guard against the "further prosecution of these dangerous designs". He asked the speaker to schedule a debate on the following afternoon, as a matter of urgency, which was agreed.

*

An emergency committee of the Corresponding Society had gathered in Thelwall's house. They agreed to raise funds for the legal and personal support of Hardy, Adams and their families, and legal advice taken that day assured them that the arrests and seizure of their papers was unlawful. Many said the arrests were simply a skilful manoeuvre to manipulate public opinion and push parliament into a suspension of habeas corpus, and a convention bill similar to the Irish one. The committee disbanded to report to their divisions and Thelwall was the last to leave his house. As he locked the door he was grabbed by a body of king's messengers and Bow Street runners and bundled into a coach. Some of the committee saw this from a distance and followed the coach to the office of the secretary of state. The news spread like fire.

*

In the House of Commons that evening, Dundas drew the attention of MPs once again to the parcel on the speaker's table. Pitt rose to speak. He loved the theatricality of it. "I move to refer the papers to the consideration of a committee," he said. "This should be a committee of secrecy. The papers were sealed up and in that state ordered to be laid by his majesty before the house. They relate to transactions of an extraordinary, formidable, and criminal nature, and contain matter that implicates a great number of persons."

Fox objected. "If the papers are sealed up and the contents therefore unknown to the House, I think it would be rashness to refer them to a secret committee." His objection proved useless and Pitt's motion was nodded through without a vote. Fox rose again. He asked for the terms of reference of the committee. "Is the object prosecution? Prosecution is already in the hands of the crown... What is the object of the crown?" He went on to ask how the papers had been obtained, "for there is an ambiguity in the words of the message, which leaves me at a loss". He wanted to know on what grounds the seizure of the papers had been made. "Was it only on the grounds of seditious practices, or on an allegation of an overt act of treason?" he asked. "Seizing the papers of a person accused of a libel is illegal and such an extreme step should not be taken unless there is an actual allegation of treason."

Dundas rose and, confident of a majority vote, weaselled around the argument. "The warrants were grounded on allegations of treasonable practices," he said. A secret committee of twenty-one was elected. It included Pitt, both Dundases, foreign secretary Lord Grenville, all of the chief legal officials of England, and other loyalists, including Edmund Burke.

On the following day the round-up of prominent radicals

continued. The attorney John Martin, who had chaired many of the Corresponding Society's major public meetings, and happened to be temporarily in debtors' prison, was served with a warrant. The Rev Jeremiah Joyce, to whom Muir had written on Moffat's behalf, was arrested. Not content with a gang of messengers and runners, Dundas sent a troop of cavalry to Chevening House, seat of the republican Earl Stanhope in Kent, where Joyce was tutor to the earl's three sons. But it was in Edinburgh that the most surprising development took place and, for Dundas, the most fortunate.

*

On Thursday 15 May in Edinburgh, bailiffs knocked at the door of an apartment in North Gray's Close occupied by the government spy Watt. They had no notion of his political connections. They were on a simple search for goods that might have belonged to a bankrupt. Watt answered the door and was told by one of the bailiffs that they were searching for the property of a Mr Neilson of Musselburgh, whose manufacturing business had gone bankrupt. They believed that a delivery of his goods had been made to Watt's home. They had a search warrant and they insisted on entering the apartment and found a large box containing twelve pike heads.

Watt was taken by sheriff's officers for questioning. He refused to answer until he had the permission of his employers, the lord advocate and the secretary of state. The sheriff made further inquiries at Watt's house, where a servant told him that two smiths called Orrock and Brown had visited him. The blacksmiths were brought in and gave evidence that Watt had ordered quantities of pike heads from them. Further investigation found that Watt was chairman of a body called the Ways and Means committee of the Friends of the People. Other members of that committee were arrested for questioning.

The dispersal of the British convention and the prosecution and conviction of its leaders had dealt a severe blow to the radical movement in Scotland. Few societies survived in public and the handful of Edinburgh branches still meeting formed a committee to maintain correspondence with sympathisers. Watt moved quickly to gain influence in the weakened movement. At his suggestion, many of the powers of this body were delegated to a secret sub-committee of seven people, called Ways and Means. It main task was to raise funds for the support of Rachel Skirving, to pay off debts from the convention, and to raise money for delegates to the proposed new British convention.

Arthur McEwan, a weaver and one of the committee members brought in for questioning, told the sheriff that in April Watt had read a paper that proposed an elaborate scheme for seizing power in Edinburgh. "A fire was to be kindled at the excise office," he said, "and a party of men to be stationed at the Luckenbooths, a party at the head of the Westbooth, and the fire was to draw the military from the garrison. When they came down past the booth, the men that were stationed there were to come in behind them, and the men stationed at the Luckenbooths were to take them in the front and so enclose them between two parties; there were different parties who were to seize the banking houses in Edinburgh, and commissioners were to be appointed for to go and demand the cash from the banks."

"And who was present when this paper was read?" asked the sheriff. McEwan replied that four people had been there in addition to himself, Watt; David Downie, an elderly goldsmith and jeweller who was the committee's treasurer; William Bonthorne, a teacher; and a medical student called John Stock.

"When Watt read this paper, what happened?"

"I objected to it as soon as I understood what Watt had proposed," said McEwan. "I said I would by no means agree to anything that was to disturb the peace, or that tended to shed the blood of my countrymen; Mr Bonthorne agreed along with me and left the committee room; the treasurer and Stock heard it in silence. Watt made no reply to the objectors, and put the paper away."

Watt was clearly trying to provoke the committee into making a rash move. Although the reform organisation was subdued, discontent was still rife in the country. New barracks were being erected and occasional rioting took place. People suffered from a succession of bad harvests that almost doubled the price of corn, and in winter about eleven thousand people in Edinburgh had to be fed by charity.

At the committee meeting two weeks later, Watt persisted with his plan and elaborated on the tactics. Only Watt, Downie, and McEwan were present. Watt read another paper containing a draft proclamation and an address to the king, both to be issued once the castle had been seized.

"There was a copy of a proclamation," McEwan told the sheriff, "prohibiting all farmers, dealers in corn, meal, or hay, to remove the same from their respective places of abode, under pain of death; and also to all gentlemen residing in the country not to leave their respective habitations for a greater distance than three miles, under the same penalty. On the other side of the paper there was a copy of an address to his majesty, ordering him to dismiss his present ministers and to put an end to this bloody war. I said, 'Mr Watt, these things do not belong to the cause of reform, and I would by no means agree to any such things'."

Watt and Downie were imprisoned on Friday 16 May on a charge of high treason, Watt all the while protesting that he was only working for the government. Downie was bemused at being charged with treason for not having publicly disagreed with Watt at the committee. On the same day in London law officers arrested Horne Tooke and John Bonney of the Society for Constitutional Information, and John Lovett and John Richter of the Corresponding Society, all on suspicion of treason.

*

High drama gripped the Commons that same evening when the committee of secrecy reported that it had uncovered a widespread, treasonable plot. It had reviewed the seized papers and come to its conclusion with astonishing speed, only three days. The forty-page report argued that the proposed British convention was "an open attempt to supersede the House of Commons"; that reform societies had corresponded with each other in England, Scotland and Ireland, and with French clubs and the National Convention in Paris, and they "must be considered as a traitorous conspiracy". There appeared to be evidence of arming in some parts of the country and the arrest of leading members had not stopped societies from meeting. "The designs which were before entertained have by no means been abandoned," the authors of the report declared.

Pitt rose before the Commons and dramatically spelt out what he thought should happen next. "There is not one moment to be lost in arming the executive power with those additional means which might be sufficient to stop the further progress of such a plan," he said. He proposed a temporary suspension of habeas corpus, the requirement that an accused person be brought before a judge to determine if imprisonment is lawful. "This is not my opinion alone," he said, "but the sentiments of all those respectable gentlemen of the committee."

Fox was scathing. He objected that there was nothing in the report that had not been in the newspapers during the past two years; the conventions were no more seditious than those that he and the minister had attended in 1780, and they, too, had corresponded with societies in Yorkshire and other places; a convention of Irish Catholics had recently secured new privileges. "To pretend alarm on that account must be gross affectation," he said. The proposal to suspend habeas corpus was "daring and impudent" and it was simply "intended to agitate and alarm the nation". Grey called the report "trumpery", and believed "the committee had been either deceived themselves or wished to deceive others", while Sheridan said Pitt's proposal was "unfounded, unjust, and impolitic in the highest degree".

The vote to bring in a bill was won by 201 votes to 39. It had its first and second reading immediately then passed its committee stage at half past three in the morning. The bill's final reading was to be at three o'clock that Saturday afternoon. The opposition fought a twelve-hour-long rearguard action and the final vote was not taken until three o'clock on Sunday morning, when it passed by 146 votes to 28.

That same Sunday, Lord Grenville, the foreign secretary, took the papers and the bill to the lords, who also formed a secret committee then and there. Stanhope called the commons report "mere humbug", but the lords' committee delivered the first part of its report on the following Thursday, 21 May, "satisfied that a treasonable conspiracy had been formed". The Commons bill was then discussed. Stanhope said, "The fears pretended to be felt are to be compared only to the windmill in Don Quixote." Lauderdale ridiculed the idea of actual danger and said it was "confined to the weak heads or insidious designs of ministers". The bill was passed at two o'clock on Friday morning. On Saturday the king signed it into law. The speed of legislation was even more astonishing than the swiftness of the Commons secret committee's report.

The act was put to use immediately and by the end of May government had made arrests on suspicion of treason up and down the country. Some were held for a few days but others were in prison for months. Some fled. Others hid only to surrender later in the year. The Sheffield and Norwich leaders were arrested and brought to London. George Mealmaker from Dundee fled and was caught in Arbroath, taken to Edinburgh for questioning and released only after a lengthy detention. Watt and Downie were incarcerated in the castle. In London thirteen leaders of the London Corresponding Society and six from the Society for Constitutional Information were detained. Hardy, Tooke and five others were committed to the Tower; the rest were sent to Newgate. Only those arrested on a warrant signed by the secretary of state and specifying high treason or suspicion of high treason, or treasonable practices could be held without bail and without trial but many provincial magistrates terrified local reformers with the false belief that they had unlimited arbitrary powers. Many were arrested without any hope of a trial, some returning to their families only after the act expired. Many more quit popular societies and some clubs closed. There had been forty-eight divisions of the London Corresponding Society in May and after the arrests, eighteen of them ceased to function.

In Ireland, the radical reformers fared no better. Hamilton Rowan had been tried for sedition in January and sentenced to two years' imprisonment. Drennan was arrested on 13 May and charged with sedition for writing an *Address to the volunteers*. On the evening of 24 May, the remaining Dublin United Irishmen were dispersed and their papers seized. The lawyer and United Irishman Thomas Emmet later wrote, "The expectations of the reformers had been blasted. Their plans had been defeated, and decisive measures had been taken by government to prevent them being resumed. It therefore became necessary to wait for new events, from which might be formed new plans."

CHAPTER 30

Mutiny

"Let us drink a good health to our schemers above,
Who at length have contrived from this land to remove
Thieves, robbers and villains, they'll send 'em away
To become a new people at Botany Bay."

'Botany Bay, A New Song', London broadside
ballad, 1790.

Captain Patrick Campbell sat at the head of the mess table in his
quarters in the roundhouse and glowered at his first mate, all the way
down at the other end, past the officers and paying guests on either
side. "So you think she's a bad sailer, Mr McPherson?" It was more
of a challenge than a question.

"It is no reflection on your seamanship, Mr Campbell," replied
the mate. He was trying to be conciliatory. "It is simply a known fact
that the Surprize is an old, slow ship and that water washes through
her in heavy seas. We just have to be prepared for it. That's all that I
meant, sir. I beg your pardon if any offence was given."

Ensign and Mrs Pattullo exchanged quick glances. Dr Thomson
and Mr and Mrs Baker, the Bostons, Pearces, Skirving, Palmer, and
Ellis all tried to look casually away. Muir asked to be excused and
retired to his cabin on the quarterdeck. Maurice and Mary Margarot
fixed their eyes on Campbell, waiting for his riposte. But it was the
captain's wife who spoke first.

"Come, Patrick," she said, "Mr McPherson is only trying to famil-
iarise our guests with what might be expected." She was worried

about her husband. He had seemed tense since the voyage began three days before. "We've had plain sailing since we left the English coast and the Bay of Biscay is not usually so kind."

Campbell retreated, but only a little. "We'll hear no more of it McPherson. No more, d'ye hear?"

This was the first time Campbell and McPherson had sailed together and their differences had grown with each step of the voyage. McPherson had wanted more crew to man the sheets and pumps; he had heard how Surprize had taken much time and effort in heavy seas, especially in the south Atlantic. She had been one of the ships of the second fleet that carried convicts to New South Wales four years before. Campbell refused to take on extra hands. McPherson quarrelled with the captain about the space given over to cargo, space that limited the comfort of convicts and passengers alike. Campbell insisted on loading the boat fully for the handsome payments made for supplies to the colony. McPherson had counted the stores for the voyage, food, water, wine, beer, clothing and blankets, and had found them wanting. He knew that many captains, and crew as well, stinted on rations because of the exceptional prices that could be had for surplus food and clothing in Port Jackson. The tension between them was now public.

Margarot turned to the captain in an attempt to deflect the conversation. "I don't understand, Captain Campbell, the logic of our course to New South Wales. We appear to cross and re-cross the Atlantic. Why is that?"

Campbell took the bait. "Simple, Mr Margarot. We head for Rio because she is a friendly Portuguese port. We can re-stock with fresh water, meat, fruit and vegetables there." His eyes took in the whole table as he paused and prepared to explain the navigation. "But that course also gives us the best of the prevailing winds and currents," he said with authority. "The north-east trade wind and the Canary current will carry us south by south-west across the Atlantic. We could run into calms around the equator but with luck and good navigation we'll pick up the Brazil current and the south-east trades to take us into Rio. After that we drop south to the westerlies and dip down to the roaring forties, where the constant wind will sweep us past the tip of Africa and on beneath Van Diemen's Land, which we round to the east and veer north to Port Jackson."

The company congratulated him on the simplicity and accuracy of his explanation. Mrs Campbell looked relieved and almost imperceptibly narrowed her eyes to a small smile, which she directed at Margarot as a gesture of thanks. Margarot was never one to shy from the attention of others. His bombast in the Edinburgh courtroom showcased his ability to put his ego on public display, and now he was enjoying the company of the captain, the officers, and the ladies. He raised a glass to the success of the voyage and the skill of the captain. The others raised their glasses in agreement, and Margarot added, with a mischievous smile, "Of course, we have to get across the Bay of Biscay first. And, you know, the French might want to know where we are, sir. You'll have to keep a sharp lookout for a rescue party!"

Margarot giggled, to indicate he was joking. The others froze in shock at what he had said to Campbell. The captain gave Margarot a level look. Everyone could see him turning the remark over in his mind. His eyes swept the table and suddenly the corners of his mouth turned up. He burst into good-humoured laughter. "That's a good one, Margarot!" The others laughed weakly, more from relief than appreciation.

Margarot could not have known how right he was. Somewhere in the great bay two French frigates, Alcide and Fabius, were searching for *"les hommes persécutés pour la cause de la liberté"*, in the words of the instructions from the Committee of Public Safety in Paris. The order, signed by Louis St Just and seven others, told the French navy to "take all necessary measures to intercept the vessel carrying them into exile". The Scottish trials and the cruel sentences of the five had been widely reported in the international press and such a rescue would be a major propaganda coup for the republic. Unfortunately, there was a persistent thick sea mist and, although it was relatively calm, the French ships never caught sight of the strong convoy. Or possibly they did, and considered it too formidable to attack. Whatever the explanation, the Indiamen, the Surprize, flying the red-and-white pennant that identified a convict ship, and the two man-of-war escorts passed through Biscay without incident.

Muir had excused himself from the captain's table and he meant never to return to it. The conversation held no joy for him and for the remainder of the voyage he had his meals served in solitude. He found Margarot annoying and disliked his forced friendliness with the captain. In fact, Muir was morose and depressed. He was desperately lonely and homesick. He came to prefer his own company and a bottle of wine. He had books to read and wanted to study the geography, geology, flora and fauna of his new home, such as was known of it, before he arrived. Food was brought to him from the captain's cook by one of the convict women, Ann Loftus, who had secured a servant's job, one of the better tasks on the ship. She had run a boarding house at Smithfield in London and could perform her service on Surprize with panache and good humour. She had been sentenced to death at the Old Bailey for complicity in the robbery of a Welsh drover of £31. One of her boarders, as she explained to Muir one evening, was a prostitute named Jane Simmons, who had taken the drover home and robbed him of his money and a silver watch. She protested her innocence throughout the trial and during the year she spent in Newgate. The sentences of both women were commuted to transportation for life and they suffered another year on the hulks before being transferred to the Surprize.

Muir and Loftus became friends. They ate together and shared Muir's wine.

"How did you get this job," asked Muir, "when so many others are scrubbing decks and washing clothes?"

"I was selected," she said.

"Selected? Why?"

"Come on, Thomas, you're not so innocent. I was selected by the captain."

"I still don't understand."

"Oh, you're so unworldly, Thomas. The captain wants me for his sea-wife," she said. "They all do it. All of the officers and men take a woman for the voyage. The high-ups turn a blind eye to it."

Muir was astounded and embarrassed. "All of them?"

"Yes, all of them, Thomas. Jane's in with the boatswain, and Bet Carter, another girl that worked Smithfield, is with the first mate. The only difference is, the captain's wife is on board and all he can do is look and flirt. That's why he wants me around the roundhouse and the quarterdeck all the time."

Muir let a little laugh escape. "You're right, Ann. I am unworldly. Sit a while and have another wine."

*

Muir was curious about the running of the ship and watched each day from the door of his cabin, a small room no bigger than a cupboard at the outer edge of the quarterdeck. The quarterdeck was the command hub, raised above the central deck of the ship and situated behind the main mast, near the stern. It was here that the captain and officers of the watch controlled every movement of the vessel and its crew, and a seasoned seaman stood at the wheel. Muir was at his door each mid-day to witness the beginning of the ship's twenty-four-hour routine. He listened as the officer of the watch took the sextant to measure the angle of the sun at its zenith and called out the degrees and minutes, which increased each noon as the Surprize voyaged south. He watched as braces and yards were adjusted to take maximum advantage of the wind, and as sailors were sent aloft to add or remove sail. He listened for the ship's bell, struck every half hour of a four-hour watch, as a marine on deck turned over the glass to measure the next half hour; one bell marking the start of the watch, through to eight bells signalling its end.

There were other patterns of activity he came to recognise. As soon as the Surprize had lost sight of land, the shackles of the prisoners were knocked off. Convicts were allowed on deck in shifts for exercise and fresh air. Their routine began shortly after five o'clock in the morning when cooks for each of the prisoners' messes were allowed up top, weather permitting, to make breakfast for their charges. Below decks, the remainder of the twenty three male and sixty female prisoners were awakened and sent for washing by divisions, issued with water and biscuit for the day, and their mess teams would swab the lower decks and the heads, the toilets at the bow of the ship. At eight they were served with breakfast, after which Doctor Thomson made his morning rounds. Bedding was folded and brought on deck for airing in nets strung along the rails. The sailors and marines brought their hammocks and blankets to the netting each day as well, once again, weather permitting. Half the prisoners were allowed on deck in the morning and the other half in the afternoon. Between scrubbing the boards with holystone, a soft sandstone block used for cleaning and whitening, or swabbing and laundering, the convicts had a chance to talk or sing or, for many of the women, to form relationships with sailors and marines.

It had been common since the first fleet sailed in 1787 for crew to take "sea wives". Sometimes this was for love, often for money, or because the women needed grog to ease the pain of transportation, or for extra food or blankets, but generally it ended in an increase in the population of the young colony two or three months after disembarkation.

Dinner was at noon, supper at five, beds were taken below after the meal, all prisoners were sent below by dusk, and after the doctor's evening rounds, candles were extinguished at nine. That, though, was never the end. Just as the daytime recreation on deck could be noisy and raucous, so with the night, assignations in quiet corners were had with background noises of fights over bedding, drink, money or men, accompanied by singing and storytelling in the dark.

It was not only Muir who withdrew from the captain's table. The Bostons had tired of Campbell's mood swings and his upbraiding of McPherson at every turn. They asked permission to set up a mess in their own cabin amidships and were joined by Palmer and his friend

308 The Liberty Tree

Ellis who, although not yet assigned a cabin, could dine from the captain's kitchen, having paid for the passage. Skirving remained in the main mess but said little. He had retreated into his Bible, which he read constantly for comfort. The first mate was weary of the friction in the roundhouse, too, and asked if he could join the Bostons' folding table. Their cabin was barely big enough to hold the five of them at dinner.

The Bostons were keen to know from McPherson what he meant when he said the Surprize was a bad sailer. He explained it was her size and construction. At just 400 tons, Surprize was a small vessel for such a trip. She was known to be a "wet ship" even in moderate weather. She had done the Botany Bay voyage before with the second fleet and stories circulated about her. The captain of the guard on that voyage, William Hill, had written home that in the rough seas and heavy gales after the Cape the convicts "were considerably above their waists in water, and the men of my company, whose berths were not so far forward, were nearly up to their middles".

The turbulent southern seas are where warm currents from the Indian Ocean and the Pacific meet ice-cold waters from the Antarctic. Gales blow up in the strong west winds and ice and snow are possible. The Guardian, another ship in the second fleet, came across pack ice and an iceberg at a latitude her master thought was too far north for such an encounter. The Surprize had limped into Sydney Cove under jury masts, temporary rigging, after damage in a Southern Ocean storm.

The faces of his companions fell. He lifted a bottle of wine, filled their glasses, and reassured them. "With good seamanship none of this should be life-threatening. Whatever you may think of Captain Campbell's behaviour, he is a first-class sailor and I pride myself with that description as well."

"How do you account for his behaviour then?" asked Ellis. "He seems to have taken sorely against you."

"Aye, true," admitted McPherson. "Some captains are jealous of their command. They don't like to be questioned. I see it as my job to double-check our readiness to sail and he doesn't like it at all. Frankly, I think he's a deeply superstitious man and I think this ship has spooked him."

"Why ever should that be?" questioned Mrs Boston.

"The Surprize has an unfortunate history," McPherson replied. "I told you she was a bad sailer, and a wet ship. But she also had a captain on her last voyage to New South Wales, Nicholas Anstis by name, who cared little for those under his charge. He starved the prisoners for money. If they died early in the voyage he would invent a later date of death to draw their allowance. And he left those starving prisoners chilled and wet, chained on soaked bedding and unable to move for days. Those that survived had scurvy and boils, flux and chest diseases."

There were about 250 convicts on board the Surprize for that voyage and around forty of them were buried at sea. Of those that were landed, more than half had to be taken to hospital. It was the same on all of the transports in the fleet. Captain Hill had commented that the slave trade was merciful compared with what he had seen. At least the slavers had a financial interest in getting their cargo to the Americas. None of the masters of the second fleet cared that much. The Rev Richard Johnson, the settlement's chaplain, "beheld a sight truly shocking to the feelings of humanity" as the prisoners from the second fleet were disembarked. "The landing of these people was truly affecting and shocking," he wrote, "great numbers were not able to walk, nor to move hand or foot; such were slung over the ship's side in the same manner as they would sling a cask, a box or anything of that nature. Upon being brought up to the open air some fainted, some died upon the deck, and others in the boat before they reached the shore. When come on shore many were not able to walk, to stand, or to stir themselves in the least, hence were led by others. Some creeped upon their hands and knees, and some were carried upon the backs of others." All were in an indescribably filthy state, "covered almost with their own nastiness, their heads, bodies, cloths, blankets, all full of filth and lice."

Surprize had previously been a slave ship on the "Middle Passage" and was still fitted out with old slave shackles during its first Sydney Cove run. They were solid bars between the ankles that prevented movement. The whole fleet had been equipped by a former slaving company, Camden, Calvert and King. But things had changed, a little. The first fleet was organised, fitted out and provisioned by the navy. Deaths on that were no more than usual in a long voyage. The second fleet was contracted to the former slavers to save money, and news of the atrocity did not reach home until after the government had signed a contract for the third fleet that sailed in 1791. One in ten died on that third voyage and Camden, Calvert and King got no more contracts from the government. Just one captain and his mate were charged and eventually appeared in the Old Bailey two years later, but the judge threw out the charges before the trial began. Neither the agent nor the contractor was prosecuted. It seemed as if the government wanted to keep the whole thing quiet in case it undermined plans for the new convict colony.

Improvements were made to subsequent contracts, with owners and captains receiving only a part payment for each convict before sailing. The rest was paid when the prisoners were delivered in decent health and the captains had brought home a governor's certificate verifying the numbers. A naval surgeon now had to sail on each transport, answerable not to the captain but to the Navy Board.

"That is a truly terrible birth for an infant colony," said Palmer, "but it doesn't explain why our captain is acting so strangely."

"As I said," replied McPherson, "I think he's a superstitious sailor. He thinks the ship is cursed by previous acts of cruelty. However, there is one more factor, I believe, affecting his behaviour, mutiny."

"Mutiny!" the others repeated in unison.

"Well, this is just my impression, you must understand," explained McPherson, "but we do have mutineers on board. The one from Quebec threatened the life of his commanding officer, Prince Edward. Mr Campbell is very sensitive to this and his feeling of bad luck aboard is strengthened by the fact that there was a mutiny on the last voyage, not on this ship, let me add quickly, but on the Scarborough. Surprize was out of sight behind when the revolt of the prisoners happened. Oh, it was overcome by the marines and crew, but it was touch and go. No one was hanged, thankfully, but the supposed ringleaders were severely flogged and chained on the open deck and the other convicts were closely confined for the rest of the voyage. Now, can you understand why a superstitious seaman might live on his nerves?"

"Indeed," replied Palmer. "But there is one more mystery. If everything is as you say, why are you here?"

"Ah! Mr Palmer, it's simple" said McPherson. "I wanted to see the Southern Ocean for myself. And I have heard it said that the climate in Sydney Cove is beautiful and heavenly. That, sir, is reason enough to risk the voyage."

*

On Friday 30 May, almost a month from the Motherbank, Muir sat by his door at noon and watched McPherson put the sextant to his eye to take the mid-day reading. "Seventy six degrees and thirteen minutes," he called to a junior officer. "What's our latitude, mister?" the mate asked. The junior officer quickly scribbled his calculation, subtracting the reading from the ninety degrees to the horizon. "Thirteen degrees and forty seven minutes, sir," he shouted.

"There y'are Mr Muir," McPherson called out. "We're near halfway to Rio, well inside the Tropic of Cancer, and about two degrees south of Cape Verde Islands. I know you take an interest in these things."

"Thank you Mr McPherson," replied Muir, stepping out into the noonday sun. He watched as eight bells were rung, indicating the end of the forenoon watch and calling the afternoon watch to their stations. A marine turned the half-hour glass to begin measuring the intervals.

"It's been a fine run south with calm weather and fair winds," McPherson went on. "In four or five days we should cross the line, unless we hit the doldrums in the Atlantic narrows. At this time of year, though, we expect to pick up the south-east trades a few degrees north of the equator."

*

Grant continued to spread rumours below decks, in carefully placed private conversations, hinting how the soldiers who had mutinied were ready to rise again. Some shunned him and told him to keep his gossip and idle talk to himself. Others, more naive, listened to his whisperings and asked for names, whether there was a leader, and if they had someone who could sail the ship. They devoured his deceit and passed the information along the lower deck. Grant had tried to place his lies among the officers by attracting the attention of Dr Thomson on his evening rounds and quietly offering him "important, confidential information". Thomson told him that, if such a thing were true, it was wrong to keep it to himself. He should go straight to the captain. But Grant was not quite ready. He was still trying to figure a way to incriminate Muir and Palmer, who had called him a spy in public and had foiled his scheme to secure a pardon on the Royal George. He had already written to Sheriff Pringle in Edinburgh telling him they had planned murder on the revenue cutter. He wanted the story to circulate in Scotland for when he achieved his freedom; he was, after all, a loyal defender of the Dundas interest. That was what had had him appointed sheriff in Inverness in the first place.

Muir was still sitting by his cabin door after his mid-day meal when he saw a barrel of porter being rolled on to the deck below. The steward called on two marine sentries to watch over it. "Captain's orders," he explained. "No one is to draw beer from it but me. It's for later tonight. A special treat for the soldiers and crew." Muir thought nothing more of it until, early in the evening, he heard raised voices from same spot. Sergeant Reddish was shouting at the two sentries.

"McLean, you are a fucking Irish idiot!" he yelled. "Not content with being a deserter, you are now a thief. This barrel is half empty!

Brotherwood, I had more faith in you but you're just as rotten as McLean. Where did the beer go? Evaporate?"

"Sir," said Brotherwood, unsteadily. "I'm sorry sir. We just had a little each, then the others kept coming by and begging for a drop and, before we knew it, the beer had almost gone."

"The-beer-had-al-most-gone!" mimicked Reddish. "The pair of you will be gone before you know it. Corporal! Lock them up below. We'll deal with them later."

McLean stuck his face close to Reddish's and stared in his eyes. "The soldiers are fools to allow themselves to be used so," he hissed. "They are able, and ought to right themselves."

Grant, who was standing a few feet away, heard the exchange. "This," he thought, "could be my chance." He requested a meeting with the captain.

Later that evening, when Ann Loftus had finished her duties, she came to Muir's cabin. She often did now, preferring it to the heat and squalor of nights below decks. They found comfort in each other's company.

Muir told her of the soldiers and the beer. "McLean threatened the sergeant," he said.

"Something's going on, Thomas," she said. "Campbell's nervous and bad-tempered. He paces about the roundhouse like a caged animal. And below decks! Well. It's edgy. Everybody is expecting something. Grant and Draper have been unsettling them all with rumours of mutiny and escape."

They sat quietly by his open door for a while, drinking wine and watching flashes of phosphorescence in the dark sea below. A marine struck four bells at the other side of the quarterdeck, and they retreated to the darkness of Muir's cabin and the warmth of his cot

*

On Saturday morning Skirving, who had the small cabin on the opposite side of the quarterdeck from Muir, looked over at his friend as McPherson called out, "All hands on deck! All hands! Sailors, soldiers, all hands!" Muir looked questioningly at McPherson, who shrugged his shoulders and nodded towards the roundhouse. He seemed to say he had been ordered by the captain to assemble the crew but didn't know why. When the seamen and the marines, including the two who had been imprisoned the evening before, had formed in ranks on the main deck, Campbell emerged from his quarters wearing his sword and a pair of daggers, with two pistols stuck in his belt. His left hand held a leather leash restraining his mastiff, a dog that had previously wandered about the decks, threatening and worrying anyone it chose to. It had been locked in its kennel on the poop deck for some weeks. Campbell stood at the head of the stairs leading down to the deck and called out the names of Draper, Evans, Neale, Barton, Griffiths, and McLean, the six deserters who had come aboard as prisoners.

"Mr Pattullo," he barked, "chain those men."

"May I ask why?" enquired the ensign.

"You'll know soon enough. Have Sergeant Reddish do it!"

The ship's complement stood still and listened to the clank of chains being dragged from the brig.

"What have we done, sir? asked Griffiths.

"If any of you dare say another word," he yelled, pulling a pistol from his belt, "I'll blow out his brains!" He steadied himself against the rail as the ship rolled. "I have uncovered a dangerous conspiracy to murder me and my principal officers and carry the ship off to France or America," he announced. A murmur of disbelief rose from the ranks. "Some Highland convicts overheard these soldiers," he pointed to the six now standing in shackles, "talking of it in Irish. These men planned to seize the ship on our leaving the fleet, by attacking my cabin and murdering me. They expected the rest of the soldiers would join them."

The marines shook their heads in denial. The sailors eyed them incredulously. "I want everyone to be on extra alert while we question these men. If you know anything or hear anything then come to my cabin and tell me. Dismiss!"

Palmer, at his cabin door at the rear of the assembly, exchanged looks with Ellis and the Bostons. They had the same thought. Had the captain's fear and superstition driven him mad? Muir wondered whether Grant had had a hand in this. He sounded like a native English speaker, but had he learned Gaelic in Inverness? He walked across the quarterdeck to Skirving's cabin and they looked round as Pattullo, with an angry set face, strode purposefully past them and flung open the doors of the roundhouse.

The mastiff barked and growled. They heard Pattullo raise his voice above the animal's objections. "Mr Campbell!" he declared, "what is the meaning of your undermining my authority in front of the whole company and crew?"

Campbell pulled back the dog and tied it to the table. It settled on the floor, eyes fast on the ensign. "Did you not hear me, Mr Pattullo? There is a conspiracy on board this ship."

"I heard you perfectly, captain, but you could have talked to me first and allowed me to deal with it."

"I am the captain of this vessel, Pattullo!"

"And I have sole authority over those soldiers," countered the ensign. "We had this argument before when your damned dog was hit by a sentry after it savaged him. You had the audacity to put the soldier in chains!" The dog barked. Pattullo pulled his commission and warrant from inside his tunic and waved it at Campbell. "See this," he said, taking a step closer to the captain. The dog growled. "See this," he repeated, "this is my authority!"

"And here's my authority, Mr Pattullo!" Campbell put his hands on the grips of his pistols. "Your mutinous marines are my prisoners. You will take them out of irons at your peril, sir!"

Pattullo turned on his heels and marched from the roundhouse. He crossed to the stairs without looking left or right. On the way down he passed Grant, who stepped up to the quarterdeck and strolled toward the captain's quarters, giving a slight but superior nod of acknowledgement to Muir and Skirving on his way.

"That might answer your question," said Skirving. "It wasn't *some*

Highland convicts who told the captain of a conspiracy. It was *that* Highland convict."

"I think you have it, William. He's a dangerous man," warned Muir.

News spread quickly on the prison deck and was embellished until some came to believe they would be granted privileges for incriminating information. Everyone now thought they had heard something; some requested interviews with the captain. Junior officers were sent below to separate the grains of fact from the chaff of fantasy. Campbell distributed arms to sailors and settlers and organised armed watches throughout the ship. Margarot was also equipped from the armoury. Two blunderbusses were mounted on swivels in the roundhouse and Campbell added a second pair of pistols to his personal weaponry. He was agitated throughout the afternoon, interviewing convicts with a tale to tell, closing the roundhouse door with a bolt, opening it minutes later. He paraded his mastiff on the main deck and Palmer thought it safer to lock his lurcher indoors. Palmer turned to Ellis after the captain had passed by. "My, my," he remarked, "that performance would do credit to any stage."

Throughout the night and into Sunday morning the six accused marines were attached to a chain on the poop deck, which formed the roof of the cantilevered cabins at the stern of the ship. They were left exposed overnight, among the caged and tethered livestock, and the corporal of the guard was given explicit instructions by Campbell. "If any of the prisoners should make the smallest noise or rattle a link of their chain in the smallest degree," he ordered, "have your sentinels immediately fire down and blow their brains out."

On Sunday morning Campbell called McPherson to the roundhouse. A file of armed sailors with fixed bayonets stood at the door. "I have received information, Mr McPherson, that the conspirators engaged someone to command this ship after they had taken control."

"That's surprising, sir, only you or I could perform that task," said McPherson.

"Exactly."

An awful realisation flashed through McPherson's thoughts. "But..."

"I also have information that you drank seditious toasts at Spithead with Palmer, Skirving and Boston..."

"Mr Campbell, I must object..."

"... and that you were overheard by the convict James Gilthorpe, telling the convict William Casswell about the plot, saying you would captain the ship, and assuring him he'd be rewarded in cash. You hoped to go to France. The same Casswell has frequently, regularly and recently seen you drinking with the seditious convicts Palmer and Skirving, until the early hours of the morning."

"Mr Campbell! Please! This is conjecture of the most insulting sort. I have not and would not think of such a thing, never mind foolishly agree to it with a convict who might be out to save his own skin. Where is your proof? What evidence have you against me? As a gentleman I demand not only proof but an apology!"

"That's enough, McPherson! Sailors! Take this deceiver away! Lock him in his cabin and post a sentry on the door!"

McPherson protested as he was led away, watched by anxious faces looking up from the gratings, and through windows and doors along the main deck.

Doctor Thomson and Ensign Pattullo hurried to the roundhouse and quickly established what had happened. "You have insufficient evidence, Captain Campbell," Pattullo said. "There is only one accuser, Grant, a convicted forger, who has nothing more than his own diary to corroborate his allegations. He could have written anything he wanted in there. The evidence from Gilthorpe and Casswell is nothing more than that they heard a rumour from other convicts and they saw people having a drink together. It hardly adds up."

"It's enough to confine him for now," countered Campbell. "We'll find more evidence, you'll see. McPherson had the impudence to raise his voice to me, a sure sign of guilt! And I have noticed other irregularities, ill treating the women convicts, and in a continual state of intoxication." There was a hint of envy in his voice.

318 The Liberty Tree

"Oh, come now, captain," pleaded the doctor, "how likely are any of these accusations, especially against your first mate? McPherson's character itself belies them."

"It is precisely his character," said Campbell with a look of distaste, "that makes them probable."

"Consider this," continued Thomson. "John Grant attempted to engage me in fuelling rumours only a few days ago. Your boatswain was standing nearby at the time and confirmed that he, too, had overheard convicts under the grating talking of such a thing. But what does that prove except the existence of rumour?"

"Rumour be damned," insisted Campbell. "There's a mutiny behind such talk."

Thomson and Pattullo gave up the argument and took their leave of the agitated captain. As they stepped from the roundhouse into the bright sunshine on the quarterdeck, Campbell shouted after them, "And damn me if I won't have those six soldiers flogged in the morning!" His brutalisation after years sailing slave ships was surfacing.

A distraught Mrs Campbell sought out Muir that afternoon and begged him help her compose a conciliatory letter of apology for McPherson to sign, in an effort to calm her husband's anxiety. The offended first officer refused to sign it, thinking it too submissive. Dr Thomson approached Palmer and together they drew up a petition to the captain praising McPherson's maritime skills, which was signed by many officers, sailors, settlers and passengers on the ship. The Margarots, strangely, refused to sign and Mary Margarot very assuredly remarked to Palmer, "I have no doubt that McPherson was at the head of the mutiny plot."

Campbell took no notice of the appeal and veered the ship off course to come alongside a nearby Indiaman. Through a loudhailer, he called for the captain and explained that a dangerous mutiny had broken out in his ship, in which a principal officer was concerned. The Indiaman promised to keep by him all night until they came up beside the Suffolk next morning, when the fleet commodore, Captain Rainier, would be informed.

Late on Sunday night, Draper gathered as much of his chain in his hands as he could manage and quietly shuffled nearer to the sentry. "Marine," he said in a loud whisper. "Sentry, over here."

The soldier looked round. "What do you want?" he whispered back. "You'll have me ironed like yourself."

"I have to speak to the captain. I have very important information."

Ten minutes later, Draper was in the roundhouse. Campbell was waiting for him in his nightclothes, with a pistol on the table. Mrs Campbell stared anxiously into the dark, next door in their bed.

Shortly after dawn, when the first arc of sun rose over the eastern horizon, the Surprize came alongside the flagship. Campbell hailed the duty officer, repeated his story and asked to go aboard and talk with the commodore. In a short time the two ships slowed and a boat took Campbell to the Suffolk. Presently another boat came for McPherson. Young Bet Carter stood helplessly sobbing as she watched her new love taken from her and lowered into the waiting launch, arms in chains. Her grief was all the greater later that morning, when Campbell returned to the Surprize and announced, "McPherson has been condemned to be ironed, hands and feet, and fastened to an iron bar on the poop deck of the Suffolk, to be exposed there day and night in all weathers, and to be fed with only bread and water."

Campbell was now convinced he had the evidence he needed to establish a conspiracy to mutiny. Draper had not only verified Grant's story but had implicated Palmer and Skirving. Draper had heard the name Casswell mentioned, so included him as a conspirator for good measure. Campbell set Draper free with a warning to keep the information to himself until he was called upon to testify the following day. He promoted Burnett, the second mate, to McPherson's position and ordered him to erect a grating against a cabin wall on the main deck and prepare for flogging. Gilthorpe and Casswell were arrested for good measure and put in chains with the remaining five accused marines on the poop deck.

The men were taken into the roundhouse one by one throughout the day and asked to confess, not only to their own parts in the conspiracy, but to give evidence against Palmer and Skirving. All denied involvement and were told they would appear before a court martial on the following day. Before being taken back to the poop they were shown the grating where they would be flogged if they did not co-operate. Each of them spent another cold, hungry, fearful night in the open, afraid to rattle a chain and afraid of what the dawn might bring.

In the evening, Campbell called a meeting with Ensign Pattullo, Dr Thomson, and Mr Baker, the superintendent of prisoners for New South Wales. He informed them that they, together with an officer from the flagship, would form a court martial in the morning. They were all officers and Baker was a former marine sergeant and therefore of sufficient rank. Baker readily agreed, Thomson and Pattullo only reluctantly, so they could influence the proceedings. Draper was called in and asked to repeat what he had told Campbell the previous night.

"This seems far-fetched, I must say," said Pattullo.

"I am astonished and surprised," said Thomson.

"I have suspected this for days now," said Campbell. "Even Mr Margarot yesterday evening bade me beware of the 'old man below', meaning Palmer."

*

At dawn on Tuesday the Surprize was under full sail and had gained another 200 miles since daybreak on Monday. Muir was wakened by the sound of many feet on the quarterdeck and the scrape of furniture being moved. He looked out to see a long table with five chairs in front of the roundhouse. Files of marines were assembling on the far side of the deck and the new mate, Burnett, began calling all hands. As the sailors assembled, a young navy lieutenant from the Suffolk, in dress uniform, was piped aboard. Muir looked over at Pattullo, who was wearing his full regimental uniform. He also noticed Draper, walking freely on the deck. Campbell, he thought, looked more like Robinson Crusoe, sporting a belt of pistols around his middle, two more tucked in his breast, and another in his waistcoat. A sword and a dagger hung from his belt. Campbell introduced Lieutenant Page to Pattullo, Thomson, and Baker and they took their seats behind the table, facing down the quarterdeck.

"Call Palmer and Skirving," ordered Campbell.

Muir was intrigued. He went inside to fetch paper and pen as Palmer and Skirving were brought from their breakfast, unaware of why they had been called. They took in the surroundings with questioning looks. Above them on the poop deck stood five of the accused soldiers and two convicts, Casswell and Gilthorpe, all in double irons. There were armed marines behind the prisoners, and the whole ship's company looked up from the main deck.

"We have been given information," announced Campbell, looking towards Skirving and Palmer, "that implicates the two of you in attempting to execute a dangerous mutiny, of intending to murder me and the principal officers, and to run away with the ship." The two stood, astonished, unable to speak or properly comprehend what was being alleged or why.

Campbell called on Dr Thomson, who read Draper's statement aloud. It claimed that, on his first night on board the Surprize, Skirving had asked for him by name as the person who came from Prince Edward's regiment, and sent him a bottle of wine. At the beginning of April at Spithead, Skirving and Palmer had confided in him that they had a plan to take the ship and had someone to sail it. They were sure the deserters would join them and asked Draper if he thought the other convicts would be on their side. The convict William Casswell, marines William Neale, James McLean, Thomas Barton and himself agreed to be the chief actors. Palmer promised money for any sailor who joined them. Draper claimed he had been liberally supplied with spirits, tea and sugar, a silk handkerchief, and other clothes. He had been given money by both Skirving and Palmer to organise the mutiny. Draper further declared that one night at nine o'clock, while still at Spithead, he had met with Palmer by the longboat for the space of an hour, along with the convict Casswell and Marine Evans.

"Lies! That's lies," shouted Casswell from the poop.

"That little bastard will lie as fast a dog'll lick a dish!" cried Evans.

"Silence those men!" ordered Campbell, and bayonets were levelled behind the prisoners' backs.

Palmer stepped forward. "I will readily be bound and hung up at that yardarm if you can prove by a single credible witness that I have ever given Draper any one thing but a single glass of rum! I employed him as a tailor, and paid him for his work. I never gave him a penny for any other purpose. Can you produce a single witness to confirm that I was ever seen to converse alone with him? It is well known that in Spithead I was so ill as to be unable to be on deck for a whole hour, or even to walk without help, never mind at nine o'clock. That was the hour when our candles were ordered to be put out and the hatchway closed upon us!"

Skirving objected that he had never given Draper anything except for work as a tailor. Draper had asked him for a small loan to buy scissors and other materials in Portsmouth to carry on his business, which he had agreed to.

Page asked whether anyone could confirm Draper's testimony. The air hung heavy with silence. Time seemed to stop in those few seconds. Then John Grant, the Inverness forger, stepped forward. Campbell turned to Page and introduced Grant. "This, sir, is the excellent young man who saved my life and the lives of a great part of the ship's company. He overheard the deserters talking in Irish of the intended mutiny." Grant gave his evidence and said he had shared a room with Skirving and Palmer at the beginning of the voyage and had often heard them in conversation with Draper, and had seen them give him money.

"Gentlemen," said Lieutenant Page, "I am going to recommend your temporary confinement."

"What?" called Skirving. "On what charge? Show us a warrant for our commitment. What authority do you have here?"

"Please, Mr Skirving," said Page. "A warrant is not necessary. I am recommending this for your own protection and honour…"

"Humbug! Tripe and humbug!" said Palmer. "We demand a speedy and rigorous trial!"

"And you shall have that. In Port Jackson," said Campbell.

"You mean to keep us confined for five months?" demanded Skirving.

"Take them away!" ordered Campbell. "Put them in McPherson's cabin in steerage."

Muir had taken a note of everything from his seat in front of his cabin, where he had a perfect view of the whole scene. He would make it his business to start taking depositions from as many soldiers, sailors and convicts as he could, to present a watertight case before the governor in the colony.

The farce of a trial continued as the prisoners were brought down from the poop to stand before their judges. Each one swore his innocence. They had been accused of plotting using Gaelic but none could speak Irish except Draper; Barton and Neale testified they were English, Evans and Griffiths Welsh, and McLean, though an Irishmen, swore that he knew nothing of the language. The convict William Casswell shuffled forward in his chains. There was fear in his eyes and his voice trembled. "Honourable sirs," he pleaded, "I swear to you that I am totally ignorant of any plot. Draper did once mention it to me that such a thing might be carried into effect. Many people were spreading rumours. But I told him that though I wished for liberty I never harboured the thought of obtaining it by blood and murder. Neither Draper nor anyone else ever mentioned the subject to me again, and neither Mr Skirving not Mr Palmer have ever spoken a word to me on the business."

"Casswell," said Campbell, "if you just confess now we shall forgive you."

"But I have nothing to confess, captain," he said helplessly.

Ellis came forward and told the officers that Grant had informed him in Portsmouth harbour that the soldiers were going to rise in mutiny to seize the ship, and that he had told him to hold his tongue. "Is it not very strange, gentlemen, that Grant should have known

324 The Liberty Tree

of such a terrible plot for so many weeks and should reveal it only now?"

"Is this true Mr Grant?" asked the lieutenant.

"I have no memory of such a conversation, sir," Grant lied.

The officers adjourned to the roundhouse. In less than ten minutes they returned to their table and Page, who had a naval officer's fondness for the lash, announced that every other one of the accused would be given twenty-four strokes, the remainder of them to be flogged the next day. If they confessed, the punishment would be withdrawn. The men, now in anguish, again pleaded their innocence and Marines Neale, Barton, and McLean, along with the convict cook Gilthorpe, were led to the grating, where the boatswain waited with the cat-o'-nine-tails.

Each of the soldiers took his two-dozen lashes in silence and was led away, bleeding and bruised, back to the poop deck in double irons so heavy they had to be carried. Gilthorpe was strapped to the grating and, after his back had been opened by the first twelve blows of the whip's tails, the pain became too much.

"Stop, stop!" he cried. "I'll confess. I promise!" Gilthorpe was taken into the roundhouse and a declaration was presented to him that he signed with his mark, after which his irons were knocked off and he was allowed to return to his convict duties.

On the following day Casswell was flogged but Evans and Griffiths were released without explanation and returned to duty.

"Burnett!" Campbell called from the roundhouse. The new mate stepped in from the quarterdeck. "What's the name of McPherson's girl?"

"He had a young woman by the name of Bet Carter in his quarters, sir."

"Find her and bring her to me."

Bet Carter was brought to the roundhouse, clearly afraid. Campbell asked her what she knew of McPherson's plans to take over the ship. She knew of no plans. He flattered her with promises of rewards but could coax no information from her.

"Mr Burnett, take her to the boatswain. Have her flogged. We'll see if you won't spill your secrets then, miss!"

Bet Carter, standing before the bloody grating, fainted on the deck. She was drenched with seawater, lifted and humiliatingly stripped of her bodice before being tied. She knew she could expect nothing but barbarity from this deranged sea captain and took twelve lashes without complaint, and with defiance and determination in her eyes.

Disgust and revulsion mingled with fear on every deck on the ship. For some, the fear drove them to further denunciations, hoping preferment would protect them. Some attempted to implicate Boston and Ellis, while others tried to settle personal scores. Many began to doubt the truth of the plot. Pattullo distanced himself from the captain. Thomson asked to see depositions and the captain's log, but was refused. He repeated his original criticism that there was only one accuser with inadequate evidence. Mrs Pattullo, Mrs Campbell and Mrs Boston went over the events and came to the conclusion that it was highly unlikely that Palmer and Skirving had been involved, and that Draper had accused them only to save himself.

Campbell, meanwhile, appointed Grant as his secretary and gave him freedom of the ship. Draper was often seen going in and out of the roundhouse. Margarot and Baker held daily meetings with the captain, and Margarot's opposition to Palmer became even more personal. He accused the preacher and his friend Ellis of "unnatural tendencies" and treated both with public contempt.

The four prisoners still on the poop deck had additional leg irons put on them. The weight on each man was sixty pounds. They spent their days and nights in the open until Rio, with only a biscuit and a half a day, a quart of water and three ounces of salt meat for each man. They were unable to lie down with comfort and were exposed to torrents of rain by night, heavy dews each morning and the burning sun by day, with their backs scabbed and throbbing. Campbell once again threatened that if they stirred or made the least noise he would shoot at them through the ceiling of the roundhouse and terrified them with promises of repeated floggings until they were hanged from the yardarm. None of them broke under his torture.

Muir approached Campbell and told him Palmer and Skirving were entitled to a copy of the charges brought against them to construct a proper defence. "There is no defence necessary," replied Campbell opaquely, "there is no court of justice here. I have nothing to do with them farther than to carry them to New South Wales. I am not the prosecutor. If the governor thinks proper to prosecute them there, I have no doubt that proper time will be given, but there is no prosecution at present."

"So why have you confined them?" asked Muir.

"They were not confined by me, but by Mr Page," said Campbell.

"But you are keeping them in custody," Muir pointed out, trying to establish some logic to the conversation.

"Yes," said Campbell, with a challenging look.

"Then that is the same thing," said Muir.

Campbell stared at him without speaking. Muir gave up and walked away, making a careful note in his papers.

*

The Surprize lost the trade winds a little to the north of the equator and was becalmed in the doldrums. The ship had to be pulled by two longboats in search of a breath of wind. On crossing the line the usual celebrations with Mr and Mrs Neptune were muted. Only a few younger sailors who had never been at zero latitude before were dunked in a barrel of salt water in a private ceremony at the fore-castle. Most preferred to keep to themselves for fear of accusation by spies and informers.

The sun blazed hot overhead and the air in the ship was stifling. There was no draught through the gratings to the lower decks. Pitch melted from the wooden seams and dripped on the decks below. Palmer recorded in his diary, "I was thrust into a cabin in the midst of that infernal brothel of which I had often expressed my dislike. The language of Newgate was virtue and decency compared to what

I was always doomed to hear. My neighbours were divided from me by only a wooden partition, the women were almost perpetually drunk, and as perpetually engaged in clamours, brawls, and fighting. The cabin was not six feet square, it was besides so close and hot in the torrid zone that we could not bear the weight of our clothes, and were obliged to take it by turns to enjoy the privilege of sitting by the door, for the sentinel had orders not to permit us to pass the threshold."

The bunk in the steerage cabin was only two feet wide and so Skirving was allowed to sleep in his own cabin but had to return below to rejoin Palmer each morning. They had two hours a day on deck, under guard, and were allowed to speak to no one but Baker, the duty officer, or the sergeant. In a further act of humiliation, Campbell at last gave Ellis the cabin he had paid for, the one from which Palmer had been evicted.

Short, violent squalls are common in equatorial waters and the passengers on Surprize were about to experience for the first time the effect that McPherson had described. A lookout called out from above, "On deck there, storm two points to starboard." Burnett put his glass to his eye and saw clearly the dark shape with bright flashes inside. As he lowered his telescope he could see the gloom head towards them at elemental speed. He called for the sails to be quickly furled and assembled the crew on deck as darkness surrounded the ship. Torrential rain and a turbulent sea sent water sluicing across the deck, down companion-ways and gratings, washing convicts from their tables and beds.

Burnett had all hands on the pumps and had just begun to suck the water from below when, just as suddenly, bright, hot sunshine exploded in their eyes as the storm passed over and raced to the opposite horizon. Dazed and sodden, the crew, the passengers and the convicts, began mopping up as the heat from the sun caused steam to rise from the deck and the masts.

In a few days the vessel had drifted westwards on the heavy, sickening swell to pick up the south east trade winds and the Brazil current, allowing the convoy to form again. On the last day of June, most of the Indiamen and the Suffolk parted company and headed south for the Cape. The Swift, Surprize and one remaining Indiaman continued west. Soon, the smell of land and vegetation reached them and on 4 July a lookout yelled from his perch on the Surprize's main mast that he had sighted the entrance to Rio de Janeiro's harbour.

CHAPTER 31

Ship of fear

"From the general tenor of Campbell's conduct, from the perpetual plotting which I discovered in the ship… I was in a state of continual terror lest it should fall to my turn to be inclosed in the same ground less accusations."

Declaration of Corporal Timothy Ryan, Port Jackson, 4 December, 1794.

Muir leant on the rail of the ship and filled his lungs with the sweet air. Those who could, stood on deck to view the narrow entrance to Rio's harbour which, after a quarter of a mile, opened into a vast bay nearly five miles across at the town. All around were small islands covered with orange trees, heavy with fruit. Crags, precipices and towering cliffs formed most of the shoreline, punctuated by green banks dotted with white buildings, each one crowned by a church or a fort. Ships stood at anchor and small boats criss-crossed the glassy surface like water insects. Behind the town, the mountains rose to dark blue summits with small white clouds clinging to their sides.

Skirving, standing under guard further down the deck, smiled at Muir. The beautiful coastline and welcoming climate caused both men to forget their gloom. Muir wanted to find out from Skirving how Palmer was, but the guard made it impossible. The preacher had fallen ill again. His gaol fever had returned and Dr Thomson was worried at the increasing cases of flux on the prison deck.

Campbell had intended to stay at Rio for only a few days, enough time to replenish water barrels and load fresh meat and vegetables, but the wooden conduits from the town water supply to the quay-side had perished and transporting heavy barrels from several miles distance caused considerable delay. In the meantime, fever and diarrhoea spread quickly among the convicts, once more chained and confined in the close and airless hold, and Dr Thomson asked the captain to wait in harbour until the outbreak was over, the convicts were returned to health, and the ship was cleaned and fumigated. Days turned to weeks, during which fresh meat, fruits and green vegetables aided the recovery of the sick. The poop deck was repopulated with two oxen, three sheep and twenty goats, and the cargo hold took in crates of fruit and vegetables, and 12,250 lbs of beef.

Prisoners and crew took the opportunity to write home. Grant wrote to his patron and namesake, Sir James Grant MP, one of Dundas's men in Westminster, explaining his heroic part in foiling a "diabolical scheme" of mutiny led by seditious Jacobins lately convicted at Edinburgh. Captain Campbell, he explained, "has in consequence assured me of my liberty upon my arrival and has been pleased to desire that I would consider myself equally as free as himself". The captain had promised to write to Sir James confirming this.

Campbell wrote to the commissioners of the navy with the same story, adding at the end, "I must, in justice to Mr Muir, say that he does not appear to have had any hand in the plot... Permit me, honourable sirs, to mention to you that Mr Maurice Margarot has throughout the whole of this business, and ever since he came on board, behaved in a manner honourable to himself, and not only pleasing but serviceable to us... Mr John Grant, to whom I am indebted for first discovering this plot, has all along behaved with a great deal of propriety, nor do I doubt of having it in my power to reward him."

The captain's vindictiveness towards Skirving and Palmer remained, and he continued to terrorise convicts into perjuring themselves and giving false evidence against them. One hot afternoon, this arbitrary victimisation fell on James Somerville, a cabinet maker who had been convicted of housebreaking. His wife was on board but they were destitute and she was without a change of clothes. Early in the voyage, Mrs Bolton had taken up a collection for her, to which the captain's wife had contributed, as had Skirving. When Mrs Campbell casually mentioned this to her husband, he sent for Somerville and ordered him to sign a paper stating that Skirving had offered him five or ten guineas to join in the conspiracy.

"He's never given me a farthing, sir," blurted Somerville. "I believe he donated to the collection for my wife."

"Sign or I'll put you and your wife in irons," said Campbell, with menace. Somerville still refused. "You'll be flogged and exposed on the poop!"

Somerville had seen the privations the others had endured in chains on the open deck and, terrified, he agreed to sign.

Campbell was still unsure of his ground for holding Palmer and Skirving. He was aware that the so-called court martial was unlawful, Muir had assured him that seven senior serving navy officers were required to form a court martial and that proper forms of law had to be followed. Campbell therefore tried to persuade the captain of the Swift, tied up near the Surprize, to court-martial Palmer and Skirving and get the whole thing over with. Captain Dowling rightly washed his hands of the affair and told Campbell to present his evidence in New South Wales.

Campbell's policy of refusing Palmer and Skirving contact with others was mercilessly enforced. While they exercised on deck each day the sentries were ordered to keep them quiet. Palmer, however, could not be prevented from chattering and the soldiers were daily reprimanded for failing to silence him. On one occasion Marine George Pitt was given a public dressing down by Sergeant Reddish.

"But sir, it's impossible to make Mr Palmer to keep silence, and equally impossible to prevent people from replying to his questions," Pitt explained.

"God damn him, he must hold his tongue," replied Reddish.

"But how am I to make him do it, sir?" he asked.

"If he will not obey you, Pitt," Reddish shouted in his face, "then, God damn him, knock his teeth down his throat with the pummel of your sword!"

None of the soldiers found it possible to carry out such an order and they, in turn, suffered the anger and blandishments of their officers throughout the remainder of the voyage. It had not gone unnoticed by the rank and file that, after the plot was said to have been discovered, the sergeant was once again eating from the captain's kitchen and he seemed to be under no restriction in his consumption of alcohol. They also saw Grant doing the same, he now dined with the duty officer on deck.

Draper used his freedom not just in spying for Campbell, but in furthering his criminal career. Many personal items and sums of money had been reported missing but no one was caught, until witnesses saw Draper break into a cabin and steal money. Campbell was ashore and Pattullo had Draper arrested and chained. On his return, the captain flew into a rage and released him. Pattullo objected.

"I'll be damned if I care," Campbell retorted.

Days later, Draper threatened Reddish and a corporal with a bayonet and Pattullo locked him up. This time, Campbell recognised the offence but time and again appealed to Pattullo to allow Draper his liberty, with the weak excuse that he had to finish off some tailoring jobs for him.

Dr Thomson was ashore with some of the officers from the Swift. He asked them if they knew of the fate of poor McPherson, in chains on the Suffolk. They looked confused and amused.

"Why, Dr Thomson, where did you hear such a fib?" asked one of the officers. "Mr McPherson is safe and well. The last we heard he is made quarter-master on Suffolk, and takes care of the signals." Thomson apologised for his misinformation and returned to the Surprize, where he first found Bet Carter and told her the news, to her great relief, and confronted the captain, who blankly denied the story and dismissed the doctor. Suspicion concerning the behaviour of Campbell and the veracity of his allegations was greatly increased.

Muir was allowed to go ashore, accompanied by an officer, usually Pattullo or Thomson. Together they explored Rio, with its straight and regular streets, where projecting overhead balconies almost touched. The houses were mostly three or four storeys high, with shops or store rooms on the ground. The grand houses had glazed windows, but most had simple shutters. There were two spacious squares, one containing a theatre and barracks, and the other housing the viceroy's palace, opera house and a Carmelite convent with a public library. The fourth side of the palace square was open to the sea with a granite pier. A fountain played at its centre, supplied from the Albuquerque aqueduct, named after a previous viceroy. Its vast two-tier brick arches crossed a valley between two of the five hills of the city, supplying residents with fresh mountain water and feeding four ornate fountains.

Streets full of English shops, such as saddlers and bakers, surprised Muir. Other stores sold English goods, with the words "London superfine" or "Birmingham hardware" on display. But it was the pubs – the Union Jack, the Red Lion, or the Jolly Tars – that made Rio seem as much a home port to the sailors as Greenwich or Portsmouth. Muir bought goods for himself and his friends, including a number of citrus trees that Palmer wanted to plant at Sydney Cove.

He counted eighteen parish churches, four monasteries, and three convents in the town. While on a visit to the Antonine monastery, he presented the abbot with the engraving of Dr Price that had hung in his cell at Newgate, and the *Memoirs of John Hollis*, a sceptic and critic of Calvinism, and in the flyleaf he inscribed, in Latin: "Thomas Muir of Huntershill, by race a Scot, in spirit a citizen of the world, has made this gift. O Scotland! O my country for long blessed and proud above others, most holy land of heroes rich in resources, fertile in men, most fortunate in its rich plains. Who could ever relate thy affliction and the extent of thy troubles, and find words to match our sorrows and base disgrace and those barbarous laws!"

He ended it with a quote from Virgil: "We leave behind the frontiers of our fatherland and its sweet fields", followed by another from Horace: "Tomorrow we shall journey again over the vast ocean". It was dated 23 July 1794.

*

The Pattullos had taken Muir on a picnic one afternoon beyond the town boundary, to the Laranjeiros valley, named after the stands of orange trees growing on each side of the stream running down its middle. They sat in the shade, pointing excitedly to macaws and toucans, eating oranges and gathering lemons and limes. Below them was a small grassy plain where women, mostly black-skinned and wearing red or white handkerchiefs on their heads, washed clothes in the stream. Set back from the stream were villas with hedges of acacia and mimosa surrounding gardens of plantains and oranges. Up above them were coffee plantations, stretching far into the mountains, all of them thickly planted with more orange and lemon trees.

The bucolic peace enjoyed by the three Scots, used to much harsher climes, was shattered as, on their way back to the ship, they took a turn into a street called Vallongo – the long valley – where none of them had set foot before. Here, the red-tiled houses were of the same design as in other streets, except that the ground floors were full of slaves, up to 400 in every house, sitting on benches behind stable doors, open at the top to allow the sea breeze to cool the packed and stifling rooms. The slaves were mostly young; some looked barely twelve years old, and were chained. Their heads were shaved and their bodies were thin. Some lay on mats, apparently too sick or too melancholy to get up. Others were being prepared by house slaves for sale, painted, if necessary, to cover bruises or give the illusion of good health. Overseers moved among them holding lashes, to keep order. Merchants lived in the houses above, and plantation owners came looking for fresh labour for their coffee fields, prodding and squeezing the young men and women, examining their teeth as they would a horse.

"Of course!" exclaimed Mrs Pattullo. "We've been blinded by the soft climate and the flowers. These are the people who make it so attractive!" All three were deeply affected. The anti-slavery movement in Scotland was particularly strong and, for Muir, very close to his heart. His mother and sister were both active in the campaign, and members of the reform associations were invariably attached to the abolitionist cause.

"And all those ships in the harbour," said her husband, "they can't all just have been exporting coffee. Many must have been slavers on the incoming run."

Rio's magnificent harbour was, in fact, the main Brazilian port for the human cargo snatched or sold on African soil. Muir came to despise the city and wished the ship would sail away from the slave harbour.

*

Muir tried to have a few words with Skirving each morning, before he was taken from his cabin to rejoin Palmer below for the duration of the hot day. Most officers and soldiers turned a blind eye to the two men briefly exchanging news, even though it had been forbidden by Campbell. Occasionally the captain would yell at Muir if he spotted him from the roundhouse. One morning Muir crossed to his friend's cabin as usual. He had been up most of the night, reading and drinking. He now often found solace in a bottle. Baker, the new colonial superintendent of prisoners, came up the stairs to the quarterdeck.

"You are acting contrary to the rules, Mr Muir," he said.

"I'm only borrowing a book, Baker!" Muir shot back with annoyance.

"It makes no difference. Talking to Skirving is forbidden."

Muir lost his temper. "Look! Look at the book, you villain! Look at it! There's no harm in a book!"

"Mr Muir, I'll ask you again to stop talking with Skirving," warned Baker. "You have no more privileges than any other convict on this ship."

"I am no convict, sir!" Muir shouted back. "And I wonder that government should send such a set of rascals and scoundrels on board to insult a gentleman. Leave us alone! I will never pay any attention to orders or directions from the likes of you. You're infinitely beneath my notice!"

Baker flew at him and landed a heavy punch on his chest, which sent Muir sprawling across the deck, coming to a halt with a thud at the rail. His assailant disappeared into the roundhouse.

*

Palmer was ill for six weeks, sometimes in great pain because of the typhus, but was fit again by the first week of August, when the Surprize, the Swift, and the remaining Indiaman made ready to sail. As they left the harbour, Boston found himself standing next to Margarot, watching the cliffs and islands slip by. He told Margarot how upset he had been at Palmer's confinement in the hot and airless cabin during his fever.

"What are his misfortunes to you, Mr Boston?" Margarot asked. "Why trouble your head about them?

"Because Mr Palmer is a friend and a man of many virtues," replied Boston.

"I'll be damned if ever I saw any of them," said Margarot. "Leave them to their fate. They are sure to be hanged."

Campbell put the word about that his prisoners would be hanged when they were out at sea, and he had already fixed the day for hanging William Casswell. He never carried out his cruel threats but they generated fear, and this in turn was supported by petty persecutions. During Palmer's two hours on deck each day, he had become accustomed to playing games with the Boltons' four-year-old daughter. Campbell ordered it to be stopped and angrily commanded Mrs Bolton not to allow the child near him. The captain claimed his life had been put in danger by the girl being used as a secret agent who carried papers back and forth. Palmer's pen, ink and paper were confiscated. He and Skirving were denied access to their own stores and equipment, including tobacco and wine. Palmer's pistols, guns and swords had previously been taken from him, but Margarot informed Campbell that he believed Mrs Bolton kept a little sword-stick of Palmer's concealed in a trunk. She was forced to hand it over and watched as it was thrown into the sea. Then Palmer's dog, the lurcher given to him by his nephew, was dumped, alive, into the ocean after a fight with the captain's mastiff. Palmer was distraught. Most others on board were sickened.

Palmer recorded later, "From the time of our leaving Rio till our arrival at Sydney, the system of spies and informers was carried to a greater height than ever. No one was safe, everyone suspected his neighbour. Ensign Pattullo and his wife, Doctor Thompson and his, and Mr Muir scarcely appeared, they kept close to their cabins, and were almost as much prisoners as myself."

Thomson admitted in Sydney that he "had lived in continual anxiety and terror from the plots and conspiracies that were daily hatching and contriving on board the ship...well knowing that no courage or innocence could defend from a false accuser, I spoke to few but on business, and rarely appeared on deck but to exercise my profession." Pattullo, too, recorded that he "seldom appeared on deck, and was fearful of speaking to any, well knowing the treachery and danger with which I was surrounded."

The Surprize had a fair passage south and out of the tropic of Capricorn. At night Muir would sit with Ann Loftus and look over the rail at the brilliance bubbling up in the sea. He would signal to Skirving to look over the side at bow-wave, illuminated by blue-green light that gleamed along her hull and formed a sparkling wake behind them. None of them had seen such magnificence in nature before, and the nightly show became a source of joy and distraction.

Soon, the ship met with squalls of wind, heavy rain, thunder, lightning and rolling seas. For days she pitched and tossed so that the prisoners had to grab hold of tables and bunks for balance. Seas washed through the ship as they had done in the equatorial storm, only now there was no way of drying clothes and bedding. Deadlights were fitted to windows in cabins and ports on the hull, to prevent the ship from being swamped, and convicts, sailors, soldiers and passengers were forced to live in darkness or gloom. Palmer complained, "The ship was so old and crazy that every wave of the sea spilled the water through its side and it ran on to my bed. Our clothes would frequently be wet through…and I was obliged to sleep in a bed soaked with water."

The air grew colder and the weather wet and gloomy. Gales carried them below and beyond the tip of Africa, where the rich Southern Ocean brought gannets and terns hunting in their wake. A wandering albatross would appear and follow them for miles, wheeling and circling above on its thirteen-foot wings. The occasional whale was sighted. But still the waves broke over the decks and the green and white freezing water rushed below to be pumped back out again. The chill never left the ill-clad, shivering convicts. The sun, which was lower at every mid-day reading, radiated no heat.

The small convoy turned north-east and in another week of hard sailing parted company at around seventy-five degrees of longitude, near Amsterdam Island, a signpost in the vast ocean that told the Swift and the Indiaman they should begin to head north for the sub-continent. About halfway between the Cape and Australia, the Surprize was on her own. Before her stretched an emptiness, unknown to both Campbell and Burnett, where the Indian and Southern Oceans became one. What lay beyond they could only imagine. The charts on the roundhouse table were those compiled by Captain James Cook twenty-five years earlier.

They ploughed the cold southern waters until Van Diemen's Land, then rounded its south east cape and sailed north. Thundery squalls drove them up the east coast and over the stretch of water that would in a few years become known as the Bass Strait, until the cry of "land ho!" brought a distant mass into sight. The indistinct bulk gradually revealed itself in a panorama of beaches and headlands framed against blue mountain ranges.

As the people on the Surprize gazed at their new home they were filled with wonder that no one had died in six months of fear and discomfort, but also with the realisation that a mere handful of Europeans before them had looked out on these sights. The headlands that mark the opening to the vast bay at Port Jackson were sighted on the morning of 25 October and the Surprize dropped anchor in Sydney Cove at eight o'clock that night.

CHAPTER 32

Oyer and terminer

"Within the Dungeon's noxious gloom
The Patriot still, with dauntless breast,
The cheerful aspect can assume,
And smile, in conscious Virtue blest!"

John Thelwall, 'The Cell', written in the
Tower of London, 24 October, 1794.

Joseph Gerrald couldn't have known it, but as he woke in a strange cell in a new prison on the morning of Saturday, 25 October, Muir and the others were on the darkened deck of the Surprize, under lanterns hanging at the masts, watching sailors prepare to drop anchor and secure the ship on the sandy bottom of Sydney Cove, a little way offshore. Gerrald had been moved from his communal cell in Newgate the day before, in a prison reorganisation carried out to make room for those who had been in the Tower since May: Thomas Hardy, John Horne Tooke, John Augustus Bonney, Stewart Kyd, Jeremiah Joyce, John Richter and John Thelwall. They joined Thomas Holcroft and John Baxter in Newgate, all of them indicted by a grand jury to stand trial for treason. The nine men were now to be tried at the court that formed part of Newgate prison, the Old Bailey.

Gerrald looked from the window of the New Compter jail into Giltspur Street. He was just up the road from Newgate but felt as if he might as well have been a hundred miles distant. "No one will think to look for me here," he thought, "in a debtors' prison." He was lonely and depressed at being locked in a miserable cell with no idea whether or when he would be sent to Botany Bay. Thelwall was convinced that the government had delayed transporting Gerrald so he could be indicted for treason if Hardy and the others were convicted. Gerrald coughed from deep down in his chest. "I feel like I'll waste away from this cursed consumption first," he muttered to himself.

Friends soon found out from the Newgate turnkey where Gerrald had been taken and John Smith, his regular visitor from the Corresponding Society, came to him that same day.

"Hardy and the others were up in the Bailey this morning," Smith told him. "They all pled not guilty to high treason. They asked to be tried separately and Hardy is first up on Tuesday."

"I thought they were arrested on suspicion of treasonable practices," said Gerrald.

"They were," said Smith, "but it was decided at some point to prosecute them for high treason. Suspension of the habeas corpus act was handy, they were kept under lock and key while the attorney general looked for evidence."

"Were you in court today?" Gerrald asked him.

"Yes, I was there, along with lots of people, inside and out. The charge said they circulated seditious literature and agreed to distribute arms for insurrection, rebellion and war," Smith said.

"Oh, that's got to be false!" said an astonished Gerrald. "It's a fabrication."

"Not only that, the war was to depose the king and kill him, and the convention was to take over from parliament and the government."

"What tosh and nonsense!" exclaimed Gerrald. "We have only ever advocated peaceful reform of the House of Commons."

"I know," agreed Smith, "but the government is determined to see a conspiracy in everything we do, especially after the sacrifice of their spy Watt in Edinburgh."

*

Robert Watt had been confident that the terrible mistake of his arrest would be rectified by the lord advocate and the home secretary. Wasn't he known to them personally and acting on their orders? Wasn't he a loyal servant of government, doing his bravest and best to expose a threat to their existence? His few pikes had been discovered by accident in May, but as details of a more extensive plot emerged from the interrogation of witnesses in Edinburgh – crucially the evidence of other members of the Ways and Means committee – they were forwarded by Robert Dundas and his officials to London. Henry Dundas passed this information to the prime minister in a series of letters and those, together with the privy council's reports from its interrogations of imprisoned reformers in London, allowed Pitt to propose another secret committee of the House of Commons and for Grenville to do the same in the Lords.

Again, the committees reported at speed, the Commons on 6 June and the Lords on the following day. The Commons committee argued that the societies were about to force a change in representation which would lead, "to the extinction and destruction of the other two branches of the legislature". The Lords concluded that the proposed convention would bring about "the total subversion of the constitution, with the destruction of his majesty's person, family, and government", resulting in "as complete a revolution in this country as that which has taken place in France since the month of August 1792". The noble lords had discovered "a seditious and traitorous conspiracy", and Pitt told the Commons there was "express proof" of the reform societies' "intention of having recourse to arms".

The law officers had still not decided on the charges to be brought in England, but Henry and Robert Dundas set the Scottish judicial system in motion. The law of treason in Scotland was exactly the same as in England, unlike the law of sedition. English treason law had been adopted in 1709, shortly after the union of parliaments and this allowed the crown to issue a special commission known as Oyer and Terminer – a Norman French phrase meaning to hear and to judge – which gave the authority to set up treason trials quickly in times of rebellion or political crisis. Robert Dundas didn't want Braxfield's controversial presence at the head of the Watt and Downie cases and on 20 June he wrote to his uncle, "*Entre nous,* I would prefer a commission were it only for this reason, that the president or chief baron would, in that way, fall to preside in place of the violent and intemperate gentleman who sits in the justiciary, and whose present state of health and spirits is such as to afford no chance of his being more soberly inclined in his demeanour than he was last winter."

Watt and Downie were brought before a grand jury in Edinburgh on Thursday 14 August, Islay Campbell, lord president of the College of Justice presiding. A true bill against both of them was found and Watt's trial was set for Wednesday 3 September. He was ably defended by Robert Hamilton and Henry Erskine, who argued that he was a spy directly employed by the lord advocate on behalf of the home secretary, and that he had attended political meetings in order to obtain information for government; at the time of his arrest he had not had time to complete his work.

Watt felt confident of an acquittal as Robert Dundas took the stand and confirmed that he was his spy, but Dundas denied having heard from Watt about plans to capture the castle and take over the banks. Watt was shocked as the lord advocate accused him of playing both sides in order to "ultimately prefer that most likely to prevail" and he was "gradually leading these men into the criminality of a scheme of treason for their ruin and for his own advantage". The agent provocateur had been publicly disowned by his master.

Members of Friends of the People who gave evidence against Watt either claimed no knowledge of the plan or told the court they had opposed Watt's wild plot. Two spies from the London Corresponding Society revealed themselves and gave evidence that suggested Thomas Hardy was part of the conspiracy. Watt's trial lasted for twenty-two hours and after only ten minutes deliberation the jury brought in a guilty verdict at six o'clock on the morning of Thursday 4 September. Watt was speechless. Alone in his cell he told himself this couldn't be happening; it was a great mistake. It must be part of a clever government plan to convict others, and he would be pardoned, eventually.

Downie was tried on Friday and found guilty but "upon account of certain circumstances," said the foreman of the jury, "we desire to recommend the prisoner to mercy." Watt and Downie were brought to court on Saturday afternoon and condemned to death.

*

Watt awakened early in his traitor's cell in Edinburgh castle on the day of his execution, Wednesday 15 October. Terror filled his eyes as they opened to the dim light. He had difficulty breathing and his whole frame trembled. "This can't be true. Why is this happening?" he asked himself repeatedly. "A pardon, a reprieve, it must come today." In his desperation he prayed. He felt hopeless. He had remained optimistic about receiving the king's mercy until two days ago, when news of only Downie's pardon arrived. His anguish was uncontrollable as the ageing jeweller was removed from the cell and set at liberty. Watt had petitioned for pardon more than once since the conclusion of his trial, but Downie's release was a deadly blow to his hopes and he asked for pen and paper to make one last attempt at influencing his masters. On Monday he began writing his confession. That evening the order for his execution on Wednesday was delivered to him. He kept writing all day on Tuesday and by eight o'clock in the evening he signed the paper and had it sealed and sent immediately to the sheriff. It contained information he hoped would earn him a stay of execution.

"At the time I was apprehended," he wrote, "there were but very few places that information was not received from; and there remained almost nothing to do, for the execution of the whole, but a visit to England and Ireland by intelligent and confidential persons. The first movement was intended to be made in Edinburgh, London and Dublin; while every town throughout the kingdoms were in readiness to act, according to the plan, on the very first notice, which was to be given by couriers dispatched by express." He named no names, hoping that the bait would be sufficient to gain time. This was ignored by the sheriff and the lord advocate.

A confusion of emotions paralysed Watt. He shook. A minister came into his cell. They prayed together for his immortal soul until ten o'clock when his jailer knocked off his chains and asked him to step outside.

"Is there nothing from the king?" he asked, weakly. The jailer shook his head. The commanding officer of the castle approached and told him he would be taken to the place of public execution at the Tollbooth. Watt had to be supported as he descended the steep stone steps from his prison to the courtyard beneath. At first he saw only the sheriff, dressed in black, wearing white gloves and carrying a white rod. As Watt's eyes became accustomed to the light he stumbled, startled when he saw a brightly coloured escort of two hundred Argyllshire fencibles in full dress uniform. When he caught sight of the cart, he fainted. It was painted black and drawn by a white horse. There were two seats in the hurdle and the first was occupied by his executioner, masked and dressed in black, holding in full view a large beheading axe. Watt was placed on his seat in the cart to be drawn backwards to the High Street. He sobbed.

As the execution party moved through the castle, Watt was unaware of the steady beat of the drum and the sound of the soldiers' boots keeping time to the dead march. His eyes rolled back as he searched the heavens for an answer. A deafening echo as the procession passed under the castle's barbican with its suspended portcullis was followed by hollow, irregular footsteps as the soldiers broke step to cross the drawbridge and Watt's hurdle rumbled behind. He had given his clothes to a creditor in settlement of a debt and now was wrapped in an old greatcoat. His shirt was dirty from continued wear in his dark cell, and his torn stockings hung loose about his legs. He still wore a red nightcap on his head. Fear gave way to shame at his appearance, and anxiety about being ridiculed. He knew he must be the most detested man in the city, despised for being a traitor, held in contempt for being a spy, scorned by his employers. Utterly alone, his humiliation enveloped him.

At the limits of the city beneath the castle, the military escort halted and the horse-drawn hurdle took Watt forward into a waiting square formed by city constables, town officers and the city guard. He was met by two junior magistrates and the Rev Dr George Baird, principal of Edinburgh university, who would attend to his last needs. The soldiers turned around and marched back to the castle and the solemn procession continued slowly to the place of execution at the Heart of Midlothian. The crowd filling the street from building to building was silent and made space to allow the condemned man and his attendants past, before closing behind them again like a river.

The cart halted at the door of the Tollbooth. Watt was taken down and into the prison. The party climbed the stairs to the place of execution on the low roof at the west end of the building. A platform and scaffold had been erected there. As the faces looked up at him from the street below Watt became aware of Baird reading from the twenty-fifth psalm, "Now for thine own name's sake, O Lord, I humbly thee entreat, To pardon mine iniquity; for it is very great."

Baird prayed for Watt's soul. At the word, "amen", Watt begged for more time, still desperate in the hope of a last-minute reprieve. He asked to read from the Bible. That was granted. Then he asked to pray. Baird told him it was time, embraced him and left the platform. The noose was placed around his neck and he dropped the white handkerchief that had been placed in his hand to signal he was ready. The tall buildings surrounding the prison enclosed the fearsome silence. Watt held his breath. The crowd held theirs. The trap opened and for an instant he was weightless, then the jerk of the rope, the snap of the neck and the flash behind his eyes mingled in his last moment before the blackness.

An eyewitness recorded the final scene. "The body was allowed to hang until it was completely lifeless, when it was cut down and placed upon a black table, with a piece of wood prepared for the head and shoulders. Then the executioner came forward with a large axe in his hand, which he held up to the crowd. This sight, to which they were totally unaccustomed, produced an instantaneous shock, and such a general cry and shout of horror burst forth, as made the executioner delay his blow, while numbers rushed off in all directions to avoid the shocking sight! The executioner then, with two strokes, severed his head from his body; which being received in a basket, was by the executioner held up to the spectators, saying, 'This is the head of a traitor!' "

CHAPTER 33

Twelve good men

"Here's a health to them that's awa,
Here's a health to them that's awa;
Here's a health to Tammie, the Norland laddie,
That lives at the lug o' the law."

Robert Burns, 'Here's a Health to Them That's Awa',
probably December 1792.

News of Watt's execution was received with mixed feelings by the prisoners still in the Tower of London. Their communication with each other was limited but on their daily walks on the ramparts they managed some stolen conversation if a sympathetic guard was on duty. Tooke and Jeremiah Joyce were walking in opposite directions around the small, square lead roof of their tower prison. They could see the Thames below them and autumn leaves on the trees on the south bank.

"He was a spy," Tooke said to Joyce, as they passed.

"He was also charged with the same crime as we are," whispered Joyce.

At their next passing Tooke said softly, "Two of the people who gave evidence were fellow spies in the Corresponding Society, little good that did him."

At the opposite side of the roof, Joyce added, "What happens in Edinburgh seems to follow us around, first Muir and Palmer; then Skirving, Gerrald and Margarot; now Watt and Downie."

A half circuit later, Tooke pointed out, "It isn't a coincidence, you know, but just days after Watt and Downie were found guilty, the special commission of oyer and terminer was issued against us." They smiled at the guard each time they passed, for confirmation that they could continue their snatched conversation.

"Don't forget English juries," said Tooke. "They're not as subservient as the Scots. Remember Thomas Walker."

In April, Walker, who was president of the Manchester Reformation Society, was tried for treason at Lancaster assizes along with seven others, on the say-so of a paid informer, Thomas Dunn. The word of this spy had previously had another two Manchester reformers jailed but Thomas Erskine, defending Walker and his colleagues, exposed the spy as a liar causing the prosecution to abandon the case and the judge to instruct the jury to bring in a verdict of not guilty. Dunn was prosecuted for perjury.

"All right, gentlemen," called the guard, "time up. Back downstairs if you please."

Joyce was taken to his room overlooking Tower wharf on the Thames, while Tooke was escorted to his cell above the western gate. His room was below those of Hardy and Thelwall. Before parting on the stairs from the rooftop, Joyce asked Tooke if he knew how Hardy was coping.

"The news of Watt's execution has unsettled him, like the rest of us," Tooke replied, "but he is still in deep mourning and grieving very badly."

Hardy kept mostly to his room, where he read, again and again, the last, unfinished letter from his dear Lydia. She had died in August after giving birth to a stillborn child. "My dear Hardy," she had written shortly before her death, "this comes with my tenderest affection for you. You are never out of my thoughts, sleeping or waking… My dear, you have it not in —" Lydia had felt weak and put down her pen at that point. She never recovered the strength to finish her letter.

Hardy turned the scrap of paper over and over in his hands and remembered with fondness how in May Lydia had persisted until she was given permission to visit him in the Tower. She was large and heavy even then and it was with effort and difficulty that she travelled from Westminster to the east of the city twice a week for only two hours of his company at each visit, which took place in the inhibiting presence of a jailer. Hardy's memories were interrupted by anger and blame, at himself for allowing his wife to become a public target, and at the church and king mob for picking on a defenceless, vulnerable woman.

At the beginning of June the English Channel fleet had won a significant victory over the French navy and the night of 11 June was set aside for celebrations. Windows were illuminated with candles and lamps to show support, and loyalist mobs roamed the streets in search of darkened panes, which they smashed for being unpatriotic. Reformers had the good sense to join in the illumination and Lydia Hardy made sure she had candles in all of the windows of the house and shoe shop. Government-sponsored newspapers had conducted a campaign of vilification of the "traitors" and their supporters since the arrests and had told the mob where they lived.

After smashing the windows of Lord Stanhope's town house, the mob made for Piccadilly, where Lydia and an older companion, a nurse, had barred the shop entrance. The howling mob smashed the windows and threatened to break down the door. The nurse got Lydia to a small window at the back of the house and called to neighbours, who came to assist. Lydia tried to climb through the window but it was so small she stuck in the frame. Neighbours dragged her through the gap and she emerged crushed and bruised. The nurse followed her and, as the mob shouted and cursed outside, they were taken in at the back entrance of a neighbouring house. Members of the Corresponding Society turned out shortly afterwards to protect her home from destruction, some armed with pistols.

Lydia visited Hardy as often as she could manage after this trauma and tried to remain cheerful for her husband's sake. On August 27 they parted at about two o'clock in the afternoon and that evening Lydia went into labour. She died the same night. On receiving the dreadful news the following morning, Hardy was inconsolable. He hid in his room for near on two weeks, refusing to join his colleagues for exercise on the Tower roof.

*

Hardy's trial began on Tuesday 28 October. It lasted for nine long days, usually finishing around midnight. His cell in Newgate was placed so that he had to walk through the felons' yard each morning to get to the court. He described the scene, "They were heavily ironed, some with single and some with double fetters. They were upon each side, and as I walked through the middle…they all expressed their good wishes towards me, in one way or another, and congratulated me on my good spirits."

The opening speech of the attorney general lasted nine hours. When gruff old Chancellor Thurlow learned in Westminster that it had taken Sir John Scott so long to outline the government's case, he exploded with rage. "Then by God there is no treason!" he exclaimed.

In the Scottish trials, the Edinburgh conventions were assumed to be an attempt to overturn the constitution and therefore seditious. At Hardy's trial the proposed British convention was held to be treasonable. There was clearly no difference in the aims of each meeting, it was the legal interpretation that had changed. The charge of treason required "imagining and compassing" the death of the monarch and had to show motive, organisation and action. Government lawyers devised a new crime of "constructive treason" in which it was sufficient to conspire to levy an imagined war against the king. Scott gave the convoluted argument like this, "The life of the prince [is] so interwoven with the constitution of the state that an attempt to destroy the one is justly held to be a rebellious conspiracy against the other."

This was a worry for even the mildest of constitutional reformers. Whig MP Charles Grey wrote, in a letter to his wife, "You see by these new constructions of treason, they have found a much better way of disposing of obnoxious persons than by sending them to Botany Bay… If Hardy is hanged, there is no safety for anyone; innocence no longer affords protection to persons obnoxious to those in power, and I do not know how soon it may come my turn."

But Prime Minister Pitt was determined to press on. During the May debate on the suspension of habeas corpus, he revealed that his great fear was the Corresponding Society, "being composed of the lower orders of people it has within it the means of unbounded extension, and conceals in itself the seeds of rapid increase". He was wary of its cell structure, in which a new division was formed when membership exceeded forty-six people. He clearly believed he was the major obstacle to their success. "My head would be off in six months were I to resign," he told a confidante.

Scott's prosecution team, a bench of seven eminent barristers, including the solicitor general Sir John Mitford and William Garrow, who later became attorney general, brought on a procession of witnesses between Tuesday and Saturday morning. Seven Corresponding Society members revealed themselves as paid government spies. They included John Taylor and Edward Gosling, who had appeared at the trials of Watt and Downie in Edinburgh. It had long been suspected that in early 1794 more spies had been infiltrated into the Corresponding Society by the government, and here was the living evidence.

The prosecution tried to link Hardy with arming the societies, simply because his circular letters had been received by Watt, and by some of the Sheffield societies who had been approached by a pike maker, as well as by a south London Society that had decided, quite legally and openly, just as loyalists were doing, to set up a self-defence militia. The parliamentary secret committees had already made this link in their exaggerated reports and some of their investigators' attempts to make the charge stick were revealed as panic, if not plain farce. An arms dump of 4,000 muskets was discovered at the Castle and Falcon pub in Aldersgate Street in London in late May. They were seized by order of the lord mayor and the home secretary was informed, only to discover that they were part of a government order newly arrived from Birmingham. Soon after, a London carpenter was arrested on information received at the Home Office that he had made sixty truncheons for the Corresponding Society. His papers were confiscated and he was held overnight, only to be released next morning by a magistrate who revealed that the weapons had been ordered by a loyalist association in the city.

Those genuine witnesses called by the prosecution who were not spies, were able to lay nothing in front of the jury that would incriminate Hardy. The spies were questioned so carefully by Hardy's defence lawyers, Thomas Erskine and Vicary Gibbs, that each one of them was branded an unreliable witness whose word could not be trusted.

Every night when proceedings finished – on two occasions it was after one o'clock in the morning – a large crowd gathered outside the Bailey to take the horses from the carriages of Erskine and Gibbs and pull them by hand to their chambers, accompanied by songs and cheering.

Hardy's defence was opened by Erskine on Saturday, when he summed up the prosecution evidence in a speech of seven hours. He was exhausted and ended his address to the jury in a whisper. "I ask you next," he said, "if their objects had been traitorous, would they have given them, without disguise or colour, to the public and to the government, in every common newspaper? ... I ask you farther, whether if the proceedings, thus published and exaggerated, had appeared to government...in the light they represent them to you today, they could possibly have slept over them with such complete indifference and silence? For it is notorious, that after this convention had been held at Edinburgh...and after Mr Paine's book had been for above a year in universal circulation, ay, up to the very day when Mr Grey gave notice in the House of Commons of the intention of the Friends of the People for a reform in parliament, there was not even a single indictment on the file for a misdemeanour; but from that moment when it was seen that the cause was not beat down or abandoned, the proclamation [against seditious publications] made its appearance, and all the proceedings that followed had their birth."

Defence witnesses took the stand for the remainder of Saturday and on Monday Gibbs summed up. He, like Erskine, was exhausted and fainted after the first ten words of his speech. Mitford summed up for the prosecution on Tuesday and Lord Chief Justice Eyre reviewed the evidence on Tuesday evening and Wednesday morning.

The jury retired at 12.30 and by 3.35pm they returned with their verdict. The foreman of the jury was so overcome that he was barely audible, but when the words "not guilty" were distinguished by the people in the public gallery there was loud applause and continuous shouts in celebration. A huge crowd, standing patiently outside in the rain, heard the happy sounds and cheered. The news flashed like lightning through the city and beyond. Hardy attempted to thank the jury but his words were drowned by a cheerful wall of noise. A coach was waiting to take him to the home of his brother-in-law in Lancaster Court, off the Strand, but some supporters took the horses out from their shafts and pulled the carriage along Fleet Street, the Strand, Pall Mall, St James's Street, and into Piccadilly, where they stopped for a few minutes' solemn silence outside his former house before taking him back to the Strand.

Hardy stepped down from the coach and asked for privacy while he visited St Martin's churchyard to pay his respects at the grave of his wife Lydia. They gave him space and silence and afterwards followed him to Lancaster Court, where he turned and briefly spoke to them.

"Fellow countrymen," he began, "thank you for the kind interest you have shown in my favour. Now, as you clearly value the cause in which you have displayed your zeal, I ask that you separate in peace. If mischievous spirits should take advantage of your joy and disturb the public peace, it will be artfully misconstrued and used to injure the other prisoners." Some called out "Home! Home!" and they quietly dispersed.

Erskine and Gibbs waited in court to allow the streets to clear but a large gathering of supporters was patiently determined to show gratitude and the two lawyers were drawn in triumph, with men again between the shafts in place of horses, from the Bailey to their Serjeant's Inn chambers in Fleet Street. They went inside and appeared at an upper window, where Erskine gave a short address and asked them, like Hardy, to go home quietly. After a few cheers and cries of "Erskine and Gibbs forever!" they did so.

*

Pitt's strategy was in shreds. The government had been so confident of a conviction that another eight hundred warrants had been prepared for a round-up of local reformers. Three hundred of the warrants had been signed, ready to be executed as soon as a guilty verdict was returned. In an attempt to salvage some of the plan the attorney general pressed ahead with Tooke's trial.

Tooke came into the Old Bailey on Monday 17 November, accompanied by Erskine and Gibbs. Tooke, unlike Margarot, was successful in bringing Pitt and the Duke of Richmond to court as defence witnesses. Richmond admitted that his plans for a reform in the 1780s were substantially the same as those in the present campaign and Pitt had to concede that he had attended reform meetings in the past. One observer thought that "Mr Pitt in particular seemed literally to have forgotten all that he had formerly attempted in the cause of reform", and Sheridan gave evidence that contradicted much of what Pitt had said.

The trial continued until Saturday, when it took the jury five minutes to reach a verdict of not guilty.

Once again supporters drew the carriages of Tooke, Erskine, Gibbs and Sheridan through the streets in celebration. Torches were lit and banners flew. As the jury left the Bailey, well-wishers formed a lane that stretched from the courthouse door to the London coffee house on Ludgate Hill. As the twelve jurors filed in, all of those inside, reckoned to be about five hundred people, rose, took off their hats and saluted them.

Outside the capital, it was reported that travellers and mail coaches were stopped and asked for news of the verdict. A man called Davey had been sent by the Norwich Patriotic Society to watch the trials and he travelled home on the overnight stage after hearing the verdict. He went straight to the Baptist meeting house where the Sunday service had begun. As Davey entered, the preacher caught sight of him and asked, "What news, brother?"

"Not guilty!" called Davey.

"Then let us sing," announced the minister, "Praise the Lord from Whom All Blessings Flow."

Joyce, Bonney, Kyd and Holcroft, were all acquitted on Monday 1 December after the prosecution offered no evidence. That afternoon Thelwall's trial began, with much the same doubtful or tainted evidence as at Hardy's. Erskine once more defended the case, but not before Thelwall had informed him in a note, "I'll be hanged if I don't plead my own cause!" to which Erskine replied, "You'll be hanged if you do!" Thelwall was found not guilty. A week later the cases against Richter and Baxter were dropped.

The immediate feeling experienced by many was relief. The old reform campaigner Major John Cartwright wrote to his wife, "A system of proscription and terror like that of Robespierre has been for some time growing in this country, and had these trials been otherwise decided than they have been, it would have been completed and written in innocent blood. But the attempt has failed." Robert Burns felt optimistic enough to write to a friend, "Thank God these London trials have given us a little more breath, & I imagine that the time is not far distant when a man may freely blame Billy Pitt, without being called an enemy to his country."

✳

Gerrald was playing a game with his four-year-old daughter on the floor of his cell. His depression had returned during the treason trials and friends suggested that the company of his daughter might lighten his mood. She stayed in the New Compter cell with him for extended periods of time, as was common in debtors' prisons. He played with her for a while, then returned to reading the news of the celebrations held by Lord Stanhope on the acquittal of Joyce.

The *Morning Chronicle* reported, "On Tuesday evening Lord Stanhope gave an entertainment at his seat in Chevening in Kent, to his neighbours and tenants, to celebrate the triumph of liberty and justice, in the honourable acquittal of Mr Joyce, the tutor of his sons, and the other persons indicted for high treason. About 400 persons of both sexes…experienced a most hearty and hospitable reception, at eight o'clock they were introduced into the ballroom, the upper end of which was illuminated with variegated lamps, arranged in the form of the letters to express *The Rights of Juries*. A ball then commenced, and five other rooms were opened for the entertainment of the company… About twelve o'clock near 200 of the guests accompanied him to the supper rooms, which were ornamented with laurel, and in which an excellent cold collation was plentifully and elegantly served up. After a variety of appropriate toasts and songs, the party returned to give place to others at the tables, and the dancing was resumed and continued till six o'clock on the Wednesday morning."

Gerrald had followed the news of the celebrations with some delight. After the final state trial a crowded meeting was held in the Crown and Anchor tavern in the Strand, with Stanhope in the chair and Sheridan as the main speaker. He turned the pages of his paper and his eyes fell on a small notice, "Died. Lately at Ivybridge, Devonshire, on his way to Lisbon for the recovery of his health, the Right Hon Basil William Lord Daer, eldest son to the Earl of Selkirk."

"Oh no," he said out loud. "Poor Daer." He had admired Daer since they met at the Edinburgh convention and was aware that he, too, had suffered from consumption. He remembered that Muir and Daer were good friends and wondered how long it might take for the news to reach New South Wales.

John Smith, Gerrald's official visitor from the Corresponding Society, came into the cell and greeted father and daughter. He had brought Gerrald his weekly allowance of one guinea and a bottle of wine for them to share, along with the news that Hardy had opened a new shop at Tavistock Street in Covent Garden, thanks to a public subscription which raised the capital. There was much public sympathy for the victims of government repression but the arrests, the spies, and the trials caused many active members to slip away. People were afraid and the societies' funding had nearly collapsed. The remaining members had spent most of the year raising money for legal costs and the support of prisoners and their families, at the expense of reform campaigning. There had been a fresh rash of provincial prosecutions of booksellers and printers and many of the country societies had dissolved, or were forced to meet in secret. There was still some activity in Scotland and Ireland, though not as open as before. Peace petitions were circulating in Glasgow and some meetings had resumed in Dublin. But much activity had been driven underground, too, in spite of the government's failure at the treason trials.

"Good news from France, though," said Smith, brightening up. "Robespierre has fallen, the Terror is over, and Tom Paine has been released from the Luxembourg prison."

"I know! At last!" exclaimed Gerrald. "Maybe now the path to liberty is clear again. Poor Mr Paine, he's been in the Luxembourg since last Christmas never knowing whether he would be taken to the guillotine each morning. He had to sit there through the executions of Danton and Condorcet, and all of the Girondin deputies. Thankfully, the Terror has ended, and Robespierre with it."

"I'll drink to that," said Smith.

Gerrald continued to receive visits from many friends and colleagues in the final weeks of 1794 and his daughter was with him throughout Christmas. On December 30, as the two of them prepared the cell for a New Year celebration the following night, the governor of the prison knocked on the door.

"Mr Gerrald," he said, "I'm sorry to interrupt but I've had a message from the Home Office." Gerrald looked at him in silence. "The order for your transportation was signed by the new home secretary, the Duke of Portland, today."

"So Thelwall was right," said Gerrald.

"I'm sorry?" inquired the governor.

"Thelwall thought they were keeping me here to be added to the list of traitors if Hardy had been hanged." Neither of them was to know it would be another five months before the order was carried out.

CHAPTER 34

The Rum Corps

"The best and noblest privilege in hell,
For souls like ours is, boldly to rebel;
To rear the standard of revolt, and try,
The happy fruits of lov'd democracy."

'The Telegraph, A Consolatory Epistle from
Thomas Muir Esq of Botany Bay', George
Hamilton, 1796.

At sunrise on Sunday 26 October the Surprize blasted off fifteen guns
in formal salute for the lieutenant governor of New South Wales,
Major Francis Grose. The batteries at the observation point on the
cove boomed in reply. Muir left his cabin and went to the rail of the
quarterdeck where, as the gun-smoke cleared, he looked for the first
time at a semicircle of dun coloured land directly in front of him.
It was dotted with white buildings, surrounded by a deep fringe of
grey-blue trees, and topped by a pale sky that was swiftly brightened
by the climbing sun to become a vivid and unending blue.

"That's your home now, Muir," said Captain Campbell, coming
up behind him.

"I see that," said Muir. "When can we go ashore?"

"Clerks will come on board to process all the convicts," he said,
"then you'll be taken ashore and put to work."

"You're wrong there, Mr Campbell," said Muir. "Captain Collins,
the colony's advocate general, came on board last night with some
other officers and informed us their orders are that we should not

work nor draw any provisions from the public stores. We are to stay aboard your ship until accommodation has been found for us, but we are free to go ashore whenever we want."

"I'll need written orders from Collins, then," replied Campbell. "I went ashore and saw Major Grose last night," he added with a sneer. "I gave him a bag of papers with the charges against your friends, along with the evidence."

"The evidence you flogged from witnesses?"

"Grose will decide," Campbell insisted.

"Then if the laws of our country run in this outpost, captain, *you* will have to answer in court as well," insisted Muir, who turned and crossed the quarterdeck to the chair at his cabin door.

Grose had already formed an unfavourable opinion of the reformers. In his mail from the Surprize was a letter from Under-secretary King at the Home Office, warning him, "Altho' directions have been given that the persons above mentioned should not be suffered to carry out with them any publications of a seditious or dangerous tendency, yet I take this opportunity of submitting to you whether it will not be highly necessary, with this in view, that their effects should be carefully examined previous to their landing at Port Jackson."

Grose knew nothing of the alleged mutiny until presented with Campbell's story. His opinion softened when Captain Collins returned from the Surprize with a stack of letters of introduction and testimonials guaranteeing the good character of the seditious prisoners. He was impressed that they should be so well connected in ruling circles. One of Palmer's letters was of particular interest to Grose. It came from George Mackenzie Macaulay, a Scots shipping magnate and alderman of the City of London. Macaulay chartered ships to the East India Company and the government, and it was on one of his vessels, suitably named the Pitt, that Grose had travelled to take command of the New South Wales Corps in February 1792. But his empathy began to dissolve on receipt of a stern letter from Margarot demanding "the restoration of my freedom, the common Birthright of Britons!" on the plausible ground that his sentence was fulfilled when he stepped on to the soil of New South Wales.

Campbell's efforts to influence the lieutenant governor were further undermined when a petition from Skirving and Palmer was delivered to Government House early on Sunday morning. It told Grose that the prisoners had not come on the Surprize at the expense of government, and that they had paid the captain for their accommodation; that towards the end of May a conspiracy of some convicts and soldiers to take the ship to America or France was said to have been discovered, and that they were accused of being instigators and leaders, which they heard with "astonishment, indignation and horror". The pair requested an immediate public hearing and "they solemnly aver and undertake, at their highest peril, to prove that their accuser, Patrick Campbell…must be the principal conspirator. That with motives black and malignant, by promises, by bribes, by threats, and by torture, he has attempted to extort evidence against them from men on whom the laws and opinion of the world have imposed the brand of ignominy." They meant to press criminal charges against Campbell and asked that he be arrested.

Grose replied immediately. "The recommendations you have brought to several gentlemen of the colony," he conceded, "will ensure you every indulgence that in your unfortunate situation can be consistently granted; but as it is absolutely requisite for the good order and tranquillity of this place that you avoid on all occasions a recital of those politicks (sic) which have produced to you the miseries…[you] must undergo." He warned them that their comfort depended on their conduct. "I hope you will never give me cause to alter my present intentions towards you," he wrote, adding as a further warning, "The letter you have just sent I cannot but consider as a very inauspicious beginning. The money you state to have paid to Captain Campbell, in addition to the usual allowance for transporting persons to this country, cannot at all alter the conditions of your banishment." All they had done was to "excite my vigilance". He avoided any mention of the alleged mutiny.

Throughout the morning, government clerks came on board to process the convicts, receiving papers from the captain and the surgeon and entering in a great leather-bound register the names and descriptions of the prisoners, together with their offences and length of sentence. They started with the men. Some of the clerks were former convicts who told the newcomers what to expect.

"You're going upriver to Parramatta," said a clerk to the first man to be entered in the book. "Some of you will then go overland to the Hawkesbury River settlement. Governor Phillip believed this was best when he was in charge, old puritan, he was. Thought Sydney had all the 'evils and allurement of a seaport', he did. Wanted you all out of its grasp, unless you've a skill in laying brick or shaping wood or milling corn."

Grose had continued this policy with new prisoners when he took temporary charge of the colony after Phillip sailed home at the end of 1792. The word spread down the line. By mid-morning every man had been transferred on shore by longboat, where many were chained together for the 25-mile tramp inland through the eucalyptus forest, while others were sent to gangs clearing bush or constructing roads and buildings.

The women were treated differently. They were kept below decks and told to wash and do what they could to look their best. Those that had anything left of their finery put it on. They were assembled on deck in groups and, when their details had been entered in the ledgers, a sign was given to the launches and rowing boats bobbing around the ship to come aboard. The officers of the corps came first. They moved among the women like buyers in a slave market. They chose which of them would be their female servants, according to their tastes, some with an eye to obtaining a mistress and with obvious lust in their eyes. Next came the sergeants and corporals, and after them the private soldiers, followed by a handful of free settlers (there were hardly any in the colony as yet), and finally some ex-convict settlers who had received the rare favour from Grose to keep a female servant. Those women who were not chosen would be set to work in the manufacture of crude linen from local flax or in creating patchwork garments from rags to clothe the chain gangs in the fields and roads.

As the women waited to be taken ashore, Muir searched for Ann Loftus and found her in a huddle on the main deck. "That was a disgraceful scene," he said. "Where are they taking you?"

"Don't fret, Thomas," she replied. "We're women. We don't like it but we've come to expect it. I'm to work in an officer's house," she said, "upriver in Parramatta."

Muir felt a surge of sadness and disappointment. He, like Ann, had expected they could continue their relationship on shore. He took her hand and held it firmly.

"Jane's being sent upriver, too, to the house of an overseer. At least I'll have a friend there," she said.

"And Bet Carter?"

"Oh, she's the real pretty one, Thomas. She's headed over there for the house of a bigwig." She pointed to a group of whitewashed houses to the left of the stream running down the middle of the cove. They stood near the two-storey government house. "I think he's one of the governor's officials," she said.

"How is she?" asked Muir.

"Her back's almost healed but her heart's still broken," replied Ann. "She hopes one day McPherson will put in at Port Jackson and find her."

Ann's small group was called to the rail of the boat and, as they climbed down the netting to the launch, Muir found it difficult to swallow. He blinked away the tears as Ann's head disappeared below the gunwale.

Campbell received the governor's order that afternoon giving the Edinburgh prisoners liberty to go on shore. Muir, Skirving and Palmer paid for a boat to the beach. Sydney still sat on the footprint of the original tented camp; some temporary buildings brought out on the first fleet had only just been replaced in brick from the new brickfields at the edge of the settlement. Essential skills were in short supply among the 3,000 Europeans, half of whom were in the Parramatta and Hawkesbury settlements. Two out of every three were convicts, and nearly seventy free emigrants had farms or small businesses, the remainder being soldiers and administrators, along with prisoners whose sentence had ended and who chose to stay put. Most convicts came from large English towns and knew little about agriculture; the majority of them had no trade, they had been day labourers or had lived off their wits. Female convicts were outnumbered by men more than three to one.

Muir, Skirving and Palmer began exploring the town, beginning at the beach and walking up the bank of the stream to a small wooden bridge. Standing on the bridge they could see three large cisterns carved in the soft sandstone bed. Dry summers made it necessary to conserve water, and Governor Phillip had ordered the reservoirs dug. From then on the water course had been known as the Tank Stream. To the east of the bridge stood the governor's residence, with a storehouse and forge nearby, above the government wharf; clustered around them were houses for the surveyor general, the chaplain and other officials. On the rising ground behind were convicts' huts and married quarters for soldiers.

The main street ran parallel to the stream on its west bank, passing in front of barracks and through a parade ground on its way south to the graveyard and gallows at the edge of town, on its way to Parramatta. To the north of the bridge, the street edged along the cove shore in an area known as The Rocks. It passed another barracks block, the hospital with its wharf, and a storehouse and prison, before climbing to the observation post and signal battery at the west point of the cove. Prisoners' huts were scattered in rows on the hills behind, some of brick, others simple wattle and daub hovels. All were whitewashed with pipe-clay. Some roofs were thatch but most now had wooden shingles. All of the roads were rough, rocky pathways and everywhere stood stumps of recently cleared gum trees. No matter where they went, they were never far from a chain gang and, dotted here and there on the outskirts, one or two of the local people, who called themselves the Cameraigal.

The reformers remained aboard the Surprize for a week, by which time houses had been found for them. The Margarots had a brick hut and garden on the west side of town and Muir, Skirving and Palmer were allocated similar huts, side by side, on the east side of the bridge, on the hill above the government buildings. They, too, had gardens, and stood on a spring that fed the Tank Stream. Money was worthless, the main currency was rum, a commodity in great demand, but Grose was good enough to make them aware of this and asked for a list of items they needed, which he would provide himself. Things were not looking quite as bad as reports at home had led them to expect.

As they acclimatised to their new homes they learned that Grose was to leave for England on the Daedalus on 15 November, only a week away. The news meant only one thing, Grose had washed his hands of both Campbell's case and their own. There would be no public justice done. Muir had begun gathering evidence in defence of Palmer and Skirving during the voyage. They had continued to add to the depositions since arriving and had persuaded reluctant magistrates to witness them. The three decided it was now of the greatest importance to get their story back to Britain to defend the reputations of Skirving and Palmer from versions that might already be circulating there.

Muir set to work finishing the depositions as Palmer and Skirving hurried to finish the narrative in time to catch the homeward-bound ship. The departing surgeon, John White, agreed to take their papers and letters and deliver them to Jeremiah Joyce. They assumed that the Unitarian minister would look after their interests at home, unaware that he had been tried for treason and acquitted. They asked him to engage a barrister to begin proceedings against Campbell in England, using their narrative and more than sixty depositions as evidence.

According to Palmer, Margarot and Campbell were obstructing the collection of evidence. "Margarot has shewn (sic) his consistency by endeavouring to terrify some persons from giving their testimony," he recorded in his narrative for Joyce. "Margarot is very intimate with Campbell and has received some very considerable presents from him. At the Governor's table, and in all companies, Campbell endeavours to exalt Margarot and deprecate us. The most improbable calumnies of me, of vices abhorrent from my nature, he is everywhere inventing and circulating."

John Stirling, a convict that Campbell had threatened to shoot if he did not give evidence against Palmer and Skirving, was one of those who gave evidence to the reformers. He had come across Campbell's chief witness, Draper, on shore and "he asked Draper if he had got any of the fine things that had been promised to him, he said no, he could not expect much now for telling lies, for every word he had said against Mr Palmer and Skirving were lies."

A letter to Joyce, signed by Skirving, Palmer and Muir, asked him to "communicate to the public the reasons of our total separation from Mr Margarot". In it they accused Margarot of being an accessory to the wrongs they had suffered and declared, "He stands a man rejected and expelled from our society."

*

Major Grose transferred his regency to the young Captain William Paterson when he took the farewell salute from his loyal New South Wales Corps as the Daedalus caught the wind and left the cove that summer afternoon in November. He was confident that Paterson's regime would continue to enrich his officers as much as his had. Paterson was his acolyte. Grose had been dissatisfied with progress under the first governor, a naval captain called Arthur Phillip. Phillip had steered the fledgling penal colony through its starvation years from 1788, living off salted meat brought from Britain or sent from India, until he left in December 1792, convinced that new settlements outside of the cove would eventually lead to self-sufficiency. He had done this by putting convicts to work growing crops for general use, and by gradually awarding grants of land and the use of tools to former convicts of good character. Hunger was shared equally and the soldiers resented it. Grose changed all that. His seventeen officers became the new elite. They enriched themselves by grants of prime land of their own choosing. They were given ten field workers each, as well as domestic servants, fed and clothed at government expense. They controlled the sale of all goods, especially alcohol, and they aimed to become gentlemen instead of jailers. Any settler could now buy convicts and then pay them as they pleased, so long as they were not a cost to the junta. To ensure their supremacy the soldiers took charge of civil administration, including justice; magistrates were replaced by officers. They were a military dictatorship.

Grose and Paterson were assisted by a genius administrator, the young Lieutenant John MacArthur who, as regimental paymaster and inspector of public works, controlled the supply of labour and capital. Their monopoly on spirits was masterminded by MacArthur in 1793, when an American ship, the Hope, put in with 7,500 gallons of booze in her hold. MacArthur bought the lot, in the name of the corps, using IOUs against regimental funds in England. From that day on, almost all of the cargo that passed through Sydney went first through the stores of the New South Wales regiment, which soon earned a nickname reflecting its true purpose, the Rum Corps. By the time a new governor could be commissioned, appointed and sent from Britain, the corps would be an armed business enterprise, difficult to control and jealous of its privileges. They were well on their way to owning a third of the cattle in Australia, more than half the horses and three quarters of the sheep.

This made little initial impression on Muir, Skirving or Palmer, for within weeks they each had a small farm as well as their houses in Sydney. Palmer bought 100 acres of cleared land for £84 from a surgeon's assistant who was going home; Skirving paid £80 for a working farm with a crop in the fields; and Muir bought 30 acres of densely wooded land on the other side of Port Jackson for £30. Each of them was given two convicts to help with the work. They were all very pleased.

Skirving wrote to his wife in Edinburgh, telling her, "I am already an heritor and freeholder in New South Wales; I have purchased a farm, crop, and work already done upon it, valued above £80; I have also got upon it a man, woman, and beast. I am not however in the slave trade, be assured, but shall treat them as brethren if they behave well. I also have the servant allowed me by the governor, and a lad by the name of Moor, belonging to Edinburgh, a free man who was left here by accident some time ago, whom I found in a very destitute condition. In remembrance of you, I have given the name of New Strathruddie to this far-away farm and, I trust, if I get any tolerable assistance sent me, to make it soon of more value than the old."

Palmer gave the news to Joyce with great enthusiasm. "The reports you have had of this country are mostly false," he wrote. "The soil is capital, the climate, delicious. I will take it upon me to say that it will soon be a region of plenty, and wants only virtue and liberty to be another America. Nature probably has done more for this than the last. I never saw a place where a man could so soon make a fortune, and that by the fairest means, agriculture. The officers have already done it, and this (I can scarcely expect to be believed) in eighteen months, yet it is absolutely fact; till then (the period of Phillip's government) all private industry was repressed, everyone was obliged to labour for what he hated. Governor Grose totally reversed the whole system; he gave land not only to officers and free men, but to convicts; he gave all the convicts half of every five days and the whole of Saturday and Sunday. By a little longer continuance of good sense, transportation here will become a blessing. I heartily wish that all the paupers of Great Britain could make interest to be sent here." He asked Joyce to send him seeds of the early York cabbage, onions, and everlasting peas.

Muir was no less appreciative. To Moffat he wrote, "We have been employed in celebrating the anniversary of the first convention, which met upon the 11th December, 1792. Last night we all supped in the Secretary's house, this night in Palmer's, and tomorrow in mine, over the water in a small farm I purchased for £30 sterling. You see we still have some little enjoyments. Of our treatment here I cannot speak too highly. Gratitude will forever bind me to the officers, civil and military." He went on to tell Moffat, "I have a neat little house here. I have another two miles distant at the farm across the water. A servant of a friend, who has a taste for drawing, has sketched the landscape. I have sent it to my mother; you may see it."

The "friend" was the departing principal surgeon, John White, whom Muir had known for only a few weeks. White made a similar impression on Palmer, who told Joyce, "It is to him that I am indebted, possibly more than my innocence, for my present comforts... He has given me a house and four acres of land."

The artist sketching for Muir was Thomas Watling from Dumfries, transported for fourteen years for forging seven Bank of Scotland five pound notes, and he and Muir had much in common: time in the Edinburgh Tollbooth and in the hulks, and a voyage involving a (fairly common) conspiracy to mutiny, but they had a grave difference of opinion about White.

Watling had spent much of his time since he landed in 1792 painting landscapes and recording the flora and fauna of the new continent. White had recognised his talent and had written scientific descriptions to accompany the illustrations, ready for publication in England (in time these paintings became famous and Watling was later hailed as the first Australian colonial artist). Watling, however, never received a penny for his work. On the back of one of Watling's paintings White had written, "The pride and vanity of the draughtsman has induced him to put his name to all the drawings, but should you publish them I think the name may be left out."

Watling complained in a letter to his aunt in Dumfries, "Instances of oppression, and mean-souled despotism, are so glaring and frequent, as to banish every hope of generosity and urbanity from such as I am, for unless we can flatter and cajole the vices and follies of our superiors with the most abominable servility, nothing is to be expected, and even this conduct very often...meets with its just reward, neglect and contempt." He described White as "a very mercenary, sordid person" to whom he was a "genius in bondage". He resented being "lent about like a household utensil to his [White's] neighbours." On the surgeon's departure, Watling was passed on like chattel to Captain David Collins, who had previously borrowed him to paint a series of illustrations of the streets and buildings in Sydney Cove for his *Account of the English Colony in New South Wales*. None of the illustrations in that successful book were attributed to Watling.

If Watling's treatment by colonial officers had been told to Muir it would have forced him to keep an open mind. Maybe all three of the new prisoners had been too generous in their estimate of them. Nevertheless, by December the wheat was being gathered in, there was enough wood to fill hearths and to build boats of a reasonable quality, there was plenty of fish in the coves and even beyond the Heads. Muir spent much of his time fishing from his small rowing boat, and the oysters were the largest they had ever seen. Muir planned to write commentaries on the Scottish sedition trials and had made a start on a treatise on the libel law of Scotland. He spent a lot of his time at his farm but regularly rowed across the bay to see his friends. Like Skirving and Palmer he anxiously awaited the arrival of a ship, any ship that might bring letters, news, and Gerrald.

On the morning of Christmas Eve, Muir spotted a signal at the South Head announcing the imminent arrival of a vessel. He had been intending to celebrate with his friends in any case but he called to his two young convict servants, a young woman called Jean and a boy by the name of Robert, to join him and the three climbed into his small boat earlier than intended to row the two miles to town. They all watched from the Sydney shore as the Experiment from Calcutta dropped anchor. James Boston and James Ellis stood with them, keen to be taken aboard to buy provisions with which to stock their business. They were refused passage on every launch heading for the ship and complained to an officer of the corps standing nearby.

"That's not how it works," he told them. "We bring the provisions ashore and you," he buried a finger in Boston's chest, "buy them from our store."

Boston and Ellis went away disappointed and with a deep feeling of injustice. They avoided making a scene for fear the power of the military would be used against them. They had had none of the help promised to free settlers since landing and had met with only hostility from the colony's officials. The Bostons were given a house in the same row as Palmer and Ellis and the others but had had to rely on Palmer's generosity to make ends meet. Boston could extract no explanation from the government clerks but word was that Campbell had told the officers he had republican sympathies and had drunk toasts aboard Surprize damning the king. The Experiment brought no news of Gerrald and certainly no news of a much hoped for change of ministry at Westminster, which the reformers believed would restore their liberty.

*

January brought heavy rains that destroyed the new wheat crops and swept away a bridge in Parramatta. Unsettling news was passed around of attacks on and by aborigines at the inland settlements. Insecurity grew as dwindling stores caused the food of convicts to be cut to allow soldiers and settlers to remain on full rations. It was March before the next ship, the Britannia, arrived from the Cape, and this time Boston and Ellis were determined to buy provisions straight from the deck. They had arranged a boat in advance and rowed out to the ship. When they climbed on board they were confronted by an officer of the corps.

"What do you two want?" he demanded.

"With great respect, sir," said Boston, "we have come on board to purchase items we require for our own use."

"You know you have to buy from the shore. Get back in your boat and wait there," the officer ordered.

"I must insist, sir," replied Boston, "on my privilege as a British subject in one of his majesty's harbours. Your refusal to allow us to trade is an invasion of our common rights."

"Common rights be damned!" shouted the officer. "Sergeant! Have your men escort these two *British subjects* off this ship!"

The officer reported the incident to Paterson, who had Boston and Ellis locked up overnight to teach them not to interfere with the monopoly of the regiment. He went further, and ordered that no grants or servants were to be given to them and that Palmer, who he imagined was the inspiration for their audacity, should suffer similar sanctions. Palmer wrote to his friend Dr John Disney in England, "My men, which I bought at a monstrous rate, with a farm, have been taken from me. A message has been sent to me to pull off my hat to the officers or I should be confined to the cells and punished. Public orders have been twice given for no soldier to speak to me, under the penalty of 100 lashes."

Ironically, the Britannia had very few provisions, bringing the prospect of starvation even closer. She unloaded only some livestock, one stallion, twenty-nine mares, three fillies and twelve sheep. Salted provisions were running so low that the meagre ration of beef and pork was halved and supplemented with extra pease. Paterson chartered the Britannia to sail to India for more provisions.

On 21 April the Colonial schooner, which had been upriver at Hawkesbury since December, returned with 1,100 bushels of corn cobs. The captain reported that the local tribe had been stealing corn and that two of them had been killed by a party of settlers. Paterson ordered a party of soldiers from Parramatta "with instructions to destroy as many as they could meet with of the wood tribe (Bediagal); and, in the hope of striking terror, to erect gibbets in different places, whereupon the bodies of those they might kill were to be hung". A farm at Richmond Hill was subsequently attacked by the tribe and the farmer and his son killed. A woman escaped by hiding in reeds in the river. Rural patrols by soldiers became permanent.

On 11 May the Endeavour put in with 132 head of cattle, quantities of rice and other goods, but no salt meat. By July the few remaining casks of salt meat were reserved for the corps and convicts' rations were reduced to only corn, rice, flour and sugar. Salt became scarce and Boston offered to make it from sea water. He was given seven men to help and Paterson ungratefully noted that he "only produced three or four bushels [about 24-32 gallons] of salt in more than as many weeks".

"The situation in the colony is at present dreadful," Palmer anxiously explained to Disney in his letter. "It is put on half allowance, and even at this rate there is not enough in the stores to last three weeks. They have begun to kill the livestock. The cows are condemned but all the stock in the colony will not last a month. The only resource is about three months' provision of Indian corn, a food inadequate to labour. In this state Mr Boston wrote to the commanding officer that he was sent out by government on purpose to make salt and cure fish, and he would undertake, with the assistance of boats and men, to supply from Lord Howe's Island in the neighbourhood, a full or even double allowance of well cured fish, at a third of the price of beef and pork. Can you conceive that little or no notice was taken of this and nearly a flat denial given?"

He went on to condemn the treatment of aborigines. "The natives of the Hawkesbury (the richest land possibly in the world, producing 30 and 40 bushels of wheat per acre) lived on the wild yams on the banks. Cultivation has rooted out these, and poverty compelled them to steal Indian corn to support nature. The unfeeling settlers resented this by unparalleled severities. The blacks in return speared two or three whites, but tired out they came unarmed and sued for peace. This, government thought proper to deny them and last week sent sixty soldiers to kill and destroy all they could meet with and drive them utterly from Hawkesbury. They seized a native boy who lived with a settler and made him discover where his parents and relations concealed themselves. They came upon them, unarmed and unexpected, killed five and wounded many more. The dead they hang on a gibbet *in terrorem*. The war may be universal on the part of the blacks, whose improvement and civilization will be a long time deferred."

Palmer pinned his hopes on the arrival of the new governor, John Hunter, another naval captain, who "will come out with just and liberal ideas, I trust, of policy, and correct the many abuses and oppressions we groan under, as well as those poor natives". His naïve enthusiasm was misplaced. While still at Plymouth, Hunter had been passed Campbell's correspondence from Rio on the mutiny, and wrote to Under-secretary King about his intentions. He was "considering on the best mode of disposing of such infamous characters. What can their advocates in the House of Commons say in their favour after this infamous conduct? Boston seems to be such a scoundrel that I think he ought not to be allowed any of the advantages promised him… These are characters over whom I will watch in the strictest manner, in short, they shall be treated as they deserve; but I cannot possibly forget the language held in their various conversations. No recommendation whatever can in the smallest degree weigh with me after such language, such infamous conduct."

HMS Providence arrived in Port Jackson in August. She was a warship and brought neither provisions for the colony nor new convicts. She did bring news that HMS Supply and HMS Reliance were some way behind her, with Governor Hunter on the Reliance. The other news that cheered Muir, Palmer and Skirving, was that Hardy, Tooke and the others had been charged with treason and acquitted by juries of their peers. This was the first they had heard of the proceedings. They guessed what might be taking place, having recently received copies of the reports of the parliamentary secret committees from the journalist John Rutt, who had sent them via the colony's Anglican minister, Richard Johnson.

Before Hunter's arrival, better news came in the form of the ship Fancy, from Norfolk Island, 2,000 miles out in the Pacific, carrying forty tons of salt pork. It wasn't much, but it helped. Hunter arrived on Monday 7 September. The Reliance and the Supply brought only a few barrels of salted meat from Rio, a town clock and a windmill. The store ship, Young William, which had been sailing with them had been too heavily laden and had had to turn back to England near the start of the voyage. Spirits were as low as provisions. Hunter held a public meeting at the end of his first week at which his commission was read out, and where he spoke about future conduct in the colony, "touching with much delicacy on that of the persons lately sent out for a certain offence (some of whom were present); and strongly urging the necessity of a general unanimity in support of his majesty's government".

Hunter began well enough by abolishing the military government and returning the colony to civil administration. He attempted to face down the power of the Rum Corps but was never going to be successful. Their monopoly was broken in name only. Nevertheless, Hunter's opening decrees were celebrated in Johnson's church. In a letter to his friend Theophilus Lindsey, Palmer reported, "It was the first Sunday after Governor Hunter's arrival. He exposed the last government, their extortion, their despotism, their debauchery and ruin of the colony, driving it almost to famine by the sale of liquors at 1,200 per cent profit. He congratulated the colony at the abolition of a military government, and the restoration of a civil one, and of the laws. Orders are this day given out that no officer shall sell any more liquor."

Hunter took a census and reorganised the distribution of labour to ensure the wheat harvest was got in and corn was planted. He still allowed Rum Corps officers their ten field labourers and three domestic servants; civilian officials got four; free settlers, two; ex-convict settlers, one; and the two sergeants of the New South Wales Corps, one each. The delayed store ship, Young William, came into harbour on 11 October, and rations were improved.

CHAPTER 35

Voice of the banished

"What though the slaves of wicked power combine,
The cause of liberty to undermine,
Her battlements the wrecks of time shall stand,
And mock the fury of each hostile band."

Lines presented to Joseph Gerrald in Newgate.

John Hunter was a sea captain. He had no experience in the art of politics or the practice of economics, although he had watched the colony's founding governor, Arthur Phillip, nurture the community during its first three years. Hunter was second captain of the first fleet that took Phillip there in 1788 and returned to Britain in 1792 to serve as a subordinate officer until, to his surprise, he was chosen to succeed to the governorship of New South Wales. Neither he nor his predecessor, nor any of the stand-in lieutenants, was illustrious. The job was that of a specialist prison governor in the eyes of ministers at Westminster. Hunter was, though, accommodating and approachable, a Scot from Leith, and naturally curious about his four most interesting convicts. He therefore asked each of them to tea in the governor's house, separately of course, for he wanted to take the measure of them.

He confided in a letter to a friend in his home town, "The four gentlemen, whom the activity of the magistrates of Edinburgh provided for our colony, I have seen and conversed with separately, since my arrival here. They seem all of them gifted in the powers of conversation. Muir was the first I saw. I thought him a sensible, modest young man of a very retired turn... He said nothing on the severity of his fate but seemed to bear his circumstances with a proper degree of fortitude and resignation. Skirving was the next I saw; he appeared to me to be a sensible, well-informed man, not young, perhaps fifty. He is fond of farming, and has purchased a piece of ground and makes good use of it, which will, by and by, turn to his advantage. Palmer paid me the next visit, he is said to be a turbulent, restless kind of man; it may be so, but I must do him the justice to say that I have seen nothing of that disposition in him since my arrival. Margarot seems to be a lively, facetious, talkative man, complained heavily of the injustice of his sentence, in which, however, he found I could not agree with him... I have to say that their general conduct is quiet, decent, and orderly. If it continues so, they will not find me disposed to be harsh or distressing to them."

Governor Hunter had clearly altered his earlier opinion formed from Campbell's letters, although he had not reinstated Palmer's helpers. He had made enemies of the Rum Corps by disturbing their hold on the colony, but possibly felt that to countermand a specific order of their leader could be tempting fate. The Bostons, however, had begun to prosper without the help promised to them as free settlers. Along with Palmer and Ellis, they had begun making beer, vinegar, salt, soap and candles for sale, and had just started distilling oil from peppermint leaves.

During one of their evening discussions in the gardens of the adjoining huts, Muir proposed a new strategy, to petition the new governor for the right to leave. They all believed that the law was on their side, that they had completed their sentence under Scots law by being banished. They only had to persuade Hunter that was the case. They agreed and on Wednesday 14 October, Muir delivered a petition to the governor, written in is own hand. It argued that "we contend with firmness, but with becoming respect" that the sentences do not "restrain our right of departure whenever we may judge departure expedient". It pointed out that Braxfield had admitted as much after the trials and that Lauderdale had quoted him in the House of Lords, saying, "That in sentencing these persons to fourteen years transportation, in consequence of which they were sent to Botany Bay, it was not in his contemplation that they should be confined to that place, or that they should be prevented from going to any other, provided they did not return here, or that they should be kept in servitude and subjected to control."

The document recorded that Gerrald's defence lawyer had argued in court that Scots law allowed no judge to confine a man who has been banished and, it claimed, counsel for the crown agreed. "The extent of our punishment is banishment," the petition reiterated. "Already the terms of the sentence are completed. We have been banished by transportation, and there can be no higher security against our returning to Britain than the forfeiture of our lives. To all the rights of free men we are entitled, with the single exception of interdiction from one portion of the dominions of the empire."

Hunter was swayed by the force of the arguments and tussled with the problem for more than a week. Finally, after dining alone on his veranda one evening, and watching the waves in the cove flash orange darts from the sinking sun, he picked up his pen to inform the Duke of Portland at the Home Office, of his conclusion. "I have examined with care and consideration the respective sentences of these people. I have perused their arguments in favour of and against these sentences, and I am obliged to confess, my lord, that I cannot feel myself justifiable in forcibly detaining them in this country against their consent... Although they have not it in their power to return to any part of Great Britain but at risk of life, they probably might have a desire to pass their time in Ireland. I hope I may receive his majesty's instructions upon this subject."

*

Boston was in an outhouse at the back of his Sydney cottage, bottling a batch of newly-distilled vinegar, when he heard the shot.

"What was that?" he called to his wife in the kitchen.

"It sounded like a gun shot," she shouted. "Hang on, I'll look in the street." She stepped outside as a boy came running to their door.

"Missus Boston!" he cried, "they've shot your pig!"

"Who has?"

"The soldiers, Missus Boston," the boy said. "They went through a close at the bottom of the stable yard over there." He pointed to the disused yard of a Captain Foveaux, adjacent to the paddock where the Bostons' pigs ran. They sometimes pushed through a dilapidated gate between the properties and snuffled in Foveaux's yard.

Boston rushed to the yard, where he saw his best sow, which was well advanced with piglets, lying dead and bleeding. He ran to the main street where he found a group of soldiers near the bridge over the Tank Stream.

"Who is the damned rascal that shot my sow?" he called.

Thomas Laycock, Rum Corps quartermaster and still a justice of the peace, turned away from his colleague, Ensign Neil McKellar, and two privates.

"Who are you calling a damned rascal?" he demanded.

"The man that shot my sow," said an angry and distressed Boston

Laycock called over Private William Faithfull, pointed at Boston, and urged him on. "That fellow has just called you a rascal. Thrash him!"

Faithfull moved toward Boston, his musket in hand. Boston grabbed an axe handle from a bystander to protect himself.

"Knock him down with your gun!" ordered Ensign McKellar. Faithfull struck Boston on the back of the head with the stock of the weapon. The blow bent the ramrod, which fell to the ground. Boston overcame the pain and stood his ground. He called for assistance.

Mrs Boston appeared in a state of alarm and stood defiantly between her husband and his attackers.

McKellar told the private to take the loaded gun away.

"Beat him again!" ordered Laycock, "for as long as he can stand." He turned to the other private, William Eaddy and pushed him forward. "Thrash him as long as he has life! Will you allow that fellow to call a soldier a rascal?"

The two privates again moved towards Boston and his wife, when a neighbour called on them to escape through the back door of her house.

"That's the rascal!" McKellar yelled after them. "He deserves a good thrashing."

A crowd had gathered looking for the fun of a fight. A sergeant at the back agreed with McKellar. "There's a whole society of them deserve a good thrashing!" he shouted over the heads of the onlookers.

Boston was taken home and his wife dressed his head wound and soothed his pride. Palmer, Ellis and Muir gathered round. Mrs Boston described the vindictive violence of the soldiers.

"Then we'll prosecute," said Muir.

"But they still control the courts," objected Mrs Boston.

"We'll do better. We'll sue. In a civil court," said Muir.

"I don't believe there's ever been a civil case taken in the colony," Palmer pointed out.

"In that case we'll make history," replied Muir.

A week later, Muir was still in his Sydney hut preparing affidavits for Boston's case when Palmer came in.

"The signal flag's gone up on the South Head," he said. "A ship's been sighted."

An approaching vessel always stirred mass curiosity, and the whole town turned out as usual. There would be news, possibly letters, maybe friends or acquaintances on board. Word passed round that the new arrival was the store-ship Sovereign and later that evening she dropped anchor in the cove. Muir and Palmer were about to return to their homes after watching the officers and some of the crew come ashore when they spotted a familiar figure in the last jolly-boat to row towards the beach.

"It's Gerrald!" exclaimed Palmer.

Ger-rald!" Muir shouted. He and Palmer waved their arms. They saw a hand slowly rise from the slight figure in the boat, then noticed Margarot crashing through the surf to welcome his old friend from the Corresponding Society. They decided discretion was required and left Margarot to accompany Gerrald, supported by the ship's surgeon, to a waiting officer, who took him at once to the governor's residence.

The surgeon saw Hunter first and explained that Gerrald was the only prisoner aboard the ship, which had touched at Rio in a voyage of 165 days. During nearly six months at sea, Gerrald had received constant medical attention for advanced consumption. The surgeon recommended that Gerrald be found a quiet and airy place to spend his days, which he thought would be few. Hunter interviewed Gerrald, who asked that he be allowed to stay with his friend Margarot and his wife in the meantime, to which the governor agreed. That night, Thursday 5 November, Hunter made a note for a future dispatch to London. "When the Sovereign store ship arrived, I found Mr Joseph Gerrald had been sent in that ship. He was landed here in a very declining state of health, which rendered it necessary that he should reside in some quiet and retired situation. For this purpose application was made to me for permission for his purchasing a small house and garden...in the neighbourhood of Sydney, but so retired as suited the weakly state he was in. Permission was immediately granted for his residing in any place that might be convenient to his health."

Gerrald moved in with the Margarots but his time there was brief. In a few days he asked Palmer if he would have him until his own place was found. Gerrald didn't reveal the difference between them, but Margarot sent a maliciously worded letter to Hardy in London. "Gerrald is arrived," he announced. "He has fled my habitation and the fraternal reception I gave him, to join others who may, in return for those good things he has brought with him, encourage his failings and feed his vanity with insidious praise."

Gerrald had disapproved of Margarot's behaviour on the Surprize; he realised he was in the company of a man who was obsessive and divisive and was too much to handle. It was strange that Margarot referred to "the good things" Gerrald had brought with him, for when he was settled in Palmer's house and felt well enough to tell his story, it became clear that he had arrived with nothing. Muir and Skirving had come to be with him on his first evening in Palmer's, and were initially shocked at Gerrald's condition. As well as an almost constant cough, he had lost the youthful bloom in his face and his complexion was drained and pale. His body was wasted and his old prison clothes hung from his frame.

From his bed in Palmer's living room, Gerrald, though breathless, explained how he was removed from Newgate to make room for Hardy and the others, brought from the Tower to answer charges of treason in the Old Bailey. "I was taken to Giltspur Street, the New Compter, where I remained until the second of May this year," he said. "The date is fast in my memory because it was the last that I saw of my daughter. It was a Saturday, about three o'clock in the afternoon, just as I had lain down to rest, for I felt ill. I was informed that Pitt, the turnkey of Newgate, wanted to speak with me. I rose and went down to the lobby of the prison, when several people seized me, put me in irons, hand-cuffing me and shackling my legs. I was not even permitted to return to my apartments, to take leave of my poor infant daughter, who was a constant companion of my imprisonment, but instantly hurried into a post-chaise with Pitt the turnkey, and driven to Gosport, where I was put on board the Sovereign transport. My removal was so abrupt and unexpected that I was not allowed time to provide myself with the common necessaries of life."

"What became of your daughter?" asked Palmer.

"Dear Dr Parr, who has been like a father to me for much of my life, already had taken charge of my son, and promised to educate him and provide for him. I understand he has made arrangements for my sweet daughter, too."

Gerrald told them how their supporters in parliament had tried to find out what was to be done with him, his health being so fragile, and had managed to privately question Henry Dundas who, although no longer home secretary, still had unequalled influence in cabinet. He had told them, "There is no intention of sending Mr Gerrald at present; and if it depended on me, he will not be sent." That had been at the beginning of April, a mere month before he was unexpectedly grabbed and taken away. "The rankness of their duplicity was made to keep pace with the rigour of their oppression," Gerrald continued. "They attempted to infuse hope, only that they might enjoy the demon-like satisfaction of blasting it; and I was hurried away, like the vilest of malefactors, fettered and without the slightest notice."

Gerrald was so exhausted from the effort of telling his story that his head fell back on the pillow. He closed his eyes and the others left the room softly and stepped into the warm November evening. They set themselves two tasks for the next month, first, to find a quiet and accessible property for Gerrald; second, to complete the papers for Boston's civil suit against the military bullies.

*

Captain David Collins, who still occupied the post of advocate-general, had allowed the hearing to go ahead but had prevented Muir from representing Boston, who would have to plead his own case. Boston v Laycock, McKellar and others was due to begin on Thursday, 3 December.

The bench of the court comprised Judge-Advocate Collins, Dr Balmain, and Captain George Johnston, all military men. Boston read from Muir's opening statement and argued that the assault on him was aggravated by the main persons being military officers, one of them a magistrate, and that they had ordered private soldiers to commit the crime. He claimed £500 exemplary compensation and examined witnesses, according to Muir's instructions, over seven court sittings during December. The judges found in favour of Boston but the two officers were ordered to pay only one pound sterling each in compensation, and the two privates were exonerated. The officers immediately appealed to the governor who, on 30 December, sat for the first time as a formal court of appeal and, to the exasperation of most of the Rum Corps, upheld the verdict to which he added, meekly, "I have thought it a lenient one".

*

The following evening's hogmanay celebration in Palmer's house saw the Bostons, Ellis, Gerrald, Skirving and his helpers from New Strathruddie, and Muir along with his helpers, Jean and Robert from his farm, all raise their glasses to 1796 and to the modest success of the first civil case heard in the colony of New South Wales. They also toasted Gerrald and his new house and garden in Farm Cove in the inlet to the east of Sydney Cove, just a short walk over the rise above Government House.

December had been unusually hot, causing much of the wheat harvest to fail. The searing summer continued into January, when HMS Supply returned from a voyage to Norfolk Island with news that cultivation there was threatened by a plague of rats and a virulent weed that nobody could control. The island's lieutenant governor, Philip King, was dangerously ill. But in Sydney the carpenters' shops and forges were busy, and some "very drinkable wine was being pressed from increasingly abundant grape harvests". On New Year's Day a brig, Arthur, came into harbour with much needed goods for sale. A theatre was opened on 16 January, giving a play called *The Revenge* its Sydney premier, which was an acclaimed success, marred only by a series of burglaries in the homes of those attending it.

Towards the end of the month Gerrald was forced to leave his Farm Cove home and return to Palmer's front room. His condition had deteriorated and he became too weak to look after himself. His coughing was painful and his sputum was tinged with blood; he had fevers and sweats and the glands on his neck swelled. He needed constant attention, which Palmer, Skirving, Muir, Ellis and the Bostons provided in rotation. Gerrald got no medical assistance from Dr Balmain, one of the judges in the Boston case. He was the principal surgeon and assistant to Dr Thomson, the new surgeon general who had travelled on the Surprize. Thomson was at the upriver settlements and Balmain was the only doctor in town. In spite of repeated requests, he failed to attend the dying man's bedside. A young convict who worked as an orderly at the hospital was the only one to offer assistance.

Another store-ship, the Ceres, arrived from England on 23 January and, apart from landing supplies, letters and newspapers, it also deposited four castaways, two French and two English, who had been picked up from the lonely Amsterdam Island in the middle of the Southern Indian Ocean. Muir went looking for them, thirsty for tales from the outside world, and found their leader, Pierre Francois Péron, in a tavern by the strand. He introduced himself and bought the young Frenchman a drink.

Péron explained that they had lived like Robinson Crusoe for more than three years. He told Muir how he and his three companions had been dropped off on Amsterdam Island as a sealing party from their ship, the Emélie, which was travelling onwards and planned to return for them when they had enough sealskins for a cargo. But the Emélie never returned. Unknown to them, it had been captured by a British warship and taken to China. They were marooned. In three years they amassed a valuable haul of skins, and they ended up dressed in them, but when the store ship Ceres found them it had no room for their furs, which they had to leave behind. They were worth a great deal of money. Péron and Muir became firm friends. They had similar views on liberty and society and shared a curiosity about the world around them.

On the morning after Ceres arrived, two more ships put into Sydney Cove. First was the Experiment, returned from India carrying calicoes, chintzes, soap, sugar, spirits, and small goods. Shortly after, the Otter from Boston dropped anchor looking for water and wood for fuel. Péron, anxious to find a berth on a trading vessel, approached the Otter's skipper, Captain Ebenezer Dorr, only to find that Dorr had called at Amsterdam Island and had picked up Péron's abandoned skins. The two men negotiated and Péron was taken on as Otter's first officer, on condition that he and Dorr had an equal share in the profits from the sale in China of Amsterdam Island furs.

Péron spent time ashore with Muir at his house in Sydney or at his farm across the bay. Muir told Péron of his time in Paris, how he met Condorcet, witnessed the debate on Louis in the Convention, and was present at the king's execution. The Frenchman told Muir of his adventures around the globe since1783 as the two of them sat in front of the hut or walked along Cockle Beach. One evening in early February, Muir asked for Péron's help to escape.

Péron arranged a meeting with Dorr. "British frigates guard the approach to Port Jackson at the moment," said Dorr. "It's possible they'll board us and search the ship."

"The seasonal fogs are thick at night and don't clear till midday," Muir said. "I have a small boat. I can row beyond the Heads in darkness. If you'll spare me a compass I can set out twelve hours before you and meet at an assigned point."

The American captain agreed and set the date of departure for 18 February.

"This has to be done without danger to myself or to Mr Péron," insisted Dorr. "Nothing in writing. We simply picked you up in distress in the open sea."

Muir gathered his friends in Palmer's house. Skirving had moved back to town from his farm to assist in nursing Gerrald, who was declining by the day. Muir explained that the Otter was to leave for Boston by way of China in a just over week and that he intended to be on her. She was to gather furs on the Pacific coast of North America and sell them in Canton, a voyage that could take up to two years before returning to Boston. He asked if any of them would join him. Gerrald was too weak to contemplate escape but urged Muir to go. Palmer reckoned by the time Muir got to Philadelphia his seven-year sentence would be almost over. In any case, he was absorbed with his enterprises along with Ellis and the Bostons. Skirving complained that he was unwell. He had stomach pains and thought he may have caught gaol fever.

CHAPTER 36

Escape

"Among the transported Mr Dorr hid on board
was one whose memory will always be dear to me."

Mémoires du Capitaine Péron sur ses Voyages, 1824.

On 11 February, the convict transport Marquis Cornwallis arrived in
Sydney Cove carrying 233 convicts, male and female, from Ireland.
The disembarkation of such a large number kept the officers and
men of the Rum Corps fully occupied. Dorr was short of crew and
busy recruiting convicts who had served their time. He took on eighteen hands for the long voyage and, in the confusion, signed on five
who had not completed their sentences.

A week later Muir was across the water at the Cockle Beach farm.
His boat was ready and he had packed only a few belongings: his
pocket bible, an engraving of his portrait, copies of his trial and
some other pamphlets. He sat with his helpers, Jean and Robert, and
told them what he was about to do. He had kept his plans from them
to avoid the chance of information leaking. He told them he had left
a note for the governor and they would not be held responsible for
his actions, but he offered them the opportunity to leave with him.
They both agreed.

They gathered a few belongings and put them in Muir's boat. In
the darkness before midnight, they moved quietly down harbour,
concealed in the deep shadows of the sandstone cliffs. In the early
hours they lost the dim lights of Sydney as they rounded the North
Head and rowed out to sea. They pulled at the oars until dawn, using

Dorr's compass and Péron's hand-drawn chart, and paddled to stay in position as best they could, enclosed by a silent mist, unable to see much beyond their own bow. By the expected mid-morning rendez-vous the Otter had still not arrived. A wind came up, blowing away the cover of mist and pushing them off course. The sea rose. They had no food and only a little water. Rowing was more difficult and tiredness turned to exhaustion. They peered out at the top of each swell but saw only a distant smudge of land. The three were cold and weak and lay in the bottom of the boat for warmth. They slept. At one o'clock in the afternoon a warm sun revived Muir and he lifted his head over the side of the boat.

"Almighty God!" he cried, "I see our saviour on the horizon."

Jean and Robert stirred into life and bent their backs at the oars. Muir pulled off his white shirt and waved it at the distant Otter. He tied it to an oar to hoist it higher. The ship signalled and hove towards them. Péron was waiting on deck with some hands to pull them aboard and lift the dinghy out of the water.

"Oh, *mon ami*," said Péron. "I was so worried. We were delayed in port and could not weigh anchor until this morning. But welcome aboard." They embraced like old friends.

*

Muir's absence was undiscovered for some time. A passing angler landed at Cockle Beach and found Muir's letter to Hunter in the aban-doned cabin. Captain Collins read the letter and later commented, "Mr Muir conceived that in withdrawing (though clandestinely) from this country he was only affecting his freedom; and meant, if he should arrive safely, to enjoy what he deemed himself to have regained of it in America, until the time should come when he might return to his own country with credit and comfort. He proposed practising at the American bar as an advocate; a point of informa-tion which he left behind him in a letter."

*

As the Otter set a course across the Pacific, Gerrald struggled; his breathing was loud and sharp and fevers troubled his nights and days. Throughout the rest of February and early March he was nursed round the clock by his friends. According to Palmer, Dr Balmain was no help. "During a three months illness, the greatest part of the time attended with danger, I could extort from him only three visits. In one of them he took away his medicines under the pretence they were not proper, but I could never get him to trouble himself to send any other."

Skirving's health also deteriorated. His sweats and chills increased and his bowels rebelled. Balmain's treatment of Skirving was no better, visiting him only once.

George Bass, the surgeon on HMS Reliance, who had been away on Norfolk Island since January, returned to Sydney on 5 March. When he heard of Gerrald's dangerous condition he attended immediately, and visited Skirving regularly. Bass left his quarters and moved next door to Palmer to be nearer his patient, but his therapy could only be palliative at this advanced stage of Gerrald's tuberculosis. At three o'clock in the morning of Wednesday 16 March Gerrald died. "Some few hours before his death," Palmer said in a letter to a friend, "calling me to his bedside, 'I die,' said he, 'in the best of causes and, as you witness, without repining'."

He was buried, according to his wishes, in a plot in his garden at Farm Cove. On his tombstone were the words, "He died a martyr to the liberties of his country, in the 36th year of his age". Three days later, dysentery took Skirving. He was buried at his farm, New Strathruddie.

Palmer was furious about the suffering of his companions. He wrote to a friend in April, "Alas Joseph Gerrald has fallen the victim of ministerial malignity. He was in such a state that none but [Dundas] could think of sending him on such a voyage. The lowest ruffian would have had more lenity showed him. The summer was unusually hot and the great variation of the climate in four months after his landing put a period to his existence. The surgeon of the

Reliance, the worthy Dr Bass, who arrived from Norfolk Island a fortnight before his death, in spite of all obloquy (for much attends the even speaking to us) attended him twice a day... Within three days of his death poor Mr Skirving died...He had the disorder a month before he complained."

Hunter received a reply from London to his query about the reformers' sentences. He was told they should be served in New South Wales and not be allowed to leave, certainly not to Ireland. He sent the news to Palmer around the time that the preacher discovered that John Grant, the fraudulent former sheriff of Inverness and the genesis of their shipboard misery, was now employed as clerk to a like-minded man, John MacArthur, regimental paymaster and the brains behind the Rum Corps. Palmer's rage grew. His disillusion with the regimes at home and in New South Wales was bitter.

"The persecution for political opinion is not confined to Great Britain, but extends to her remotest connections," he wrote to Joyce on 5 May 1796. "They are all aristocrats here, from ignorance and being out of the way or desire of knowledge. Governor Hunter is a furious one and sees with no friendly eyes those of opposite principles. This my friends Boston and Ellis and I woefully experience. He has defeated or discouraged every attempt of theirs to benefit the colony or themselves. We are told by a person high in office and high in his confidence that it is his intention to do so in order to drive them into the woods or a farm; or from the country. With talents capable of the most beneficial exertion in this colony they are doomed to starve as far as he can make them as useless characters."

*

On the morning that Gerrald died, Péron at last found a clear channel out of the scattered islands and reefs of the Friendly Isles and set the Otter on a course towards America. The 27-year-old navigator had guided the ship across more than 2,200 miles in the month since they left Sydney Cove, on an ocean known only to a few seafarers. The outlines of New Zealand, Fiji, Tonga, the Friendly Isles, Samoa and

Hawaii were on his charts but were mostly unexplored by outsiders. Muir, to whom Captain Dorr had given the privileges of a passenger in an after-cabin of the 168-ton three-master, was fascinated by the skill of his new friend. He stood watch with Péron and assisted each day as, with sextant and compass, the Breton plotted their position from the mid-day sun. The routine reminded Muir of McPherson, and he wondered whether the much abused mate of the Surprize might at that moment be in seas around India or China on board the Suffolk.

Péron kept a careful log of their voyage and amended his charts as they went. "19th February am", he had recorded, "153.60E, 34.56S, 107 miles from Port Jackson. Noticed sandbank, or coral reef, about 300 feet circumference in 15 to 20 fathoms of water." And later, "7th March, 2am, Tropic of Capricorn. Light N'ly winds perfumed by flowers on nearby island, still unseen." Five days after that, "Mid-day 183.30E, 20.22S, Rotterdam Island about 8 miles NW, with small island between, great many native canoes came out."

Rotterdam Island was called by its inhabitants Nomuka, and the first canoe to reach the Otter brought five people carrying gifts of cooked fish wrapped in leaves. Their chief was invited on deck by Dorr, who, by signs and gestures, indicated that he wanted to find a safe anchorage. The chief understood and piloted the ship to a bay on the south-west of the island. His people were aware of strangers in large wooden ships, having been recently visited by the new breed of Pacific fur traders, but their memory of outsiders stretched back to two visits by Captain Cook in the 1770s and by Captain Bligh in HMS Bounty just seven years previously.

"All the time we were searching for an anchorage," Péron wrote, "we kept up a very active bartering with the natives. By eight o'clock that night the decks were laden with five or six kinds of bananas, water melons, the lightest weighing about 12 pounds, oranges, yams, sweet potatoes, pineapples, coconuts, breadfruit, sugar cane... When night came we fired a cannon, the natives understood the signal, took to the canoes and went back to the island. There were more than one thousand tall and vigorous natives who were renowned for their adroitness and their tendency to steal anything that appealed to them. In case they made an attack, and as a precautionary measure, we had all the swords and guns on deck, and our ten cannons were charged and run out."

"The night passed," he went on, "and at sunrise we fired a cannon. At this signal the sea became covered with canoes, and a most picturesque sight opened up before us. It was a race as to who should reach us first. A hundred canoes swarmed around the ship. Bartering started again for scissors and knives. We had seen pigs but the natives seemed reluctant to part with them; they asked for axes but we did not have any."

On the following day, however, the chief brought a 250lb pig to trade for knives and scissors and during that day's busy bartering the Otter lost one of its former Sydney Cove convicts in a manner reminiscent of Captain Bligh's deserters. The advances of one of the island's beautiful young women had been too much for him and he paddled off in her canoe to a different life. "The women," noted Péron, "that is to say, the ones we saw, did not appear to posses the slightest degree of modesty, and gave themselves to the first person to pass by." In the eight days it took Péron to find a passage out of the islands, another five convicts slipped ashore, reckoning on a life well away from British authority.

On Wednesday 16 March, Péron sailed the Otter between the islands of Tongatapa and Eua into deep, clear water where, for six days, the ship caught a fair wind and sighted Niue, called Savage Island by Cook, in the distance. Samoa was later passed well to its east and on 3 April three more small islands were spotted. As the Otter approached them on the following morning, the lookout shouted to the quarterdeck that people were on the beach waving mats.

"Four men and myself, accompanied by Mr Muir...entered the ship's boat," Péron recorded in his memoir [he always addressed Muir formally in his writing]. "I directed it into a village I had seen through the trees. As we rowed inshore the natives went down to the spot at which we would probably land. We were, however, suddenly stopped by a coral bank covered by not more than a foot and a half of water, and less in some parts. I lifted our oars, and by signs enticed the natives to come towards us; they remained for a long time undecided. However, six of them came armed with spears and clubs, but at a short distance away five of them stopped and the sixth, holding a club in one hand and a branch of cocoanut palm in the other, came out as far as the coral ledge. Supposing the branch to be a hospitable sign I got out of the boat with Mr Muir and stood on the coral ledge. My sailors were ready to fire at the slightest sign."

The locals were reluctant to barter but, seeing how easily a steel knife cut through the palm branch, they accepted a few as gifts. Péron and Muir made to move closer but the islanders became alarmed and readied their clubs and spears. "Mr Muir, imagining that they had not quite understood him," continued Péron, "started pleading in his own way, and tried to point out that we did not have any weapons by throwing up his arms. The natives thought by this we wanted to capture them and ran away, only turning around from time to time to see if we were following them."

Péron ordered the boat back to the ship, but they were pursued by a canoe party, which they outran. The canoes hovered round the ship and Péron gingerly approached them once again and successfully traded trinkets for coconuts, mats, and stone axes as souvenirs.

"It is probable and even certain that they had never seen strangers," he wrote. "They were afraid of our appearance, of the whiteness of our skin, and of the shape of our clothes, and they were completely ignorant of our tools and the objects that we bartered. Everything united to convince us that we had the right to attribute to ourselves the honour of having discovered three new islands, and with this conviction I gave them the name of the Otter Islands... In order to distinguish them we named the eastern one Péron and Muir, the one to the north Dorr, and the name of Brown was given to the third, after one of our officers."

On 5 April the islands were left in the Otter's wake as Péron laid a direct course north-north-west to avoid the outlying reefs of the Hawaiian Islands. During the night of 29-30 April they left the Tropic of Cancer and shortly after rounded Midway Island at the western extremity of the Hawaiian group, tacking to the north-east on a straight line for the American coast. For a month Péron held this course until one morning a lookout yelled, "Land ahead!" The officers lifted their glasses for a clearer view of the craggy inlets on a long, continental shore framed by high, dark green, pine-covered ranges stretching upwards and away into the purple-blue distance. On Sunday 29 May, Péron took the Otter into the Juan de Fuca Strait at the south of what is now known as Vancouver Island and on the following morning turned north-west towards Nootka Sound on the island's western coast.

*

Ebenezer Dorr was a hard-headed, tight-fisted Massachusetts master, scion of a Boston mercantile family who had built, and named, the Otter especially for this trade. The Dorrs must have read the published journal of Captain James Cook, explorer of the Pacific Northwest in 1778, who described the abundance of sea otters there and told how their silky pelts could amass a man a fortune in the markets of Canton. Vessels from many seafaring countries had begun a scramble for the spoils and the newly-built Otter, she was less than a year old, was there to join them.

Dorr was pleased with the seamanship of Péron. He could leave his first officer in charge of the quarterdeck while he supervised the crew. He worked them like regular navy to keep his vessel scrubbed and shined, greased and painted. The hard work was probably one reason why five of the convicts had jumped ship. He was aware he had come to Sydney short of men but he had reckoned on picking up more hands in the port, which was becoming a regular stopping point for American ships heading for the Pacific fur coasts. He needed extra hands for gathering pelts. Dorr was surprised at the additional two brought on board by Muir, but had put Robert to work with the crew and sent Jean to the galley to assist the cook.

Muir stood next to Péron on the quarterdeck. "There's a good anchorage at Nootka Sound," Péron told him. "We can work both sides of the bay and start to trade for furs there, according to Captain Dorr."

Muir asked whether he was in danger and if British ships patrolled these waters. Péron explained that Spain and England had both claimed this section of the coast when the fur trade began. The English wanted to be able to range down as far as San Francisco and the Spanish wanted to set their border at the Straits of Juan de Fuca. They had come to an agreement the previous year to allow equal access, but both sides left the border question unresolved and each of them abandoned their settlements. "So to answer your question, Thomas, it is unlikely you are in any danger."

While sailing up the shoreline the ship was approached by a canoe, paddled by men who were, according to Péron, "of rather small size and whose only clothes consisted of a piece of cloth fastened round their necks by two leather straps, opened in the front, and hanging to the middle of their legs at the back; their heads were covered with small plaits which were like many rays diverging from the same centre... Their roughly built canoes and the coarseness of their manners did not give us a good impression of this tribe. They had nothing to exchange and when we asked them for otter skins they made us understand that they would bring some along. Another canoe 20 to 30 feet long, which approached us toward 7 o'clock, gave us an otter skin for a fathom of cloth."

Further along the coast others refused to trade for cloth and demanded copper, which the Otter did not have. At Barkley Sound, a large inlet called Out-Cha-Chel by its inhabitants, two canoes approached, "singing a war song in a strong sonorous voice and beating time with their paddles against the sides of their canoes. Coming closer the natives discarded their leather garments and stood up naked in the canoes, while the chief addressed a long harangue to the ship's company, of which nothing was understood." They then turned and went away.

Contrary winds blew the Otter south, back to Juan de Fuca, where Dorr ordered Péron to anchor in a deep natural harbour to look for wood and water. The captain had a cannon fired to announce their presence and presently a canoe with four men and three children came alongside with fresh salmon. "Their faces were as black as our chimney sweeps, the smell of their bodies was unbearable," recorded Péron. "On the same day, June 4, I got on board the dinghy with Mr Muir and four good rowers with the intention of visiting the river. At its mouth a column of smoke drew our attention and we rowed in that direction. Fifty steps from the river we came across a hut belonging to five or six Indians. One of them came towards us and beckoned us to come closer. He led us to an old man sitting in front of a hut. After a lot of gestures to greet us he urged us to go in and immediately unrolled several pelts and placed them on scooped-out wooden stumps, inviting us to sit down on them."

The hut was a longhouse constructed of rough beams and boards. It was large, about 50 to 60 feet in length and 18 to 20 feet wide. A fire was burning in the middle of the room, around which several bear joints were roasting; above the fire were a dozen large salmon being smoked on a trellis and all around the hut lay discarded mussel, oyster and scallop shells. The smell inside was the same as from the men in the canoe, their clothes and skin had become impregnated with smoke, fish, meat and fat. But there were no otter skins to be had, neither here nor in other settlements around the harbour. They moved the Otter to the southern side of the strait on Wednesday 8 June and found some locals dressed in European clothes, but there were still no skins for trade. Captain Dorr ordered Péron to make way north again and head for Nootka Sound once more.

Péron turned the ship and began to tack up the coast, accompanied for a time by war canoes "one of which was fifty feet long and ornamented with crude carvings representing the sun and immensely long snakes". Four days later the Otter sailed back into Barkley

Sound, a massive square inlet dotted with islands. Soon they were surrounded by canoes, some carrying women and children, which they took to be a sign of peaceful intentions. The women wore two bear skins fastened at the shoulders, one hanging down their fronts and the other at the back.

The ship lay there for three days and the chief, Out-Cha-Chel, after whom the area was named, came on board. Péron and Muir visited his village while he was busy with Dorr. The two men were greeted with cries of "Vacache! Vacache!" and replied using the same strange words. They came to the chief's large hut, where more demonstrations of friendship were given, accompanied by "naive flirtations with Out-Cha-Chel's wives who were in cheerful mood". Then a stony-faced Out-Cha-Chel appeared at the doorway. They paid the chief compliments and he replied with long mimes of his prowess as a warrior. They made to leave and the chief shook his head. "Out-Cha-Chel answered no with a nod and told us by another sign to wait a little longer, and taking us to a big chest, the outer sides of which were inlaid with human teeth, touching his own to make us better understand what they were. He opened one of the chests and brought out a man's head which he held by the hair. I must admit this princely politeness made me shiver with horror. I think he even noticed my emotion, anyhow he calmly put the head back in its place and stretching his arm toward the other end of the chest, seized another head and showed it to us… Mr Muir told me it was quite possible he would put our heads next to these. 'I think so,' I answered, 'but let us not show our fear'."

The chief showed them his weapons, long wooden bows, iron tipped arrows and two broken muskets. He dressed himself in leather armour of buffalo skins with a leather helmet and a war mask, and displayed his martial skill, after which he allowed them to return to the ship.

The following morning a fresh, headless corpse was found on the shore. They took the warning seriously and weighed anchor. Two of the seamen were attending to the anchor lines in a dinghy when a canoe full of painted braves sliced through the water towards them. The braves attacked with spears and clubs and the two men fought back with knives and oars and finally broke free, clambering aboard the ship, bruised and lacerated. The war canoe retreated to the sound of paddles beating on wood. There were clearly no pelts to be had in Barkley Sound.

The Otter hove to in Nootka Sound on Tuesday morning, 21 June. "Sail to starboard!" announced the lookout. Dorr put his telescope to his eye. "Spanish," he said. "There's a boat approaching." The captain welcomed on board a Spanish officer, who introduced himself as Captain Cuba of the Sutil from San Blas in Mexico. Cuba offered Dorr one of his officers to guide them into the harbour, which he called Friend's Creek, and invited him aboard the Spanish ship to meet Don José Tovar, commander of the expedition. Dorr paid his respects to Tovar and presented to him a passport issued by the Spanish consul in Charleston, giving permission to enter the area. Tovar explained that the viceroy of New Spain in Mexico, the Marquis of Branciforte, had noted the increasing number of British and American vessels operating in the Nootka area and had ordered the navy base at San Blas to send a small vessel to the region every six months to monitor ships in the sound.

"As you may be aware, Captain Dorr," said Tovar, "British and Spanish vessels have equal rights to the temporary use of this haven. Captain Broughton in HMS Providence has been at Nootka recently and is expected to return soon." Dorr told Tovar of being attacked by Indians along the coast and suggested they sail north together for security. Tovar explained that of his small company of fifteen only nine were seaman and six of the sailors had been stricken by illness; their health had not improved during a period of rest at Nootka. Dorr offered to lend Tovar five of his crew to supplement the invalids. Tovar was uncertain; he risked official reprimand if he agreed. There was a vice-regal edict against the entry of foreigners, especially Protestants, into New Spain, but he eventually considered it a risk worth taking if it allowed him to complete his mission. The five could be returned to Dorr on the voyage south again.

Dorr reported the conversation to his officers on board the Otter and ordered them to make ready to leave the sound. Five convicts willingly left the harsh employ of the Bostonian and the risk of being boarded by a British ship. Muir was equally perturbed by the danger. HMS Providence had been at Port Jackson in August 1795 and he remembered Broughton, the captain. It was possible he would be recognised by some of the officers and men and captured. He made a quick calculation. Dorr had told them Tovar would eventually head for California and on to Mexico. He would surely be safer there than on the Otter and could find a ship in Mexico to take him to the United States. That would avoid the uncertainty of another eighteen months of hiding from the British navy on the high seas and especially in Canton, India, and at the Cape of Good Hope. Muir asked permission to join the convicts in the ship's boat to the Sutil. Dorr agreed and Muir quickly said his farewells to Péron, Jean, and Robert, and scrambled over the side into the waiting craft.

After a long interview with Tovar, Muir was accepted as a passenger. Both vessels sailed very early on the following day, no doubt wishing to quit the sound as fast as possible in case a returning Providence found runaway convicts on each of them. When they had cleared the head of the sound and entered the Pacific, Tovar left the quarter-deck to Captain Cuba and retired to his cabin to compose a letter to the viceroy, explaining why he had accepted a fugitive Protestant on board a ship belonging to his Catholic Majesty of Spain.

"I bring to your notice," he began, "that Don Tomas Moro, of the American ship Otter, Boston, while being in the port of Nootka, requested me to offer him passage to proceed via New Spain to the States of America, to go with General Washington. This individual, as far as I was able to understand him, is a high-ranking gentleman from Scotland who has been persecuted by the English government for defending his mother country and the Christian states of Ireland until his ultimate banishment from the isles; but being able to go to other parts of the world and finding himself in New Holland, he took the opportunity of embarking in the said vessel."

The weather in the Pacific worsened and a gale separated the Sutil and the Otter. The Boston ship was swept further north while the Spanish vessel was blown to the south in a storm that lasted several days. Tovar gave the order to stay on a southerly course and in less than two weeks, on Tuesday 5 July, they rounded the point at Santa Cruz and gradually reduced sail as the Sutil entered the wide bay of Monterey.

From the deck, Muir could make out the white-washed, red-tiled fortification the Spanish called the presidio. It was a square adobe fort containing a chapel with a domed belfry, storehouses, quarters for about fifty soldiers, and the residence of the governor of Upper and Lower California, Don Diego de Borica.

CHAPTER 37

New Spain

"Rome of the New World in a golden century
Venice in form, a Tyre in wealth,
in artifice a Corinth, a Cairo in trade,
Athens in knowledge, in treasure a Thebes."

Mexico City described by Arias de Villalobos
in 'Canto Intitulado Mercurio', 1623.

Don Diego de Borica was the seventh governor of the Californias and had accepted the post reluctantly, leaving his circle of friends in the busy New Mexico town of Chihuahua for a lonely outpost on the ocean shore peopled only by soldiers, priests and their Indian converts to Christianity. Muir was taken by Captain Tovar to the governor's residence. He introduced himself in broken Spanish and, after vain attempts in English and Latin, the two men soon settled into conversation in French. Each found in the other an educated and cultured companion. Tovar had asked permission for his ship to sit in the harbour for at least two weeks and so Borica invited Muir to stay in his house, with his wife and young daughter.

Borica and Muir were eager for each other's company and the governor expressed his pleasure in a letter to the viceroy in Mexico, telling him that Muir, who "was in Paris during the great revolutions of '92 and '93, gives very circumstantial accounts of all that occurred, and paints with very vivid colours the characters of the principal personages, such as Mirabeau, Condorcet, Lafayette, Brissot, Robespierre, Danton, Tallien, Egalité and others, and appears not less informed as to the political state of England".

Muir wrote a detailed description of his political history and travels for Borica to send to the viceroy, along with a Spanish translation of an excerpt from his trial, the English language original of the transcript, and a copy of his portrait. Borica's letter of introduction to Branciforte explained, "He [Muir] is proceeding in the Sutil to San Blas, hoping to be allowed to continue his journey until he is able to put himself under the protection of Washington, president of the United States, awaiting the downfall of the English ministry, which he forecasts will take place in a short time."

Muir's letter to the viceroy was carefully worded to appeal to Branciforte's sense of justice and patriotism. He explained the purpose of the Scottish convention: "The assembly of delegates framed and concluded their resolutions in the course of three days. These resolutions, loyal to the king and faithful to the country, appalled a guilty ministry who were the enemies of both. Recovered from their consternation, they attempted by every device of arts and of intimidation, to terrify and to disunite us."

He appealed to the viceroy's religion, "In Ireland, to the catholics they held out some paltry, unavailing privileges intended to skin the surface of the wound, but not to effectuate its cure." And then to his nobility, "In Scotland, defenceless and unarmed, they directed the storm in its most envenomed fury. The first in action, it is my glory likewise to have been the first in suffering. Disdaining every form of law, I was exiled to New Holland with certification of death if in the course of fourteen years I should return to Britain. The country trembled with horror and with rage. The emotion extended to England and we, who in Scotland and Ireland had lately in consequence of the artifices of the ministers been considered by that people in a state of rebellion, were now regarded as the champions and as the martyrs of our country. With invincible eloquence my cause was pleaded in both houses of the English parliament. I count in the number of my advocates and friends the illustrious names of Sheridan and of Fox, of the Earls of Stanhope and Lauderdale." Muir also reinforced his position as a tolerant patriot, "To have defended the ancient laws and constitution of my country, to have contended for the instant and immediate emancipation of three millions of professors of the catholic religion, these are no crimes." He asked the viceroy's permission to travel through Mexico in an effort to secure a passage to the United States.

A fortnight of rest and good company in the family's home gave Muir the opportunity to write a number of other letters to friends and family. But first, he sought the protection of the president of the United States. To George Washington he wrote a similar explanation of his political history and his travels, adding, "We have arrived at Monterey. In a few days we sail for St Blas, where I will remain, waiting for the permission of the Viceroy of Mexico to pass through that country. Sir, I have claimed the protection of your name. I hasten to Philadelphia to solicit it in person."

He wrote to Lauderdale, Stanhope, Fox, Rev Theophilus Lindsey, Dr Joseph Priestley and to an old friend John Millar who, like Priestley, had emigrated to America. He told them of his whereabouts, praised the hospitality of the Spanish and let them know he would be in Philadelphia within six months.

In the daytime Muir was free to explore the presidio, as well as the small settlement outside and the nearby mission on the banks of the Carmel River. The friars there had a community of twenty-six Indian families, all baptised into the Catholic church, who worked the fields around the mission. They had begun to wear European clothes but most of the unconverted natives went almost naked, covered only with a small cloak of rabbit or hare skin. The women wore a short apron of red and white cords twisted together, which extended to the knee, or ones woven from green and dry marsh grass. Soldiers in the stockade wore a knee-length sleeveless leather coat made of seven layers of buckskin and weighing eighteen pounds. It was designed as armour to deflect arrows and gave the frontier troops their name, *soldados de cuera*, leather-jacketed soldiers.

Muir was invited to dine with the Borica family in the evenings and they would sit on the veranda afterwards and talk. Borica was keen to

extend the colony by bringing in new blood and building more settlements. There were four presidios in New California, San Francisco
and Monterey in the north, and San Diego and Santa Barbara in
the south, but there were only two civil settlements, the pueblos of
San Jose and Los Angeles, small farming communities providing
grain and vegetables for the forts. A chain of missions claimed most
of the coastal land and the friars monopolised Indian labour and
actively opposed the growth of civil towns and private ranches.
Borica explained to Muir how he had made requests for colonists of
good character and skill to come and exploit the country, especially
"healthy young maids". But no single women had responded and
officials had begun to send him married convicts, prostitutes, orphan
boys and girls, and other unfortunates from Spain and Mexico. "It
is a pity Thomas, but I think we are beginning to develop a reputation as a Spanish Botany Bay, which does little to appeal to potential
immigrants," he said.

Before he left Monterey Muir wrote to his mother and father in
Huntershill, "The governor of this part of the world, a nobleman
of high rank, has shown me such civilities as could not be believed.
Every refreshment has been sent aboard for me. Could you imagine
that even this lady could have employed herself in making some
portable soups for me during the remainder of my voyage at sea. I
never can be sufficiently grateful to heaven nor to these people."

The crew of the Sutil had all returned to health and as the ship
was being prepared for the voyage to San Blas, Borica handed Tovar
a parcel for the viceroy that included the documents given to him by
Muir and the letters Muir wanted sent on to Britain and America, as
well as the governor's letter of introduction for the political refugee.
They left Monterey Bay for the 2,000-mile voyage to Mexico on
Thursday 21 July. In three weeks of sailing they followed the shore
with the coastal ranges looming behind it, took the Santa Barbara
and San Pedro channels past the little pueblo of Los Angeles, caught
a glimpse of the southernmost mission at San Diego, then sailed
down the coast of the peninsula of Baja California, before crossing

the mouth of the Gulf of California, rounding the group of islands called the Marías, and on 12 August put into the harbour of the naval base at San Blas, which stood at the outflow of Mexico's longest river, the Rio Grande de Santiago.

Muir found the voyage exhilarating; he felt he had lived a lifetime of adventure in just four years. San Blas, however, was less than appealing. It was a dirty, mosquito-ridden place and the town, a little way to the east of the base, was no better. Muir was separated from the five crew members of the Otter, still on board the Sutil, and he spent an uncomfortable week in San Blas, among the packed tenements and rowdy taverns.

To his surprise, he was allocated new quarters in the pleasant and friendly town of Tepic, in the foothills of the western Sierra Madre. Most of the officers and their families lived here in cool plazas with fountains and patios fringed with orange trees. Muir reached Tepic on 19 August and stayed there for a month, during which time he made several Spanish friends and spent much of his time with a fellow Scot, Robert Gibson, who was preparing a business trip to the Philippines. The hermetically sealed empire of Spain, which had been closed to outside political, religious and commercial influence, was already leaking under pressure from the industrialising countries of northern Europe. Cheap contraband textiles from Britain had been smuggled into Mexico for thirty years. By the 1790s, this trickle had become a flood.

Muir wrote to the viceroy, the Marquis of Branciforte, from Tepic informing him of his arrival and asking, very politely, to get on with the job of issuing his passport to Philadelphia. "Last night I arrived in this city and await with the highest respect your lordship's orders," he wrote. "Permit me in this letter, with the same frankness and sincerity as in the former, to state the cause of my anxiety. Three years have almost passed since I enjoyed a regular and uninterrupted communication with my friends and relations. In this impending crisis, motives the most powerful, private and public, urge me to accelerate my course to resume my station in the scenes of the world." He asked permission to travel to Havana and looked forward to waiting on his Excellency in Mexico City.

A month later, Branciforte replied and told Muir he had assigned a senior naval officer, Don Salvador Fidalgo, to escort him to the capital. Muir wrote back, "Last night the order of your lordship for me to proceed to Mexico was communicated. I hasten to testify the deep sentiments of regard and of respect with which my mind is impressed. The circumstances in which I came into your dominions were singular and uncommon. Falsehood and disguise, to you unjust, to me dishonourable, became not the occasion. Unreservedly I reposed in your humanity. Without artifice I exposed my situation. My confidence has not been betrayed."

Muir, Fidalgo and his aide, a junior naval officer, along with their attendants and guards, formed a small caravan for the month-long trip. The old Aztec road from Tepic went first down through the savannahs of the Santiago river valley to Mexico's second city, Guadalajara. The roads were dangerous and attacks by *banditti* were sporadic, so caravans of mules and carts accompanied by traders on horseback and protected by soldiers were common sights. Muir was on horseback, as were the two officers, followed by foot soldiers and attendants coaxing pack mules along the track. The road had been widened at several points to take traffic from the silver mines in the Sierras and there were small forts at strategic points. As darkness fell, the little group would stop in the safety one of the many *mesones* along the way. These one-storey, fortified hostels built around a cobbled courtyard, also allowed the horses and mules to spend the night munching hay, safe from predators, human and animal, out on the trail.

The party passed through mining country and into the great wheat fields around Guadalajara, dotted with ranch buildings, which were similar to the *mesones*, set around courtyards and with watch-towers at each corner. A broad roadway continued from Guadalajara to Queretaro along the river valley. It climbed to the high plateau and over the ridge of the mountains to reveal the Valley of Mexico below

where, in the distance, the snow-capped volcanoes of Popocatepetl
and Iztaccihuatl formed a backdrop to a gleaming city dotted with
green gardens and sparkling silver canals. The twin towers of its
cathedral rose above red roofs on white houses and in the centre
stood the palace of the viceroy. The caravan gathered speed down
through the pine-covered slopes into the lower oak forests.

Muir was astonished. Beneath him lay the largest, most cultured
city of the Americas. Its university was 250 years old and could
compete with the best in Europe. Immigration from Spain to the city
had doubled in the eighteenth century, and more than 150,000 people
now lived in its streets. Muir was speechless, he hadn't expected
such mature, civilised urbanity. From a distance it looked like the
legendary Eldorado.

They passed through the suburbs, a ring of communities, mostly
Indian, and crowded with workshops producing the goods swallowed
by the city every day: pots, soap, brooms, herbs, flowers, vegetables
and *pulque*, the traditional, sweet alcoholic drink. As they entered
the teeming capital on Wednesday afternoon, 12 October, Muir
was reminded, in one respect, of Edinburgh, the different classes all
mingled in the same districts, often in the same buildings, and in
the same order as in the Scottish tenements, with the wealthy, white,
pure-blooded Spanish in the desirable upper apartments, and mixed
race, Indians, and blacks in the garrets or damp basements.

They didn't stay long. As soon as Fidalgo received his orders from
the palace, they climbed aboard a carriage provided by Branciforte
and drove to the Atlantic port of Veracruz. The viceroy had decided
he must follow official procedure for the treatment of foreigners who
had arrived on Spanish soil without permission; Muir would be sent
to Spain to appear before the Council of the Indies. He had already
sent instructions to the governor in Veracruz that Muir should be
placed on the first available ship to Cadiz or Coruña. Branciforte
read the letters Muir had written in Monterey and kept Spanish
translations of them. He forwarded the originals to Spain. They were
never delivered to their intended recipients.

When Muir heard the news from the Veracruz governor he was distraught. He was now so close to his objective, so near to Havana, a mere day's trip from the mainland of north America, that he could not comprehend Branciforte's decision to put him once again in harm's way on an Atlantic crossing, where the chances of being intercepted by the British navy were high. He paced back and forward in his room in anger and frustration. Could he smuggle himself on board a ship for Cuba? No, that would be too risky, his bad Spanish and his appearance would soon betray him. Could he persuade Don Fidalgo to ignore the viceroy's instructions? Unlikely.

In a while he overcame his helpless indignation and decided to appeal once more to the palace. He sent another conciliatory letter of thanks to the viceroy coupled with an entreaty to be allowed to travel to North America. "I have heard that hostilities have commenced upon the part of Britain," he wrote. "… If war is commenced, in passing to Europe in a merchant vessel I am exposed to some danger. It may be safer for me to embark on a ship of war to the Havannah [sic], where I may find some neutral bottom for Europe and for the United States of America. But in this I submit myself entirely to your humanity."

Spain had abandoned a recent treaty with Britain and resumed its traditional alliance with France. Suspicious of Pitt's intentions in the West Indies, Madrid thought Spanish interests were at risk and declared war on Britain in October. Muir could not be freed. On 9 November he was put on board a packet for Havana to take passage in the frigate Ninfa, carrying treasure alongside a sister ship, Santa Elena, both bound for Cadiz, and both armed with 34 guns and carrying 320 men. However, it would be four months before the ships were ready to sail.

The governor in Havana took no chances with his unwanted enemy renegade. Muir was locked away in one of the city's forts but was free to move about within its walls, and he was given a modest daily allowance of money. He became irritable and ill and was removed to the military hospital for while. He wrote to Hamilton Rowan, who had escaped from prison in Ireland to the safety of America, that he was "well and humanely treated, though at present a prisoner as an Englishman". That description, though, was probably to avoid the displeasure of his jailers. Much later, when he was free of Spanish authority, he swore that while he received humane and honourable treatment in Mexico, in Havana "the scene changed. The governor, without deigning to give me any explanation, treated me forthwith as a prisoner. I remained four months shut up in one of the forts, during which time I suffered every kind of harsh treatment."

The Ninfa and the Santa Elena left Havana on 25 March, 1797, and for four weeks drove steadily through the waters of the Atlantic until they spied the coast of Spain. On the night of 25 April the lookout of the leading frigate spotted bobbing lights on fishing boats from Cadiz. They hove to and sent a boat to the fishermen, where they learned to their alarm that in February the Spanish fleet had been defeated off Cape St Vincent by the British navy and that Admiral Sir John Jervis had mounted a blockade of Cadiz ever since. The main part of the Jervis's fleet was stationed five miles offshore but an inshore squadron lay within gunshot of the lighthouse at the entrance to the harbour.

CHAPTER 38

Citizen Thomas Muir

"For a' that, an' a' that,
It's coming yet for a' that,
That Man to Man, the world o'er,
Shall brothers be for a' that."

Robert Burns, 'A Man's a Man for a'
That', first published anonymously in
the *Glasgow Magazine*, August, 1795.

Captain George Martin stood on the quarterdeck of HMS Irresistible and, adjusting his telescope, took in the details of the ships heading south a few miles ahead of him. "Their hulls are out of the water," he said to his first lieutenant, Andrew Thomson. "They must have unloaded their cargo in the night."

He was right. The captains of the Ninfa and the Santa Elena had transferred their treasure to the holds of the fishing fleet, whose crews had taken it safely into Cadiz harbour, under the eyes of unsuspecting lookouts of the British inshore squadron blockading the city. The two ships had not gone unnoticed by the main body of Sir John Jervis's fleet. In fact the officer of the watch had reported their appearance to the captain of Jervis's flagship, but they were assumed to be either friends or neutrals, probably the two Venetian ships that had sailed from Cadiz the night before, and were allowed to pass without being stopped and examined. The Spaniards had been unaware of the enemy fleet but when dawn broke they realised that two British warships had breasted the horizon behind them.

"They show no colours," said Martin to Thomson, "but all their boats are out towing as fast as they can. They must be Spaniards." The captain was aware that there was very little wind driving any of the ships, but for the two in front to deploy boats could only mean they were running for cover.

"Mr Thomson," he ordered, "set all sail and come up with the chase; signal Captain Berkeley in the Emerald to do likewise."

By half past eight the British ships were closing on the Spaniards; a puff of smoke and a flash of fire from the stern of the Ninfa was followed by the boom of an explosion. A ball splashed in the water well out of range.

"That's it!" called Captain Martin. "Clear the ship for action, Mr Thomson!"

By noon the gap had closed to about two miles and thirty minutes later the Spaniards hoisted their colours, ready for battle. They fired several rounds at the British ships, all of the balls falling short. The Spanish sailors rowed furiously under the bows of the frigates, pulling them to a bay beneath the small town of Conil de la Fronterra. The Spanish captains knew they were outclassed by the 74-gun Irresistible and the 36-gun Emerald and hoped to reach the safety of the bay, whose northern approach is guarded by a submerged reef, the Lajo de Cabo Roche, on which the British might founder. Ninfa and Santa Elena rounded the rocks and anchored close to the shore, ready for battle.

Muir approached the captain and requested that, as a civilian, he be allowed to leave the ship. The captain could spare neither the time nor the men to take Muir ashore and asked him to go below for his own safety. Muir thought quickly. It was either fight or hang, so he claimed French citizenship which he said a decree of the French Convention allowed, and offered to fight side by side with the Spanish crew as an ally. Muir was hurriedly equipped with a sword and pistol to ward off boarding parties, while the guns of the Ninfa and Santa Elena fired at Irresistible and Emerald, still out at sea.

At two thirty the British ships safely rounded the reef and stood at broadside to the Spaniards. A continuous barrage of shot and ball hit Ninfa and Santa Elena for a full ninety minutes. All seemed chaos to Muir, the noise was deafening and, blinking through tears and gun smoke, he saw many sailors fall amid a hail of iron shards and wood splinters. Ninfa's captain was struck by flying debris and died on the quarterdeck. Santa Elena was holed beneath the water-line and listing. As British jolly-boats headed towards them loaded with marines, Ninfa's first officer, who took command, ordered the colours to be struck and the company to surrender. But just before the Spanish flag was lowered, a last shot from Irresistible crashed through the woodwork of Ninfa, exploding in a murderous whirl-wind of shrapnel and jagged slivers of timber. Muir didn't know what hit him; shock and surprise jarred him for a conscious moment; he felt no pain; all was black.

*

Muir regained consciousness among the wounded. Throbbing, hot pain pumped in the left side of his face. His vision was blurred. He slowly realised his impaired sight was from just one eye. He felt his face. Its left side was an open wound. He winced as he touched the spot where his left cheekbone had been. His left eye was gone. Blackness enveloped him again. He felt a hand move his head. A voice comforted him. It spoke in English. Was that a Scottish accent?

Darkness once more was followed by light and nausea. His wound had been dressed. Red jackets of marines mingled with blue jackets of British naval officers. He heard the officers call each other by name, Ferrie, Thomson, Maxwell. He was sure there were Scottish voices among them. Could he know any of them? Would they recognise him? Was he imagining this? He slipped in and out of consciousness. He heard his own name. "Was there a Thomas Muir aboard your ship?"

"Yes sir, there was," a Spanish voice replied in good English. "But I saw for myself he was killed. His body was among the dead put on shore."

British officers took a muster of Spanish prisoners as they were loaded into boats and taken on board Irresistible. Muir was barely aware as he heard the same Spanish voice identify him with the name of a dead seaman. Both fit and wounded prisoners were housed below decks together as the Irresistible set sail north to Cadiz once more. Muir was feverish and numbed with pain. He slept or was unconscious for most of the six days in the hands of the British, but he remembered fragments of talk from those around him: after the surrender the crew of Santa Elena cut her anchor cables and ran her ashore to make their escape; some of Ninfa's crew escaped, too; eighteen Spaniards were killed and thirty wounded; Irresistible had just one dead and one injured; Emerald escaped without a casualty; British officers were still on the look-out for an escaped traitor.

Awake. Asleep. In pain. In dreams. Being lowered on a stretcher. The rocking of a boat. Consciousness once more in an unfamiliar room. The feel of clean sheets against his skin. A nun bathing his wound.

"Where am I?"

"You are safe, my son. You are in hospital on the Isla de Leon, in Cadiz harbour."

The authorities at the Royal Hospital soon realised they had in their care a person who might be of some importance and so informed the governor, who sent officials to confirm Muir's identity. Muir was aware that the near presence of the British was still a danger to him and he knew he could not count on the protection of the Spanish authorities. He had, after all, come here as a prisoner. He requested the assistance of the French consul, who visited him in hospital. Consul Roquesant was convinced of Muir's identity, and wrote at once to Charles Delacroix, the minister for foreign affairs in Paris, informing him of the battle at Conil Bay and the arrival in Cadiz of "le fameux Thomas Muri", now recovering from his wounds. He told Delacroix he had secured a private room in the hospital for Muir and proposed that, when he was well enough, he would stay with the consul at Cadiz and later travel to Madrid to be under the protection of Citizen Pérignon, the ambassador there.

News soon reached the senior officers of the British fleet that Muir had been aboard the Ninfa but had slipped from their grasp. An envoy was hurriedly despatched to the governor of Cadiz, requesting that "the Englishman of quality" in his hospital be restored to them. In return, they would hand back the captured frigate, Ninfa, with its officers. The governor was tempted by the offer, but the consul intervened to stop negotiations over the fate of a citizen of the Republic.

Delacroix reported to the French Directory that "the celebrated Scotsman" was back among them. "I need hardly recall here," he explained, "the motives which should influence the French government to offer a refuge to all those men distinguished for their courage and their genius, who have dared to maintain the lamp of liberty amid the enemies of France, at a time when Europe was leagued against her. The Directory knows how greatly this kind of national gratitude honours the Republic and multiplies its friends." He asked the five Directors to approve the consul's plan, which they did.

Muir, though, spent the summer in the Royal Hospital as a prisoner of war on orders from Madrid. Ambassador Pérignon had applied for his release to the prime minister in June and August, but the oddly named "Prince of Peace", Manuel Godoy, ignored his requests. The young Godoy, lover of Queen María Luisa, who had been appointed prime minister to King Carlos IV on the queen's advice five years previously at the age of 25, was politically inept. He had brought Spain into the war against the French Republic, was invaded and forced to sue for peace, changed sides and went to war with Britain, and in so doing brought about the blockade that cut off Spain from its empire. He ordered the governor of Cadiz to keep Muir under close guard and to have him periodically interrogated on suspicion of being an English spy.

Strength was returning to Muir. A leather mask had been fashioned to cover the horrific wounds on the side of his face. He was conscious of his impaired vision as he took up his pen to lobby for his release. He wrote first on 14 August to his old acquaintance, Tom Paine. "Sir, I greatly rejoiced when I heard you were still in Paris. I flatter myself to be there in the course of this winter and to have an opportunity of cultivating that friendship which I value so highly. Since that evening I parted with you in the Palais Royal, my life has been composed of many agitated and some uncommon scenes. These I will have the happiness of relating to you in a few months. Contrary to every expectation, I have almost recovered from my wounds. The Directory has manifested to me the most flattering attention. The Spaniards detain me as a prisoner because I am a Scotchman, but I have no doubt the interposition of the Directory will soon obtain my freedom. Remember me in the most affectionate manner to all your friends, who are the friends of liberty and of human happiness."

More directly, on the following day he wrote to the new French foreign minister, Charles-Maurice Talleyrand. "I have almost recovered from my wounds but I am detained here as a prisoner, for no other reason, doubtless, than that of my having been born in Scotland. Permit me, Citizen Minister, to solicit the immediate interposition of the French government to secure my liberation, all the more so as my health is suffering from my present position. The ambassador and the consul are no doubt doing all they possibly can, they have already made strong representations on this subject, but as things go with this government your mediation seems to be absolutely necessary."

Talleyrand wrote back to Muir, "*Homme estimable*, I have just learned with as much astonishment as annoyance that you have been detained as a prisoner at Cadiz, where you hoped to find hospitality. I am writing to the ambassador of the Republic at Madrid to bid him demand that you be set at liberty. Be assured that your adopted country will not abandon you to new persecutions. It gives me pleasure to be at this moment the instrument of the Directory to testify to you the great interest it takes in you."

To Roquesant at Cadiz, Talleyrand wrote, "Thomas Muir tells me, Citizen, that he is detained at Cadiz as a prisoner. I am instructing the ambassador of the Republic to demand that this celebrated Scot be set at liberty. Please...be good enough to give him freely all the assistance he may require."

And he sent an official instruction to Ambassador Pérignon. "Thomas Muir belongs no longer to the nation which has proscribed him. France is his adopted country; she has offered him a refuge and awaits the moment when she may number him among her citizens. By this he ought to be protected in Spain as a Frenchman. I request you, Citizen Ambassador, to demand that Thomas Muir be at once set at liberty, and to inform Consul Roquesant of the result of your negotiations."

Pérignon renewed his request to Godoy on 11 September and the prime minister scribbled a truculent note in the margin of the ambassador's letter, "This person has behaved badly in America and I have not the details. See if it is known what this devil was doing." Either Godoy had not read the dispatches from California, Mexico, and Cuba, or he had chosen to ignore them. However, on the following day he changed his mind, possibly realising that a powerful ally might take offence, and signed the order for Muir's release on condition he never set foot in any Spanish territory again. Pérignon informed Talleyrand, of the decision, noting, "The conditions might have been expressed more graciously, but at least they will meet our desires and those of a friend of the Republic."

By mid-October Muir was strong enough to travel and Roquesant provided him with one of his staff, a young soldier named Molet, to act as Muir's aide and secretary, along with transport to take them over the sierras to the great, high plain of central Spain. On the first day of November he was received in Madrid by the ambassador who, keen to see his charge safe on French soil, arranged for a post-chaise to carry the injured refugee and his aide all the way to Paris. Muir wrote to Talleyrand on 3 November expressing his sincere thanks, "Two days ago I arrived in this city and I hasten to set out tomorrow on my journey to Bayonne. I have been received here by Citizen Pérignon in a manner the memory of which will imprint itself for a long time on my heart."

On the following day, a Saturday, Muir and Molet climbed into their carriage and began a journey across the northern plateau towards the winter passes of the Pyrenees. It was slow going. The officials of small towns from Bayonne and on through Aquitaine were the first to greet the celebrated radical with the leather half-mask covering wounds of war that disfigured one side of his face.

Near the end of November they arrived at Bordeaux to a tremendous civic welcome. On 4 December the imposing Société de la Grande Quille in the Grande Place was decorated with republican bunting and emblems. All of its windows were ablaze with lamps to greet "le célèbre Thomas Muir" and a group of *citoyennes* presented him with flowers, myrtle and victor's laurels. Muir waved from the balcony to the large crowd outside, who cried "Long live the defenders and martyrs of liberty!" To the sound of a band playing in the hall, he was escorted into the main assembly room where a banquet was prepared for five hundred guests, who toasted the Republic and the brave young Scottish advocate, a new *citoyen*. Speeches were given in his honour and at length he replied.

"Citizens, I am not accustomed to speak the French language in public," he began, "but were I endowed with all the facility of speech and eloquence it is possible to possess, I should not be able to express the sensations I now feel. I am transported with joy to find myself at this moment among you, but when I compare my present situation with my brethren and countrymen, who sigh in dungeons or languish in exile, I experience sentiments of the most profound melancholy... The liberty of the universe is not yet lost. The patriots of England, Scotland, and Ireland will soon break their chains... The same spirit which animates you, animates them also." He paused. His hands gripped the edge of the table as he tried to compose himself, but before he could continue he fainted and collapsed on to the American consul, sitting to his left.

It was several days before Muir felt strong enough to travel again. Molet brought to his hotel room a copy of an engraving that was on sale in shops throughout the city. The hand-tinted representation of Muir showed him with a black eye-patch and a lopsided face. Muir was warmed by the flattery but the image shocked him. It reminded him of the damage done to his face and the frightening sight of torn flesh, exposed teeth and an empty eye socket that lay beneath his mask.

Molet also brought an armful of the French newspapers, many of which reported Muir's reception in Bordeaux, as did those in England, Scotland and Ireland. As the two men continued their journey north in short, easy stages, the Paris paper, *Le Moniteur*, prepared the population of the capital for Muir's arrival. A front-page article announced, "He arrives in France at the very moment when the *Grande Nation* is menacing England, and is taking steps to realise the project which he had conceived. Let this apostle of philanthropy come among us, let him find in his new fatherland friends and brothers, and may our victorious cohorts call him back to the country which gave him birth, there to establish liberty."

CHAPTER 39

Exile and intrigue

"Plant, plant the tree, fair freedom's tree,
Midst danger, wounds and slaughter;
Each patriot's breast its soil shall be,
And tyrants' blood its water."

Chorus from 'Plant, plant the tree',
attributed to Robert Crossfield, 1796.

Charles-Maurice Talleyrand stood uncomfortably at the head of the welcoming party in a state room of the Foreign Ministry. His club foot hurt. He always felt uncomfortable but his manner disguised his awkwardness. The combination of his limp and his deep, reassuring voice seemed to add gravitas to his easy, well-honed social skills. As Muir was shown into the grand apartment, Talleyrand moved towards him with arms outstretched and clasped him to his breast, kissing his good, uninjured cheek.

"Citizen Muir, *homme estimable*, on behalf of the Directory, welcome to the French Republic," he said, and the assembled bureaucrats and guests applauded the new hero. Muir and Molet were seated at table prepared for a banquet lunch and, after the toasts had been made, the food had been eaten and the tables cleared, Muir stood and, although still weak and tired, made a short speech of thanks for his benefactors.

"Citizens, I arrived two days ago at Paris, in a very weak and sickly state," he explained. "Permit me to express to you the extreme devotion and gratitude of my heart. To you I owe my liberty, to you I owe my life. But there are other considerations of infinitely superior importance and which ought to make a more forcible impression on my mind. Your energetic conduct has saved the liberty, not only of France, but also of my country, and of every other nation in the world at present groaning under oppression. It is unnecessary for me to make protestations of my love and veneration for the Republic. To my last breath I will remain faithful to my adopted country."

After lunch Muir had a private interview with Talleyrand, where he told the former bishop – Talleyrand had resigned from the church in 1791 to pursue a political and diplomatic career – of his desire to defend the Republic and extend liberty to his former home. Talleyrand was amenable and indicated to Muir that his door would always be open for him.

But Muir also needed finance. "I do not lack, and I shall not lack, money of my own," he later explained in a letter to Talleyrand's private secretary. "You know my character and you know my resources. There is, however, a law which has been passed in England which makes it high treason to send money to France. I cannot correspond with my father and my mother; I fear to compromise them by writing to them. It is necessary for me to have French money. I shall not receive this as an act of charity. I shall not receive it as a loan. But I shall receive it only in the name of the Scottish nation and if the government is sincere in projecting a landing in Scotland, all that is furnished to me will be paid in Scotland with interest and enthusiasm."

Talleyrand was agreeable, even though the Republic was overwhelmed by financial crisis. Muir had been careful enough to describe his frugal existence in his letter. "My table is not elaborate. It consists only of a soup and a dish of meat, in the company of one or two friends. I have no personal expenses, as those who know me can attest, but in my position I require a lodging not unworthy of my former status and which is not capable of inviting the wretched criticism that patriots have no standing in France... [M]y heart is wholly French. I have sacrificed everything for the sacred cause of the

Republic. I have very little blood remaining in my veins, but the little that does remain will flow another time."

There were two further requests in Muir's letter, "My wounds, the feeble state of my health, the loss of one eye and the impaired vision of the one that remains, oblige me to have a carriage," and "For the reasons I have just indicated it is necessary for me to have a secretary to write what I dictate. My secretary is that fine young fellow Molet, whom you have seen, who has fought for four years in the armies of the Republic. It is only fitting that Molet should receive honourable treatment, not only because he has left the army with the consent of his commanding officer and that of the French consul at Cadiz, in order to be of service to me on my journey, but as continuing in the service of the Republic."

Muir was an asset to Talleyrand, a recognised leader in a disaffected country to the north of France's main enemy. The foreign minister knew how to build his assets. He encouraged the Irish in their belief that the Republic would send an overwhelming force to assist in their independence struggle. Since late summer he had kept up regular personal contact with the conquering young general, Bonaparte, victor in Italy who forced the Austrians to sign a peace treaty. England was now without active allies in Europe and Talleyrand had recommended to the Directory that the young Napoleon be put in charge of the *armée d'Angleterre*, then massing in the channel ports. He had long felt that Scotland and Ireland had a similarity of interests but had as yet only the Irish voice in Paris, chiefly through Wolfe Tone. Now he had an independent Scottish voice to add to his entourage.

*

Molet answered the knock at the door of the apartment he and Muir shared in the Rue de Braque. A tall, shabbily dressed man with bright, dark eyes and a noticeable aquiline nose, introduced himself, "Good afternoon, Monsieur Molet. My name is Tom Paine and I have come to see…"

"Tom!" cried Muir from the sitting room. "Tom, come in. Welcome."

The two men embraced and Paine explained how he had read of Muir's coming to Paris and had heard about the reception at the Foreign Ministry the day before. Wine was poured and Paine was anxious to learn about Muir's adventures while Muir sought from Paine the story of his remarkable escape from the scaffold during the Terror.

"No man could count upon life for twenty-four hours," Paine said, recounting the story he had told over many bar-room tables. "Robespierre and his committee were at such a pitch of rage and suspicion that it seemed as if they feared to leave a man living. Scarcely a night passed in which ten, twenty, thirty, forty, fifty or more were taken out of the prison, carried before a pretended tribunal in the morning and guillotined before night."

He told how in July 1794 his name, and those of his cell-mates, was on the execution list. "We were four, and the door of our room was marked, unobserved by us, with that number in chalk; but it happened, if happening is a proper word, that the mark was put on when the door was open, and flat against the wall, and came on the inside when we shut it at night, and the destroying angel passed it by. A few days after this, Robespierre fell and Mr Monroe [the US ambassador] arrived and reclaimed me, and invited me to his house."

Paine was now living in the Rue de Théatre Français with Nicolas de Bonneville and his family. Bonneville owned and edited a newspaper, *Le Bien informé*, to which Paine was a regular contributor. He invited Muir to meet Bonneville and to write for him. But first, Paine stressed, Muir must meet other political exiles in Putode's café on the Rue des Marais or in the United Irish club in the Rue du Colombier. The cafés, he explained, were still buzzing with celebration at Napoleon's return to Paris after his Italian victory and the treaty signed with the Austrians at Campoformio. But the new excitement in the air was over an expected invasion of England, not only in cafés, but in theatres, where dramatised French landings were enacted, as ministers held fund-raising banquets to pay for the expedition.

One such banquet was hosted by the Minister of General Police. The event was reported in the Paris press and, on reading the article, Muir decided to respond and dictated a letter to Molet. "I read with the greatest sensibility in the journal *Les Amis des Lois*, the toasts given at your civic feast. I am a United Irishman; I am a Scotchman; I can answer in the name of the two nations. The tears of affection and sympathy will flow when they shall be informed of the wishes of your heart. You drank to the victims of English despotism, and may the blood they have shed speedily ripen in their country the seeds of liberty and equality! That blood has been shed; I myself have seen it. Alone I called for justice on the assassins; and that was one of the causes of my proscription. You drank to the United Irishmen, the people of Scotland who wait only for the French to break their chains – I assure you in the name of the Irish and the Scotch that we will break our chains on the heads of our tyrants. An effort remains to be made by the Great Nation. It is not with the people of England it fights. It is only with a hundred scoundrels. Let them fall and the peace of the universe is established. Health and respect, Thomas Muir."

Muir was convinced that only a tiny clique of ministers and advisers surrounding the Hanoverian throne prevented reform. He was now stating in public his belief that insurrection in Ireland and Scotland was the only way to achieve democracy in independent republics. This would at least force a change of government in England, led by the peace party, who would negotiate with France in good faith. The Whig parties in London and Dublin had begun to boycott the parliaments in favour of a mass public campaign for peace and reform. Muir's letter was published and soon picked up by the British press in early January 1798. One paper, the *True Briton*, accused Muir of encouraging the French "to put to death one hundred of his countrymen".

It was time to engage in politics once more and Muir had to reach deep inside to find the courage to walk the city streets, knowing he would be the object of unwelcome stares at the strange appearance of a man with half a face concealed beneath a leather mask. He was still weak and tired easily from the constant pain in his wounds but Molet encouraged him and they made tentative expeditions into the poor, impoverished city that war had diminished. To Muir, it looked so different from the Paris of 1793. Much of it was in need of repair; many of the old aristocratic mansions not leased to speculators had become public buildings with little thought for their fabric; filth was piled high in the streets and the latrines were full.

Muir and Molet went first to the Irish Club in the Rue du Colombier where they met Wolfe Tone and Edward Lewins. Muir was welcomed as a member of the United Irishmen. Tone had been in Paris since 1796, urging government support for an Irish republic, and although he had read Muir's announcement he showed no outward annoyance at having a possible competitor for French attention. Tone had been forced into exile in America by the Dublin government and applied to the French ambassador in Philadelphia for official recognition. The ambassador gave him a letter of introduction to carry to Paris. Lewins arrived from Dublin a year after Tone, the official representative from the United Irishmen, but Tone seemed comfortable with this; they knew each other from the Catholic Committee some years before, and the two men rubbed along.

Lewins was an attorney. Some said he was the caricature of a lawyer, standoffish, rather dry and a bit too pedantic. His sunken eyes, guarded by bushy eyebrows above and a prominent chin below, told of much peering at documents in poor light. He liked to control access to government ministers but was wary about sharing information, seemingly even with his comrades in Ireland. The lack of intelligence passed to Dublin throughout 1797 meant another envoy had to make his way secretly to Paris by way of Hamburg to amend the request to the French government to reduce the troops required because of the great growth in United Irishmen membership, and to increase the arms needed because of the British army's campaign of violent coercion and disarming of the people. This was especially true of Ulster, where the army was aided by a terror campaign waged by the newly formed Orange Order. James Coigly, a Catholic priest, had travelled from Paris to Dublin that winter to carry the information that Lewins seemed reluctant to send.

Tone, who had been appointed as an officer in the French army, had attempted a landing at Bantry Bay in the winter of 1796. It had failed because of foul weather but, he later recorded, "We were near enough to toss a biscuit ashore." They had been "six thousand of the most carefree fellows in Europe" he noted in his diary, and set sail with little except enthusiasm. "We have not one guinea; we have not a tent, we have not a horse to draw our four pieces of artillery; the general in chief marches on foot... we have nothing but the arms in our hands, the clothes on our backs and a good courage," and for good measure, "we have no horses for our cavalry". They had hoped, of course, to pick up recruits, equipment, and supplies after landing but it was "the dreadful stormy weather and the easterly winds, which have been blowing furiously and without intermission since we made Bantry Bay, that have ruined us". They had reached the bay on 21 December and waited for eight days for a change in the weather. On 29 December, "At four this morning, the commodore made the signal to steer for France."

Unfortunately, the attempted arrival of the French at Bantry Bay was completely unexpected by the United Irishmen in Ireland because of the awful communications and it was, inexplicably, planned for a place where the movement was weak.

Back in France, Tone was sent to the army of General Hoche, a champion of Irish independence, and posted to Texel in Holland, France's new ally, where the Dutch fleet was ready to embark with an army of 13,500. It was the summer of 1797 and nothing stood between the fleet and the Irish shore. The British navy was under the control of "the floating republic" of mutineers and Irish sailors made up about a quarter of the lower deck in the Channel and North Sea fleets. But contrary winds kept the Dutch bottled up in the North Sea port.

Tone later recorded in his *Memoirs*, "Twice, within nine months,

England had been saved by the wind. It seems as if the very elements had conspired to perpetuate our slavery. The persecution in Ireland was at its height, and the people were beginning to lose confidence in themselves and their chiefs, whom they almost suspected of deceiving them. The great crisis of the mutiny was suffered to pass by, without the French government making the smallest attempt to profit of it."

Later that year a landing in Scotland was considered, taking Edinburgh and using the Forth and Clyde canal to transport troops and equipment to Glasgow, holding the ground around the canal and using it as a defensive barrier. That would have distracted London while a force of five thousand climbed aboard ships again in the Clyde estuary and made for Ulster. But Hoche died a premature death from tuberculosis in September and the British navy, with the crisis over and the mutineers' leaders hanged, sailed toward the Dutch and defeated their fleet at Camperdown in October. The engagement was commanded by Admiral Duncan who, five years before, had defended Henry Dundas's mother from the mob in Edinburgh.

*

Putode's café was where Paine met with other radicals. Muir was reunited with old friends, among them James Smith, the gunsmith from Gorbals whom Muir had met in the Palais Royal in January 1793. Smith had married a Frenchwoman and had arranged for his son to join him from Glasgow. They were now settled in Paris. Often present were John Stone and Helen Williams, to whom he had been introduced in the British club at White's Hotel. Williams had, like Paine, been imprisoned in the Luxembourg with her mother and sister during the Terror and found safety in Switzerland when they were released, where she travelled with Stone. Back in Paris, Stone divorced his wife Rachel and now lived with Williams in the family apartment in the Quai Malaquais. Muir remembered attending one of their Sunday soirées in the Rue de Bac in 1793, where he met Condorcet. Stone now owned a printing business, *Imprimerie Anglaise*, which published Paine's works as well as those by Thomas

Jefferson, and Constantin de Volney, among others. Stone was kept informed of events in England by his brother in London.

Muir learned that after the London treason trials both Hardy and Tooke had withdrawn from public life and the Corresponding Society had fallen away for a time. But from spring 1795 it resumed agitation and held a vast meeting of 100,000 people in London's St George's Fields in continued support of annual parliaments and universal suffrage. The provincial organisations revived during that summer and by autumn a further great demonstration of 150,000 people was organised in Copenhagen Fields in Islington. Days later the king's carriage was attacked by a stone-throwing mob on its way to the opening of parliament and the government replied with its usual severity. A proclamation was issued against seditious assemblies and Pitt introduced in parliament what became known as the Two Acts. These made it treasonable to incite hatred or contempt of the king, constitution or government, and banned meetings of more than fifty people, except by permission of a magistrate. There was a brave last stand of the reformers. In the month between the introduction of the "gagging acts" and its royal assent in December, the Corresponding Society called another emergency demonstration in London at which 200,000 people showed up, entire families with children came. Yet another was held in Marylebone and demonstrations took place all around the country. But the Acts were successful and although the society tried a policy of defiance, leaders were arrested and prosecuted and the organisation gradually collapsed. In July 1797 another huge demonstration was held in St Pancras in opposition to the new laws but it was dispersed and six leaders were arrested.

Muir had until then only a superficial idea how severely repressive the British administration had become since his transportation and what had happened to the radical movement. He learned how the Corresponding Society had now split into two parts, one of which, the United Englishmen sometimes known as the United Britons or the True Britons, was secretive and oath bound, just like the United Irishmen, and the other remained an ineffective debating club. After the naval mutinies, during which radical and United Irish cells were discovered among sailors, marines and soldiers, another two Acts were passed by parliament imposing the death penalty for illegal oaths or for attempting to suborn the armed forces.

From his fellow Glaswegian, James Smith, Muir learned of current events in Scotland. The news was patchy, put together from what was read in the press and whatever information came through Hamburg. They knew that the old Friends of the People had kept going for as long as they could under the repressive laws but had to become secretive and many of the local branches had joined the new United Scotsmen. They felt that the constitutional route had been closed to them but they wanted to keep in touch with Ireland and England, so they took on the model of the United Irishmen. Towards the end of 1797 the French agent in Hamburg had reported that he had information from London claiming that 50,000 were ready to rise in Scotland and 200,000 in England, and the Irish were waiting for a French landing before rising. But they had no way of verifying that. What they did know was that the authorities were worried enough to have George Mealmaker arrested.

Muir remembered the Dundee weaver who had written the handbill that led to Palmer's transportation. Mealmaker was now the effective leader of the United Scotsmen and had been charged with administering illegal oaths under the new legislation. His trial was taking place in Edinburgh as they spoke and they had heard of further arrests there, as well as in Perth and Dundee. What they could not know was that the organisation was not compromised thanks to its watertight structure and the seriousness with which its oath was taken.

That was a headache for the lord advocate. Robert Dundas had complained to the Home Office about his belief there was "mischief going on in the west of Scotland", but he couldn't get to the bottom of it. "It will be impossible for me, however," he admitted to Portland, "to get into the secret of their proceedings unless they act with more boldness than they have hitherto done; or unless you can procure for me some more precise information from Ireland as to the names of the persons corresponding from Scotland."

A watch was set on boats crossing from Ulster to Portpatrick. Nearly a thousand escaped the beatings, burnings, rapes and cappings with hot tar, taking place all over Ulster during that spring. "We still have swarms from Ireland," wrote the lord advocate, "but have sent back as many, indeed more, persons than in strict law we are authorised to do. But we must not stick at trifles."

In fact the United Scotsmen were expanding. At their secret national meeting in Edinburgh in May 1797 the membership was recorded as 2,871, about the same as the number of people allowed to vote in the country. By September that year the figure was 9,653. But that was before Mealmaker was taken up.

Robert Dundas had a second headache to nurse. Between July and September riots broke out all over Scotland in opposition to the Militia Act. Six thousand nineteen- to twenty-three-year old men were to be drafted into the newly created militia for the duration of the war plus a month. The counties were given a quota to be filled by ballot. Opposition began in the Borders, then spread to the Lothians, Galloway, central Scotland, Fife, and even to the highlands of Perthshire and Aberdeenshire. In August a massacre had taken place when eleven people were killed and more injured by English cavalry at Tranent in East Lothian. The riots were quelled by soldiers that had to be requisitioned from Northumberland.

*

Muir learnt from Paine about some of the plans for an invasion of Britain. Paine was certain that a French army of liberation would be supported by local risings and he had already submitted plans for a fleet of gunboats, which could be built cheaply and easily, and with little fuss, all the way up the Channel coast to Holland. "A fleet of a thousand of those boats each carrying one twenty-four pounder canon and rowed by forty oars would be a very formidable force in passing the North Sea and would...be better adapted to accomplish an invasion than a fleet of seventy or eighty sail of the line," he wrote. They could easily out-run English ships of the line and land on the firm, sandy shores that stretch from the mouth of the Thames to Scotland. "But my own opinion is that the expedition should go directly up the Thames." Napoleon had appointed Paine as political adviser to his *armée d'Angleterre* and the Directory had ordered the first 250 gunboats.

In their more public discussions in Putode's café, Helen Williams threw in a note of caution. "Beware of promises made by second rate revolutionaries," she said. She distrusted the Directory. "Some are former Jacobins who have sacrificed their principles for power, others are speculators and gamblers, but most are indifferents who generally voted with the moderate side of the house." Her criticism of them was acid. "When debating food shortages and peoples' hunger, they would leave the debate when their stomachs rumbled, and the first sound they utter is *soup à la tartare!*" She viewed with contempt the people who restricted the vote to those with property and neglected the rights of women. The question was not whether women "have gained by the revolution, but whether they have gained as much as they ought".

Paine agreed with her that the answer was an obvious no. He had made public objection to the restriction of the vote but, nevertheless, thought what they had was better than the despotism of monarchy, or the tyranny of the Terror. They had to work with what existed, and one of their assets was Napoleon.

*

There was a coffee house in the Rue de Condé where Paine often met with other Irish, English and American radicals. It was here that Muir met two other Irish exiles that were to be key to the next twelve months. One was James Napper Tandy, who had already fled Ireland when Muir was there, and the other was Nicholas Madgett, a Kerry man in his sixties, who had been a priest in France before the revolution.

Tandy's reputation was legendary, a leader in reform politics in Dublin and Ireland from the 1760s, he was prominent in the volunteer movement of the 1780s and founder, with Tone and Drennan, of the Dublin United Irishmen in November 1791. He was its first secretary. He fled Ireland two years later, having been charged with distributing seditious literature and, suspecting that a more serious, capital charge was to be laid against him for taking the oath of the Defenders, he took a small boat to Wales and journeyed to America, landing in October 1795, and was soon invited to France by the French ambassador at Philadelphia on behalf of the Directory.

Madgett became a translator for the Convention during the revolution and then worked for the Directory in the department of foreign affairs, where he dealt with all things Irish. It was he who advised Tone, Lewins and other Irish exiles on their arrival in France. Tone didn't think much of Madgett. In his diary he noted, "Madgett has the slowness of age, and at present the gout about him."

In fact, Tone didn't think much of Tandy either. Tandy, now in his sixties, had reached Paris via Hamburg in May 1797 and his arrival threatened the supremacy of Tone and Lewins. Tone became infuriated by Tandy, although he appreciated that his name and position were useful. He revealed his private thoughts in a letter to his wife. "What in God's name is Napper Tandy doing in Paris? And especially why does he go by a name so notorious?" Tone and the others used *noms de guerre*. "I will whisper that 'tis out of pure vanity, but let it go no further."

However, Tone sought to co-operate with Tandy for a time. Tandy believed Ireland needed immediate French assistance and was frustrated by the longer, patient, and often secret game played by Tone and Lewins. It was Tandy who had sent the priest, James Coigly, to Ireland for an accurate assessment of needs, and also to attempt to have Lewins, whom some thought was a spy, removed as official representative.

Tandy's presence in Paris was reported in the Irish and English press and he became regarded as the leader who would command the

French forces in Ireland. He wrote frequently to his son in Dublin and his optimistic reports reinforced popular belief that a French landing was imminent. However, the lack of communication with Ireland from Tone and Lewins led two members of the United executive, Edward Fitzgerald and Arthur O'Connor, to attempt to establish direct contact with Tandy. The Irish camp in Paris was split into two factions. O'Connor who, like Fitzgerald, was also a Whig MP in the Dublin parliament, decided to travel to Paris to take control of negotiations. He left Dublin in December 1797, but first stayed for some months in London to spend time with the Whig opposition at Westminster and to meet with the radicals and the growing number of United Irishmen in the capital, forced to flee from the military clampdown at home. He was watched closely by Whitehall.

*

Muir and Molet sat in the glow of the candles on the table in their apartment and Muir began dictating the first of many memorials to Talleyrand. His eyesight was weak and he relied on Molet for proper French usage. Molet set down Muir's political description of Britain before he was transported: the dangerous church and king mobs in England; the reactionary Anglican church; and the networks throughout England of radical dissenters. He described how a small elite around Pitt and Dundas controlled parliament, the Bank of England and government contracts and placements; they were dominant because of the feebleness of the official opposition. In Scotland the popular societies were widespread.

At the same time Tone was having meetings with Napoleon. At their final meeting in January 1798, Tone gave the general a sheaf of papers containing his analysis of Ireland, in which he described the dissenters in the north, who numbered about 900,000 as the "best informed of Ireland". He wrote that they are "to a man, sincere republicans and devoted with enthusiasm to the cause of liberty and France; they would make perhaps the best soldiers in Ireland, and are already in a considerable degree trained to arms." There were more than three million Catholics, from whom "there are five hundred thousand men who would fly to the standard of the Republic, if they saw it once displayed in the cause of liberty and their country". The Defenders "in June last embraced the whole peasantry of the provinces of Ulster, Leinster, and Connaught, three fourths of the nation; and I have little doubt that it has since extended into Munster, the remaining province. These men…are completely organised on a military plan".

What neither Tone, Tandy nor Muir knew was Talleyrand and Napoleon were discussing options that even the Directory was unaware of. In August 1797 the general wrote to Talleyrand encouraging his colonial ambitions and suggesting it was "necessary to seize Egypt". The minister replied, "As for Egypt, your ideas in this matter are grand and their usefulness should be understood." On 27 January 1798, he sent the Directory a memorandum arguing that the Ottoman empire could not last for another twenty-five years and France must act to take strategic possessions from it. Egypt, Crete, Lemnos and Malta would guarantee French dominance in the Mediterranean. This discussion was, of course, top secret.

In February, Napoleon rode all along the Channel coast and reviewed his *armée d'Angleterre*. From Dunkirk to Ostend he saw under construction the flat-bottomed gunboats championed by Paine. But at the end of the month he submitted a report to the Directory that strengthened Talleyrand's hand. "Whatever efforts we make, we shall not for some years gain the naval supremacy," he argued. "To invade England without that supremacy is the most daring and difficult task ever undertaken. If, having regard to the present organisation of our navy, it seems impossible to gain the necessary promptness of execution, then we must really give up the expedition against England, be satisfied with keeping up the pretence of it, and concentrate all our attention and resources on the Rhine, in order to deprive England of Hanover and Hamburg…or else undertake an eastern expedition which would menace her trade with the Indies."

In the Paris cafés, talk was still of an invasion across the Channel.

However, Tone, Tandy, Paine, Muir and the others were no longer the strategic allies for Foreign Minister Talleyrand that they had been, but reduced to tactical assets, valuable for "keeping up the pretence" of an invasion to wrong-foot Pitt and George III.

Meantime, Paine wrote articles in Bonneville's newspaper advocating invasion and praising Muir. Muir wrote in praise of Tandy. Muir began using his influence with Talleyrand to secure passports for exiles coming to Paris. He intervened with the Directory on behalf of Irish sailors taken prisoner from British ships, to the annoyance of Tone, who thought he was officially in charge of monitoring all new Irish immigrants to France. A London newspaper reported in February, "A Paris paper…contains the following article, 'Several Irishmen, flying from the despotism of the British government, have been taken in English ships and carried into Bordeaux where they have been confined in the Castle of Ila. After having undergone a strict interrogatory, the error was discovered and, at the recommendation of the celebrated Thomas Muir, they enjoy the best of treatment and will not be exchanged, as their political opinions would be fatal to them'."

In fact, Madgett had secured the authority to recruit, from among the prisoners of war, Irish sailors who were willing to join an invasion fleet. The British foreign secretary, Lord Grenville, received a spy's report that informed him, "I have frequently been in company with him [Madgett] at Thomas Muir's lodging… The day I left Paris he set out for Orleans, to tamper with the Irish prisoners there, in order to get them to engage in the expedition, on account of their knowledge both of the coast and of the country, and to serve as sailors in navigating their vessels."

Tone was unhappy. He recorded in his diary, "The number of Irish refugees is considerably increased… We all do very well except Napper Tandy, who is not behaving correctly. He began some months ago by caballing against me with a priest of the name of Quigley [Coigly], who is since gone off, no one knows whither."

The factionalism within the Irish émigré camp became destructive. Tandy called a meeting of all the United Irishmen in Paris to settle the leadership. Lewins refused to attend. Tone was under the impression some charge was to be levelled against him but "when I appeared, there was no one found to bring forward a charge against me". However, a vote was taken on who should be the main spokesman and a spy reported the meeting to the foreign secretary, Grenville. "Napper Tandy having quarrelled with Lewins and Tone, called a meeting of the United Irishmen in conjunction with Muir, Madgett and Stone. At the meeting a division took place, the numbers being pretty equal. Muir waited on Talleyrand with a petition, which Talleyrand took immediately to the Directory. In consequence Tandy was appointed general." The Directory had, in effect, recognised that two Irish parties existed and wanted to keep both on side.

"In consequence of this manoeuvre," recorded Tone, "I have had no communication since with Tandy, who has also lost ground, by this mean behaviour, with all the rest of his countrymen; he is, I fancy, pestering the government here with applications and memorials, and gives himself out for an old officer, and a man of great property in Ireland... He has got lately a coadjutor in the famous Thomas Muir, who is arrived in Paris, and has inserted two or three very foolish articles relating to the United Irishmen in the Paris papers, in consequence of which, at a meeting of the United Irishmen now in Paris (with the exception of Tandy), it was settled that Lowry, Orr, Lewins, and myself, should wait upon Muir and, after thanking him for his good intentions, intreat (sic) him not to introduce our business into any publications which he might hereafter think proper to make."

They arranged a meeting in Muir's apartment. "Of all the vain, obstinate blockheads that ever I met, I never saw his equal," Tone wrote. "He told us roundly that he knew as much of our country as we did, and would venture to say he had as much the confidence of the United Irishmen as we had; that he had no doubt we were very respectable individuals, but could only know us as such, we having shown him no powers or written authority to prove that we had any mission."

Muir, said Tone, claimed that everything he had written about the United Irishmen had the sanction of "the most respectable individual of that body, who had, and deserved to have, their entire confidence and approbation, and whose authority he must and did consider as justifying every syllable he had advanced. This most respectable individual of the body, we presume to be Tandy... We gave Mr Muir notice that he had neither licence nor authority to speak in the name of the people of Ireland, and that if we saw any similar productions to those of which we complained, we should be obliged to take measures that would conduce neither to his ease nor respectability, for that we could not suffer the public to be longer abused. On these terms we parted very drily on both sides."

In London, Grenville received another piece of information, possibly deliberately placed by Talleyrand, giving some details of plans to establish three separate republics in Ireland, Scotland and England, and naming the members of each Directory. Scotland's was to include Muir, and Lords Sempill and Lauderdale; the English Directory included Paine, Tooke, Thelwall and Lord Lansdowne, with Thomas Hardy as minister of justice; and in Ireland, Tandy, Fitzgerald and Hamilton Rowan (still in America) were named, but not Tone. Grenville naturally used this to advantage by secretly passing the intelligence to the loyalist associations in England who appealed to their members "to assemble in order to strengthen the hands of government and to keep a vigilant eye on the motions of domestic enemies" assisted by "traitors who have fled the gallows at home".

Tone's influence in Paris was further diminished in March when he was posted to Le Havre to help prepare for the French landings in Ireland. He was distressed at what he left behind. He noted in his diary, "I have seen lately in the paper called the *Bien Informé*, two articles relating to Napper Tandy, which are the most ridiculous rhodomontades. They describe him as an Irish general to whose standard 30,000 United Irishmen will fly the moment he displays it, and other trash of the like nature." (The numbers seemed small compared to those Tone had presented to Napoleon in January.) He thought Paine "was vain beyond all belief" but forgave him because "he has done wonders for the cause of liberty, both in America and Europe". However, "He drinks like a fish, a misfortune which I have known to befall other celebrated patriots [an oblique reference to Muir]. I am told that the true time to see him to advantage is about ten at night, with a bottle of brandy and water before him." And he complained about a St Patrick's Day dinner organised by Tandy, Muir, and Paine, that included the Who's Who of radical exiles in Europe, including the French-Irish generals Kilmaine and O'Shee. Kilmaine was commander of the centre column of the *armée d'Angleterre*. Tone saw this as public posturing and thought Tandy and Muir were "puffing one another...for the private advantage".

Lewins, too, was out of Paris for much of the spring of 1798, leaving Tandy as the main negotiator for the United Irishmen. Tandy, Paine, Muir and Stone met regularly to review events and were joined by John Ashley, former secretary of the London Corresponding Society, and Samuel Turner, a leader of the Belfast United Irishmen who now was their representative in Hamburg. It was Turner who suspected Lewins of treachery and had informed both Fitzgerald and O'Connor of this.

*

In Ireland from the summer into winter of 1797 General Lake imposed martial law in most of Ulster. He quartered his troops on villages and burnt down houses where sedition was suspected or where arms might be hidden. Soldiers sliced off ears and raped women as they gathered up pikes and small arms. Confessions were beaten out of poor people or they had scalding hot tar poured on their heads to give up information. United men were hung or flogged to death before ending up in graves that the soldiers called croppy holes. Thousands had to flee to Scotland, England or France. Many went to America. Now, in spring 1798, the Northern Committee wanted to press ahead with the revolution without waiting for the French and Coigly, the priest from Armagh who had been sent from

Paris to Dublin, was also in favour of an immediate national uprising to encourage and invite French intervention. The Dublin committee, however, wanted to wait for the French, even though little or no information was coming from Tone or Lewins. There were two dissidents on the committee, Fitzgerald and O'Connor, who pushed for immediate action in Leinster and beyond but were overruled by moderates such as Emmett and McNevin.

General Lake had by now extended martial law across the whole of Ireland, and sporadic, uncoordinated rebellions were breaking out all over the south. It was defensive, often led by priests or poor peasants who had different objectives from the United Irishmen. They called for reinstatement of ancient land rights, death to the protestant landowners, and a Catholic state. It was driving a wedge between them and Protestant revolutionaries, especially Presbyterians in the north.

The Paris committee knew the United Irishmen had to gain control if a democratic revolution was to be achieved. They needed to let the French know they could support the insurrections if they acted soon. Otherwise the chance would be lost, again.

Tandy received news from a messenger sent by Coigly and O'Connor to let him know they were on their way to Paris. The messenger reported that Coigly had stayed in London for about three weeks, to assist with building an alliance between the London United Irish and the republican dissidents in the Corresponding Society who had formed the United Englishmen. They had a new national committee of United Britons, which included delegates from Scotland. Coigly and O'Connor were anxious that Paris knew of this and understood how it could be important in creating diversionary actions when the uprising in Ireland began.

"Can you add anything more recent to that, John?" asked Tandy, turning to Ashley, recently arrived from London. Ashley explained that Coigly had gone on to Ireland with three delegates from the London committee. They met with Fitzgerald in Dublin then travelled to Belfast with the delegates from the United Britons and told the provincial meeting there that the French were going on with the expedition and that it was in a greater state of forwardness than was expected. Coigly had crossed back to England and in Lancashire met the twenty-seven secretaries of the Manchester United Irish before returning to London. The organisation of United Irish and English was strong in the North and the Midlands. Back in London he reported to the committee that he and O'Connor were going to Paris to give the French assistance in their plan of invading Ireland, Scotland, and finally, England. Not only would they encourage the prompt despatch of a fleet to Ireland, but they were to depose the Irish envoy, Lewins, whom they had begun to suspect. "The last I heard was that Coigly and two or three others were waiting on O'Connor to finish his business in London," Ashley concluded.

Most of what Ashley conveyed was correct. But the United Englishmen were not as tightly knit as the Irish organisation. It was still an umbrella network connecting different groups. The intensive United Irish recruitment in England and Scotland was, though, impressive and fanned the embers of the old radical societies in both countries. But Ashley's assessment of the importance of those societies was exaggerated. His claim that 30,000 men in London were ready to rise in a diversionary move to assist an Irish rebellion may have buoyed the exiles around the table in Paine's room, but it must have prompted some to raise a sceptical eyebrow.

*

Across the city, in the Foreign Ministry, Talleyrand received private word from the Directory that Napoleon's plan to seize Egypt had been approved. In early April began issuing orders to prepare, with the greatest secrecy, an expedition comprising thirteen ships of the line, seventeen frigates, thirty five smaller warships, 280 transport craft, 16,000 sailors and 38,000 officers and troops, to be accompanied by 187 scientists, writers and artists. Not one of the five Directors seemed to have thought to ask why Napoleon's objection to the invasion of England, the unpreparedness of the French navy, could not equally be levelled at his plans for Egypt.

"Bad news," said Muir to Molet as he scanned the main stories in that day's newspapers. "O'Connor, Coigly, and three other United Irish have been arrested in Margate trying to book a passage to France. They have been charged with treason."

CHAPTER 40

A flame extinguished

"We have achieved a great duty in these critical times. After the destruction of so many years we have been the first to revive the spirit of our country, and give it a national existence."

Thomas Muir, 1798.

The tall, balding, well-built man in his fifties who strolled though the Palais Royal with the aid of a walking stick was newly arrived in Paris from London. His name was Dr Robert Watson and he was looking for Hôtel de la Marine, which he had been told at Muir's old apartment was somewhere near the Palais. Muir and Molet had recently moved there. Watson was one of four delegates chosen by the committee of the United Britons to travel to Paris as their representative but he was the only one who managed to complete the journey. The government had ordered mass arrests of radical leaders throughout Britain in April and five hundred or more were rounded up in London, Manchester, Leicester, Birmingham and different parts of Scotland.

Watson had avoided arrest but was known to the authorities, who put a bounty of £400 on his head. He had been active in the London Corresponding Society almost from its beginning and was at one time president of the executive committee; he had spent two years in Newgate for circulating a handbill attacking the English Militia Act; and the Home Office was informed by a spy in April 1798 that, "when the accounts of the mutiny on board the fleet at Portsmouth came to London the society expressed the greatest satisfaction & actually sent delegates, namely Dr Watson & John Bone (the one being at that time a member of the executive committee of the Corresponding Society and the other the secretary) down to Portsmouth to confer with the leading mutineers, and that when the mutiny also broke out at the Nore they endeavoured to communicate with sailors on board the fleet there, and actually did so in one or two instances." The informant went on to explain how the Corresponding Society repeatedly tried to influence soldiers in Hyde Park and elsewhere by distributing handbills to them, and encouraged their own members to join the militia and the supplementary cavalry.

Watson leant heavily on his stick as he mounted the stairs to the Hôtel de la Marine. He had suffered a leg wound during the American war while fighting in Washington's army, which he left with the rank of colonel after the defeat of the British. He found Muir's apartment and introduced himself. Muir was aware of Watson's reputation in London, he had read Watson's rebuttal of Edmund Burke's criticism of the French revolution, but they had never met. Muir warmed to the soft tones of Watson's Elgin accent and after a very few pleasantries Watson began to explain his mission.

He told Muir how he had been smuggled on a Swedish ship and made his way through Scandinavia to Hamburg, where he had had previous contact with the French agent who secured his passport to Paris. One of the other delegates trying to get to France was Charles Williams of the United Englishmen, who was arrested in the raid on the leadership of the London Corresponding Society on 18 April. The two others were James Kennedy and Angus Cameron from the United Scotsmen and Watson believed they were still free and attempting to cross the Channel.

Kennedy had been Skirving's assistant secretary at the British Convention and was arrested in 1794 and subsequently released. Since then he had been working for the Friends of the People and, later, for the United Scotsmen, travelling all across Scotland. The authorities lost sight of him from May 1794, when he was unsuccessfully called as a witness for the Crown in the trials of Watt and Downie.

Cameron was a Highlander, a United Scotsman from Lochaber,

who spoke both Gaelic and English, and a great orator. When the militia riots spread to the Highlands in August the previous year it was Cameron who took the lead. He commanded thousands and tried to organise them into something like an army, which surrounded Castle Menzies to extract a promise from Sir John and other local gentry that they would not implement the Act and would not prosecute those who opposed it. They did the same at other great houses along the Tay, and for eight days this near insurrection went on, with Cameron on horseback, leading his followers and addressing the people in Gaelic. There was talk of plundering Lord Breadalbane's armoury, and the ones at Glenlyon House and Castle Menzies, and of capturing the guns at Taymouth Castle and taking to the hills to fight a guerrilla campaign. Cameron and his lieutenant, James Menzies, were arrested from their beds by a party of Windsor Foresters early one morning and the carriage taking them to Perth had to outrun a huge mob who pursued it throwing stones and even firing a few shots. Cameron escaped from the prison but Menzies stood trial and was sentenced to seven years in Botany Bay.

Watson brought the news that Mealmaker, too, had been sentenced to transportation for fourteen years, and that three men and a woman from Eccles, in the Borders, were handed the same sentence by Braxfield for just being at the scene of a riot, in spite of a plea from the jury for mercy. Even Robert Dundas subsequently admitted that Braxfield had once again been too severe, making later juries wary of convicting. In the end, only eighty people were charged with rioting in Scotland and, of these, twenty three failed to appear and were outlawed, twenty-one were found guilty and transported or imprisoned, nineteen were acquitted, and the other twenty seven were released without charge.

Watson arrived in Paris at the end of May as the trials for treason took place at Maidstone in Kent of Coigly, O'Connor and the three other United Irishmen arrested in Margate in April. Coigly had been found with incriminating evidence in his coat pocket, an address from the United Britons urging the French government to invade, and he was the only one convicted. He was offered his freedom if he would implicate O'Connor, which he refused to do. He was sentenced to death. O'Connor was re-arrested at the close of the trial and sent to Dublin where he was imprisoned in the Castle.

Throughout Ireland the rebellion was in disarray. In March most of the Leinster provincial committee and four of the five-man national executive had been arrested. Only Fitzgerald remained free and in hiding. Others filled their places right away – that was the secret strength of the organisation which, in spite of murderous assaults by the British army, still had more than quarter of a million men in the movement, a hundred and ten thousand in Ulster, a similar number in Munster, and forty five thousand in Dublin and the surrounding countryside.

Fitzgerald and the new executive at first refused to name a date for the national uprising until their planning was complete. It was clear that the scale of government terror now made it necessary for an independent attempt without French aid. They had, in any case, had word from France at the start of May that an expedition would not sail until August. Organisation of a mighty blow at the functioning of government in Dublin now became central to their plans.

On 20 April, Tone received news in Le Havre that Napoleon was to leave Paris for Toulon, where a great flotilla was being prepared. He was confused. "All this, I confess, utterly deroutes me," he wrote in his diary. Sure enough, at the beginning of May the general set out and two weeks later the French fleet sailed from the southern port for Malta, en route to Egypt.

In France, the exiles were unaware that the United Irishmen had now no choice but to set a date for the revolution and 23 May was agreed. Nor did they know that Fitzgerald had been captured and fatally wounded and others of the new national executive were taken prisoner as well, leaving no one free to give the signal to rise. An uncoordinated insurrection was still raging in the countryside and on the agreed date only the south rose in any numbers; Dublin remained peaceful and the Ulster committee delayed for a week and then voted to wait for the French, or at least for the fall of Dublin. Army and militia poured into Ireland from Britain, where no diversionary skirmishes took place.

*

Muir and Watson, who had become Muir's close adviser, had extensive discussions with Paine and Tandy and the others. Would the Scots rise and fight a rearguard action? Could Cameron and Kennedy rouse the Highlands? Some said 50,000 Gaels would rise, many more than had ever gathered under the standards of the Stewarts in their rebellions. During the American war loyal regiments had been raised in the Highlands by lairds but this was because tenants' sons were compelled to make up a quota or see their parents turned out of their homes. Though they came from what was still a warrior culture and had a loyalty to the chieftain, Highlanders since then had been enrolled by lairds in temporary fencible regiments for home defence, only to be sent away to another part of the country or abroad to the Indies. The rumour during the militia riots was that the government planned to get them into a local unit and then draft them into the regulars and send them overseas. The trust with the chieftains had been broken. The Paris committee recognised this, strengthened with the knowledge that from the beginning the Friends of the People had been careful to take their message into the Highlands and Paine's *Rights of Man* had been translated into Gaelic and sold in its thousands in villages of the north.

Muir prepared a second memorandum to Talleyrand, nineteen pages outlining the political constitution of Scotland and its injustices; the Scots' moral character and physical strength; and how a revolution could be ignited and sustained from France. The Scots would fight to establish an independent republic and 100,000 patriots would rise. However, much more preparatory work would be required to overcome anti-French propaganda, and a proclamation that guaranteed the people's right to choose their own religious leaders and their own form of worship would be crucial. French troops would have to conduct themselves as allies, not occupiers, under a Scottish provisional government.

Muir was by now well enough known in the Foreign Ministry to be received by Talleyrand or his officials without difficulty or ceremony. Accompanied by Molet, he made his way to the ministry building in the Hôtel Gallifet, set back a way from the Rue de Bac. He passed through the first of its two courtyards and into the inner square which housed the main buildings, fronted by a peristyle of thirty-foot columns. Talleyrand lived, worked and entertained on the ground floor, one wall of which had great doors and windows looking into the garden. Molet waited in the courtyard while Muir was shown into the minister's office.

Muir explained that he had brought along another proposal for intervention in Scotland, once again in Molet's handwriting, which he placed on the desk that stood between them. He told Talleyrand of the arrival in Paris of Watson and the news he had brought of the United movement in England and Scotland, including the previous year's widespread riots against the Militia Act.

Talleyrand knew that one of the reasons Napoleon had blown hot and cold over invading Ireland was the conflicting views in the reports of different Irish envoys. He also knew that Tone had been continuously protesting against a force being considered for Scotland and was convinced that "nothing will ever be done unless we first begin in Ireland". Large contingents of the *armée d'Angleterre* had by this time been reassigned to the Rhine or sent to reinforce the Egypt campaign.

Outside in the courtyard, Molet was waiting in the spring sunshine. Muir emerged from the ministry and stumbled on the bottom step. Molet steadied him, holding him fast by the elbow. Muir's face was drained and ashen; he leaned on one of the tall columns. On some days the pain in his face and head was acute and he asked Molet to get him home to take some tincture.

*

It was weeks before news of the Irish rising was confirmed in France. In Le Havre, Tone read of the May insurrection in the French papers of 11 June. They also carried the shocking news of the arrest and death of Fitzgerald on 4 June, and the hanging of Coigly in England on 7 June. Tone was frustrated at his isolation from developments at home; he scarcely recognised the names of the arrested leaders and could not guess at the reason for O'Connor's and Coigly's attempted trip to France. Lewins had been in Holland for months and had still failed to establish regular contact with Ireland.

But if Tone was unprepared so were the other exiles and so was the Directory. The Republic's navy had sailed away to Egypt with most of the army and its best generals. Hurried plans for assistance to Ireland had to be made. Talleyrand urged the Directory to action and sent them an up-to-date assessment of strengths and weaknesses, taking into account the submissions of the exiles, and argued for a more hawkish policy of supporting the revolt in Ireland, spreading disaffection in England, and threatening India from Egypt. But word was sent to Tone on 20 June that, because of English naval superiority, the expedition would be postponed until autumn. He was furious. Ireland was in revolt and being left to fight Britain's army on its own. It dawned on him that there would be no major French expedition, a few forays to draw the heat from Napoleon, maybe, but no great military campaign of liberation.

The insurrection in Leinster was over by the end of May. A rank and file revolt against the sluggish Ulster leadership saw 11,000 rise in Antrim and County Down, but they were defeated in mid-June. By the middle of July the revolt was confined to Wexford, where a rebel government exercised real power for a time. At sea, there were many attempts at support through mutinies led by Irish sailors. These were met with iron discipline in shipboard courts martial and quick executions. The First Sea Lord said the hangings were needed "as the most effective means of checking a new species of mutiny…connected with the rebellion in Ireland".

Still the Directory was slow to respond. General Humbert sailed with a force of a thousand officers and men in mid-August and put ashore at Killala, in County Mayo on the lonely west coast. In London the *Morning Chronicle* reported, "Those who can see further through government despatches than other people, assure us that the French landed at Killala are not soldiers but officers; and that Hamilton Rowan and Napper Tandy are among the number, perhaps Thomas Paine, Thomas Muir and others." The landing sparked a second insurrection that had some initial success but ended in defeat on 8 September. Napper Tandy was not at Killala but was rushing equipment to Humbert's forces on board the Anacreon, one of the fastest-sailing corvettes in the French navy. She left Dunkirk on 4 September and sailed around the north coast of Scotland, arriving too late, a full week after the final battle at Ballinamuck. Tandy briefly put ashore and, learning of the slaughter, sailed away again. A second expedition to reinforce Humbert sailed on 14 September. There were three thousand men under General Hardy, with Wolfe Tone on board the flagship Hoche, together with eight frigates and a schooner. They had no idea Humbert's army had been defeated, or that the British navy lay in wait for them off the coast of Donegal. The French fleet was dispersed and Tone was taken prisoner on 31 October.

*

Since Muir's painful attack outside the Foreign Ministry in May, his health had not improved. In fact, ever since the fainting incident at the banquet in Bordeaux he had done his best to disguise his pain and discomfort. Molet had been attentive, making sure he had an adequate supply of opium-based pain killer and ointments. At one point in June they had talked of Muir's future and had decided to apply to the Directory for a country place where he might retire. Molet, as usual, drew up the petition, which began by once more thanking the Directory for rescuing him from Spain and for their kindness towards him in France. "Nevertheless," he went on, "I am very unhappy. I eat your bread and am no use to the Republic. If my physical forces had answered to my inclinations I should have sought from you the honour of fighting your enemies on the frontiers but, alas, that is impossible."

He explained how it was difficult for him to make a claim on his estate in Scotland, although he was investigating ways to achieve this. However, he explained, he was also busy compiling "all the materials of my travels and of the events of my exile", which would amount to two volumes that are "awaited in England with the greatest eagerness" and would be worth around £3,000 from a London publisher. "The object, then, citizen directors, of this petition is to beg you to accord me the permission to buy a National Domain of the value of one hundred and fifty thousand francs, which I hope to be able to pay for entirely within two years, and to be good enough to put me in possession of it immediately, as a means of subsistence and to free me from the necessity of depending any longer on your outstanding humanity."

It was now September and they had heard nothing from the ministry about the petition but, in any case, Muir felt that the responsibility of leadership forced him to put that idea aside. With Tandy gone, only Muir and Madgett remained of the Paris exiles committee that managed Irish and Scottish affairs – Paine, Stone, Williams, Watson, Smith and others were consulted, naturally. Samuel Turner, the Ulster United Irish agent in Hamburg, who was often in Paris, was invited to make up the third member of the triumvirate. Turner wrote, "Madget and Muir swore me into the secret committee for managing the affairs of Ireland and Scotland in Tandy's place, there are only we three of the committee."

Turner had written that note to Lord Portland, the British home secretary. Neither Madgett nor Muir could have known, nobody did, that Turner was a spy. He had been since 1797 when he approached the government in London with information. He was a barrister from Newry and initially one of the shrewdest leaders of the United Irishmen's northern executive. He revealed the names of committee members and how correspondence between Paris and Dublin and

London came by way of Hamburg in the personal mail of Lord Edward Fitzgerald's sister Lucy and was identified by special seals and ciphers. Turner later arranged to become the United representative in Hamburg and ingratiated himself with the Fitzgerald household there.

His distrust of the Catholic leaders and his fear of a religious tyranny in a priest-led sectarian Catholic state led him to become an informer with the aim of destroying that goal. It was he who planted suspicion about Lewins, whom he resented for his support of the Catholic faction. Turner's information had led to the discovery of Coigly and O'Connor in Margate; he supplied the British with details of preparations for invasion at the French Channel ports, and later of the expeditions to Ireland by Humbert, Tone and Tandy; he gave away the identities of all the exiles active in Paris; but he played a long and cautious game and was never discovered. The invitation to become the third member of the secret Paris committee was treasure trove for Turner.

News of the Irish defeat began to filter through to the Paris cafés at the end of September. No one was yet aware of what had happened to the leaders of the expeditions but they were acutely aware that the planned diversionary risings had not taken place in either Scotland or London.

"Why did the movements fail?" Muir, Watson and Paine asked themselves. The arrests and trials of Coigly and O'Connor, coupled with mass arrests across the country in April had severely weakened them; more arrests in May and June, when the rebellion was in full swing, took place among the Irish in England, more than thirty at the end of May and more in June and July. That would have led to extreme caution in Scotland and in the Lancashire stronghold of the United Irishmen. Some Scottish regiments refused to leave their barracks in Glasgow, but only for a brief period. They went to Ireland in the end. In London the union between English and Irish organisations was still fragile and they were certain to be aware they were too weak and too closely watched to mount a diversion.

They wondered whether everything was lost or whether it was

still possible to revive an insurrection in Scotland. Muir decided to approach Talleyrand once again. He bypassed Madget and Turner – this was a Scottish affair – and didn't call on Molet, as he usually did, to write the memorandum in his neat, small hand and perfect French. On the evening of 18 October he sat and wrote alone and in secret, this time in English.

"*Citizen Ministre*," his covering letter began. His handwriting was better than he thought, in spite of his poor eyesight, but not as legible as it had been in earlier days. "I have the honour of transmitting to you the enclosed memorial. It is ill transcribed, as upon the importance and delicacy of its contents, I was obliged to transcribe it myself. It relates to three important objects. 1st Insurrection in Scotland. 2d Insurrection in London & 3d Insurrection aboard the English fleet." He explained that he believed the Republic could still strike "a rapid and decisive blow" with small expense and little danger. "If I had the means by a safe and confidential messenger who, furnished with no written instructions, could invite one or two persons from Britain to meet me not in Paris but in some other place less suspicious, I could give instructions and arrange the plan of operation."

He appealed to Talleyrand to consider carefully the dilemma of English sailors. "In their highest irritation, if attacked by a foreign force they will fight well and desperately. No hopes, founded upon their discontentment will be realised on the day of battle. The Republic must avail herself of their discontentment while they are in a state of inaction brooding over their wrongs and meditating revenge."

He expanded these themes in the memo but first asked the ministry to find a capable confidential agent to travel to Scotland and "survey and calculate the force of the patriots", arrange preparations and fix the timetable for action. No arms needed to be sent. A sum of £20,000 would buy all necessary weapons in the country. Only powder would have to be transported. Artillery could be got in the Carron Iron Works and in the foundries of the Clyde. He suggested guerrilla warfare. "You know the topographical plan of Scotland.

Her mountains, her lakes, her hazardous and narrow passes might be so fortified by an invisible foe as no army could either march or act."

The Directory should give assurances to sailors that they would receive the full value of every vessel brought into a French port, and be promised better pay and promotion. "More than two thirds of those employed in the marine service are Scotchmen & Irishmen... The Republic has it in her power to annihilate the English navy by the navy itself."

Muir was scathing about the London mob, which he said would follow whoever offers the most money. This had been evident in earlier riots that included burning effigies of Paine. They could be bought. "The sum of 20, or 30,000 £Stg prudently employed and distributed would be sufficient to accomplish that effect, once produced." Some of the radical leaders in the capital, such as Tooke or Thelwall, he considered too far removed from the people, but he named others, including Hardy, who could be relied on.

He repeated again the potential of a Highland uprising. "Cameron has been outlawed and is now concealing himself in London. He could easily be found. Kennedy I sincerely hope is upon the road to Paris." The Scots would not rise prematurely and would not risk the fate of Coigly or O'Connor. "There is a very momentous class of people, highly discontented, who wish a revolution but who, tinctured with deep-rooted prejudices declare that they will never accept of liberty if it is not entirely of their own manufacture... Let me then earnestly entreat the French government to attack the tyranny of the English government in its interior. The attention of the government is now drawn to Ireland. Let it be fixed there... Ireland has now committed herself." While the preparations for a Scottish revolt were undertaken in secret, "the English government would be lulled into security". When Scotland was "completely disposed and completely organised" with the help of a well-organised invasion, a revolution could be achieved at very little cost and with very little bloodshed.

Muir now made preparations to leave Paris and await the presumed arrival of Cameron and Kennedy. He found a safe house in the small village of Chantilly, about thirty miles north east of the capital. In the middle of November, about the time they heard of the conviction of Tone for treason and his suicide in a Dublin jail, Muir moved there in secret and without company. Only his most trusted friends knew where he went and why. Only they could direct the expected Scottish agents to him.

At Chantilly Muir took a room in the house of Mme La Bussine; he lay low and kept to himself. No one in the village knew him and he made no attempt to make friends or acquaintances. Only Mme La Bussine's twelve-year-old son was allowed into his life. The boy brought his food and ran errands for Muir. Newspapers and documents arrived daily from Paris and were delivered by the local postman. They were brought to Muir's room by the boy.

The cold December stretched into January and still Muir was alone. He knew that his health was failing but was determined to see through his plan before even thinking of rest and retirement in a country *domaine*. On the morning of 26 January, young Bussine brought Muir bread and coffee. It was about six o'clock when the boy knocked on the door. He received no answer. He pushed the door open and saw Muir still in bed. He called *"Monsieur!"* and gently shook him. He placed the bowl of coffee and the bread on Muir's table and tried again. He touched Muir's hand and was surprised to find it cold. He had never encountered death before but the fact of it slowly and reluctantly became personally known to him.

"Maman, maman! C'est Monsieur Muir. Il est mort!"

CHAPTER 41

Epilogue

"When you're called for jury service, when your name
is drawn by lot. When you vote in an election, when you
freely voice your thought. Don't take these things for
granted, for dearly were they bought. Remember Thomas
Muir of Huntershill."

Adam McNaughton, 'Remember Thomas Muir of
Huntershill', 1992.

It was the postman, Jean Lepauvre, who reported Muir's death to
the mayor, Jean Philippe Levasseur, at the town hall. Lepauvre was
the only other person in Chantilly who knew Muir's name, and that
was only because of his mail. No one knew his age or his nationality
or where his permanent residence was. The mayor, the postman and
the town official in charge of weights and measures went to Mme
Bussine's house to confirm Muir's death, and arranged for him to be
buried in the local cemetery. It has since been built over and there is
no trace of his grave. Only the headstones of those who had a permanent plot were transferred to a new graveyard. Muir's must have been
a temporary, public plot and there is no known remaining record of
his burial.

However, someone in Paris must have known of his death because
a short obituary for Muir appeared in the *Moniteur* just four days
later, on 30 January. It read, in part, "Thomas Muir, the Scotsman so
celebrated for his love of liberty, for his misfortunes…has just died
from the wounds which he received about two years ago." He was
thirty-three years old.

And someone must have collected his belongings from Chantilly, for the small bible given to him by his mother and father when he boarded the Royal George revenue cutter in Leith Roads, bound for the Thames hulks, was returned to them in Huntershill. Peter Mackenzie, in his 1831 biography of Muir, says, "On his deathbed he carefully sealed up the bible which they had given to him...leaving an injunction that it should be forwarded to his parents by the first opportunity." Whether this is true we have no way of knowing. Much in Mackenzie's book is dubious history, written from fragmentary material for a directly political purpose, part of a campaign that led to the 1832 Reform Act. However, it is thought he did have the benefit of interviewing some surviving relatives of Muir and the story of how the bible was returned may have come from one of them.

How news of Muir's death got to his family is unknown but the shock must have been severe. According to Michael Donnelly, author of the 1975 pamphlet on Muir, Huntershill was permanently closed and his parents spent their final years in the Glasgow apartment above the shop. They decreed that the driveway gates should stay shut in his memory. Donnelly says he found the rusted lock to the gates and presented it to the Australian Museum of Democracy in Canberra.

An inscription left in Huntershill House read:
Doomed from this mansion to a foreign land
To waste his days of gay and sprightly youth,
And all for sowing with a liberal hand,
The seeds of that seditious libel truth.

Christina Bewley, who wrote the 1981 biography of Muir, claims that the inscription was underneath a portrait of Muir, which his mother, who died in 1803, asked to be permanently kept in the house. She quotes an article in the local paper in March 1971, but no further evidence of the existence of the portrait is available. A letter from Sir Patrick Dollan, the former lord provost of Glasgow, to Muir's unpublished biographer GP Insh in 1949 claimed, "A copy [of Muir's portrait] hangs in the gallery of famous Glaswegians in the Lord Provost's room at the City Chambers". Was this a portrait that had been removed from Huntershill or a different one? There is no record of a portrait of Muir in the archives of Glasgow council today.

Muir's parents must have lived in hope that the report of the death of their son was mistaken. James Muir's will, his "disposition and settlement", dictated shortly before his death in 1801, left the bulk of his estate to trustees on behalf of his son and his heirs.

Did Molet, or Paine, or Stone, Williams, Watson, Madgett, or any of the other Paris exiles know what Muir was doing in Chantilly and did one of them collect his things? Were any of them in regular contact with him? Who was sending him newspapers and documents? Did any of them know he was expecting the arrival of Cameron and Kennedy, who, as far as we know never got there? Or was there more to it? Did Muir feel his life ebbing away and decide to die alone? If so why? Without further documentary evidence we can't answer these questions.

Muir had said he was compiling a book about his travels, but that material has never been found. However, on 3 March 1821 Thomas Hardy received a note from a Mr Witherspoon of Cheapside saying that he had a box of manuscripts, letters and papers belonging to the late Thomas Muir. Hardy replied to this note and sent Witherspoon a print taken from the cast of Muir's face made aboard Surprize while she lay at Portsmouth. What happened to those papers? Hardy didn't say whether he saw them or collected them.

It seems that any letters or papers that may have been in the possession of Muir's family have gone without trace as well. Bewley claims in her biography to be descended from another branch of the Muir family. "There are few family papers because the Muirs were an unlucky family," she wrote. "Thomas had one sister, four of whose sons were killed in accidents. Of her children only one daughter, Louisa, lived to forty. My grandfather was a descendant of one of Muir's uncles, and was only eight when his parents and sisters were lost at sea." Janet Muir's great-grandson, JG Lockhart, confirms the family's unfortunate fate. "With one exception," he wrote, "none of her offspring reached the age of forty." Her eldest son, a lieutenant in the navy, was drowned at sea; another was killed when he fell from his horse; a third had a fatal accident on board a ship; a fourth died of sunstroke in India; and a fifth disappeared in the Australian outback. "Even the happy exception – the daughter who married my grandfather – died on her fortieth birthday." He also revealed that his great-grandmother, Muir's sister Janet, "was burnt to death in her bed".

The final trace of Muir in the French archives is an entry on his request for a country property. It must have emerged at the top of a bureaucrat's pile some time after January 1799. Scribbled in the margin is a note, which reads in translation, "Since then Muir has died".

The verdicts of later historians on Muir's endeavours in Paris have been harsh. Meikle, referring to Muir's October memo to Talleyrand, dismissively concludes, "Such was the extraordinary document that Muir, diseased in body and mind, submitted to his benefactors." Insh adds, "The value of his estimate may be judged by his assertion that an invading force might expect the ready assistance of fifty thousand Highlanders. This represented eight times the number of Highlanders who had come out in the Forty-five." Bewley is judgmental and hostile about his earlier submission in May. She calls it "a sorry piece of clumsy propaganda and childish diatribe, giving a totally misleading picture", "exaggerated" and a "farrago". She goes on, "He was a sick man who had suffered great hardship and was struggling for official support... Force of circumstances arrested and distorted his political development, sharpening his radical and chauvinistic opinions."

Only MacMillan, who notes that "foregone conclusions seldom have existence prior to hindsight", tries to go beyond explanations that rely on personal failings. "Accept that the radical estimates refer to militant support, rather than a gathered army," he says, "and the figures begin to look almost modest... The radical leaders were intelligent men, well versed in history, and none would have expected the figures quoted to be assembled armed and ready for the fray; but at a time when half a regiment of determined infantry could hold most towns to ransom, they had every reason to believe effective bridgeheads could be established." Unlike the historian, who weighs the available evidence to reach a conclusion, the political activist weighs risks according to partial information and takes gambles. Outcomes are never certain.

The reality of continued radical activity in Ireland, Scotland and England, is incontrovertible, no matter what the debate on Muir's numbers concludes. In Ireland the United Irish society outlived the rebellion. The surviving leaders, including O'Connor, Thomas Emmet and McNevin were imprisoned in Fort George in the Moray Firth in Scotland, while hundreds of ordinary members who lived through the rebellion and its aftermath were sent to the army or the navy, or transported to Botany Bay. A new, exclusive, secret organisation led by Robert Emmet was fashioned for a political coup rather than a popular uprising, while nationalist Defenders revived in the countryside. Negotiations were renewed with the first consul, Napoleon, who had taken over from the Directory in the coup of November 1799. Emmett and his associates attempted another rising on 23 July 1803, which was premature and ill-conceived. He was tried for treason and executed in October that year.

In England, a revival of radicalism in 1799 was assisted by the flow of rebel fugitives from Ireland and more than 15,000 United men were reported to be organised in the Irish areas of London, with 8,000 in Manchester. A new democratic offensive by English radicals in 1800-1 included a programme in Lancashire and Yorkshire towns to revive mass petitioning, accompanied by similar attempts at a peace campaign in the counties and in London. In the West Midlands, riots demanding "No King! Give us bread" sparked fears of insurrection. On 8 November, Under-secretary King at the Home Office thought that "an insurrection of a very extensive and alarming nature" could engulf the region. Suppression of attempted mass meetings followed, which cowed the petitioning movement by June.

The United British organisation was revived following the release of the English state prisoners in March 1801. The act suspending habeas corpus was due for renewal and this had been carelessly overlooked, obliging the authorities to set hundreds of unconvicted radicals at liberty, and the organisation grew in London and the north of England in the first half of 1802. It was expected that war with France would be renewed soon and the United British worked with the United Irish to secure a French landing in Ireland. The government moved too soon and arrested some United men in London in what became known as the Despard Conspiracy. They were convicted of treason on the word of spies but the full extent of the United preparations was not uncovered. News of Emmett's premature rising put a stop to continued preparation after August 1803.

In Scotland, where the United Scotsmen had gone to ground, a similar revival took place, leading Robert Dundas to believe that by the end of 1800 secret correspondence had been renewed with England. In the following year a new lord advocate, Charles Hope, found that the local societies were still meeting and, although their numbers were not great, they had an executive committee sitting in Glasgow that he was unable to penetrate. In the spring of 1802 one of his spies at last informed him that in Fife United Scotsmen cells were regrouping and a rising was intended.

Similar information reached him from other parts of the country. The Glasgow executive began gathering membership figures from weaving villages and other old radical strongholds and found a respectable cadre still at local level, 93 in Auchterarder, 59 in Dunning, 133 in Crieff, 29 in Foulis and 483 in Perth. Arms were being gathered in many places, using the tested Irish method of pretending to assemble for a funeral. There were cells in the Fife Militia, and in the Dundee, Perth, and Strathmingo volunteers. Food riots in 1801 engulfed the whole country and the lord lieutenant of Renfrewshire told Hope, "The spirit of 1794 has burst forth, and politics is mixed with the present scarcity to excite the disaffected to tumult and insurrection." By April 1803, the lord advocate could report that the societies were "all alive again". Following the arrests in London in November 1802, renewal of war with France in May 1803, and the crushing of Emmett's revolt in Ireland in June, they went to ground once more.

So, if effective leadership and coordinated strategy had been provided by France in Ireland, England, and Scotland, maybe Muir's persistence and his numbers were not so fanciful. An observation of George Canning, a disciple of Pitt who became prime minister in 1817, is telling. He dismissed "the trite and futile argument that our would-be reformers and revolutionists are few in number... When was a revolution effected in any state but by an active and enterprising minority?"

That observation was tested and proved throughout the nineteenth and twentieth centuries and into the early years of the twenty-first. Muir's strength was not only in being well known and a recognised leader, especially in Scotland, but in his organising ability. He gathered together the disaffected of the early 1790s and forged a nation-wide platform, and he had the guts to show bold leadership. It was possible, in spite of his horrific injuries and failing health that, given the right circumstances, he could have become a figurehead to rally that desire for change once more. At least we can assume that is what he hoped for.

The radicalism never ceased, although it hid its face from time to time. By 1809 it had taken on a more industrial form when a combination of weavers was formed in Glasgow and surrounding districts. In 1812, 40,000 of them struck over declining wages. By 1816 a campaign of mass public meetings and petitions for parliamentary reform emerged again, drawing in the 1812 veterans and even some of the old reformers from the 1790s. This agitation had intensified so much by the end of 1819 that yet another new repressive code was introduced in parliament. The so-called Six Acts were directed against possession of arms, printing of seditious libels and holding large meetings. Those early years of the nineteenth century also saw unrest from Luddites; strikes against the Combination Acts; a march of Staffordshire miners and Manchester weavers, the Blanketeers, to London in 1816; a rural uprising in Nottinghamshire in 1817; the Manchester spinners' strike of 1818; and the massacre in the following year of eleven people, with 140 more injured, at a reform meeting in St Peter's Fields in Manchester. This tragedy, which came to be known as Peterloo, inspired Shelley to write his 92-verse poem, *The Mask of Anarchy*, which includes the lines, "Shake your chains to earth like dew, Which in sleep had fallen on you, Ye are many, they are few".

In February 1820, twenty-seven delegates of the Glasgow central committee of the United Scotsmen were arrested on suspicion of being involved in arranging simultaneous risings in Scotland and England. On 2 April, manifestos posted throughout the west of Scotland called for a strike the next day in support of the formation of a provisional government. Around 60,000 answered the strike call, thought to be the work of *agents provocateurs* to force a premature uprising. But the expected rising, and a simultaneous insurrection in England, failed to materialise. A skirmish took place at Bonnymuir and forty-seven were arrested and charged with high treason; eighteen were transported and three executed. In the aftermath of the so-called Radical War the societies again briefly subsided, but trade unionism was boosted by the repeal of the Combination Acts in 1824. Popular political societies regrouped for the agitation surrounding the Whig Reform Bill in 1830-2 and continued with the Chartist agitation of the following two decades.

The second reading of the Reform Bill in 1831 led to public rejoicing and in Glasgow one of the illuminations displayed was a transparency of Thomas Muir. The English Act was passed on June 7, 1832. According to Meikle, "Inasmuch as the system of representation in Scotland was more irrational than that of England, the Scottish reform bill, which received the royal assent on the 17th of the following month, was a more revolutionary measure. According to its provisions, householders rated at £10 replaced the electorate of self-elected town councils. In the counties the qualifications of parchment barons were abolished and the franchise conferred on the proprietors of real property valued at £10 a year, and on tenants with a nineteen years' lease, paying a rent of £50. Eight members were added to the representation of Scotland, two members being allotted to Edinburgh and Glasgow respectively, and one each to Paisley, Aberdeen, Perth, Dundee, and Greenock." MacMillan is more circumspect. "The final result of this great Whig reform bill was that Edinburgh had two MPs instead of one, Glasgow had two instead of a quarter of one, and nearly ninety per cent of Scotland's population was still denied the right to vote."

But they celebrated, nevertheless. More than 100,000 joined the Edinburgh Grand Reform Jubilee organised by the Trades Council on 10 August 1832, carrying more than a thousand banners and flags. One had the motto "For a nation to be free it is sufficient that it wills it", which would have been familiar to readers of Paine's *Rights of Man*. Another banner, carried by the chair and cabinet makers, was black and had the legend, "To the memory of Muir, Gerrald and others who suffered for reform." The United Hosemakers' banner remembered the later "patriots who have suffered in the cause of Reform" and made special mention of Muir, Skirving, Gerrald, Margarot, and Palmer.

*

The Rev Thomas Fyshe Palmer served his sentence and was freed in 1801. In the years since Muir's escape he had built a substantial shipping business with the Bostons and Ellis and they began the journey home in a ship that had been taken as a prize from the Spanish in the Pacific, which they subsequently bought. They made first for New Zealand in El Plumier to collect timber for sale in the Cape but were delayed there after the ship was damaged on a sandbank. Short of supplies for the voyage to South Africa, they made first for the Pacific Islands then headed for China. They put in at the Spanish colony of Guam in January 1802 but were held for a year and a half by the governor as prisoners of war. Palmer's chronic dysentery returned, this time fatally. He died in Guam in June 1803, aged fifty-five.

James and Mrs Boston left Guam along with Ellis that year and appear to have continued their business together, for some of the time back in Sydney. Boston was killed on the Pacific island of Tongatboo in 1804. The fate of Mrs Boston is unknown. Ellis's end is similarly obscure. According to an 1873 publication, *Dundee Celebrities*, Palmer and Ellis "together amassed a considerable sum of money. Ellis was appointed Palmer's executor, but dying soon after, the relatives of Ellis, three sisters who resided in Dundee, succeeded to the money".

Maurice Margarot was the only one of the five reformers to make it back to Britain. He and his wife, Mary, accompanied by "a servant" arrived in Liverpool in mid-1810. The passage cost them £450 and they landed with only three guineas to their names. During his time in New South Wales, Margarot fought the corruption of the Rum Corps by informing Governor Hunter and the Colonial Office in London of their activities. Margarot offered the same service to the new governor, Philip King, who dismissed him as an insolent spy. King suspected that Margarot had some hand in a rising of Irish convicts in 1804, mostly sent there for their part in the 1798 insurrection, and confiscated his personal papers and diaries. King kept Margarot where he could see him for a time but in 1805 transferred him to Norfolk Island, then on to Van Diemen's Land, and finally back to New South Wales, to the small coal-mining camp at Newcastle. He was reunited with his wife at some point and spent his final four years in New South Wales without incident.

In England he sought compensation from the Home Office for the loss of his personal papers, for the regime's failure to treat Mrs Margarot properly as a free settler and, above all, for being forced to serve two years beyond his fourteen-year term. None of this was successful but he was invited to give evidence to the 1812 House of Commons inquiry into transportation. He spent the summer months of 1813 and 1814 in France in an unsuccessful attempt to re-establish his old wine business. Margarot died in London on 11 November 1815, aged seventy, and was buried in St Pancras churchyard. His wife Mary survived him by some twenty years and Thomas Hardy and other surviving members of the old Corresponding Society organised a subscription for her upkeep.

George Mealmaker arrived in Sydney on 21 November 1800 aboard the Royal Admiral. He was sent to Parramatta where, because of his weaving skill, he was set to work in the linen and woollen shops. In 1803 he was awarded "conditional emancipation" and appointed superintendent of the textile industry. Mealmaker died in Parramatta on 1 April 1808 at the age of forty.

Tom Paine had attempted to leave France and return to America several times, in 1795, 1797 and again in 1799, but each time he changed his mind for fear of capture by an English ship. In 1801 he was offered safe passage in a United States warship by the new president, Thomas Jefferson. This gesture whipped up a storm in America because of Paine's pantheistic ideas expressed in his book, *The Age of Reason*, but more immediately because of his public attack on George Washington, whom he had called "treacherous in private friendship…and a hypocrite in public life". He asked Washington "whether you have abandoned good principles, or whether you ever had any". Paine was furious that his old comrade had done nothing to have him released from the Luxembourg prison by publicly announcing his protection as an American citizen, believing Washington had been prepared to sacrifice him to protect United States neutrality and negotiate an alliance with England. He called the president "a cold blooded traitor".

Jefferson's political enemies turned their hostility on Paine. The opposition Federalist newspapers described him as "that living opprobrium to humanity", "a drunken atheist and scavenger of faction". Fortunately, the Treaty of Amiens brought temporary peace to Europe in March 1802 and Paine took a passage on a commercial ship from Le Havre to Baltimore. Despite warnings of riots when the "lying, drunken, brutal infidel" came ashore, his arrival passed without incident. Paine returned to his farm in New Rochelle and lived in relative obscurity. This champion of democracy was refused the vote on the grounds that he was not an American citizen. In 1808 he moved to Greenwich Village in New York, where he died on 8 June 1809, aged 72.

Of the remaining Paris exiles, Tandy lived out his days in Bordeaux, where he died in 1803 at the age of about sixty-six. After leaving Ireland in the French corvette following the defeat of Humbert, he eventually made his way to the free port of Hamburg, where he was betrayed by Turner and seized by the British. He was tried for treason in Dublin and sentenced to death. Released at Napoleon's insistence, ten days before the peace of Amiens was signed, he was repatriated to France and awarded a general's pension.

Robert Watson died in suspicious circumstances in London in 1838 at the age of eighty-eight. He had remained in France as the United Englishmen's envoy until Napoleon appointed him as his English language tutor and principal of the Scots College in Paris. Later, Watson discovered the official papers of the Stuart dynasty under the ceiling of an old palazzo in Rome, and he sold them to the British government, from whom he received a pension and a pardon.

Helen Williams and John Stone stayed in France and became citizens in 1817; Stone died a year later and Williams died in 1827. They are buried together in the Père Lachaise cemetery in Paris. Ashley remained in Paris until his death in 1829, and is thought to have prospered in business as a shoemaker. John Smith, the gunmaker from Gorbals, also stayed in Paris and became prosperous, financially assisting Watson in his purchase of the Stuart papers. Nothing more is known of Muir's faithful amanuensis, Molet.

Nicholas Madgett continued his government career in Paris until his death in 1813. He was involved in the purchase of Louisiana from France by the United States in 1803. Edward Lewins or Lewines seems to have ceased as United Irish ambassador after 1799. Following the restoration of the Bourbons in 1814 he was made inspector of schools for France, was awarded the *Légion d'honneur*, and died in 1828. He, too, is buried in Père Lachaise. Samuel Turner was named in the Fugitive and Banishment Acts of 1798 to preserve his cover as a United Irish leader. At the same time he was secretly awarded a British pension of £300 a year. He eventually made his way back to Dublin, where he was arrested, quickly released, and the warrant against him nullified. He worked as a barrister until his death in 1810. His treachery remained undetected.

William Pitt not only banned radical societies by name, but in 1799 had the Combination Acts put on the statute book, which outlawed the infant trade union movement. In 1801 he won a majority for abolishing the Irish parliament and joining the two countries with an Act of Union. He built a second coalition of European powers from 1798 in a further effort to defeat France, but military setbacks led to its failure, losing Pitt crucial support in the Commons and among his ministers. But it was the refusal of George III to admit Catholics into the parliament at Westminster that finally forced Pitt's resignation as prime minister in 1801. He was out of office for three years but the renewal of war with France in 1803 brought him back into politics and he formed a new administration in 1804. Again, the war with Napoleon initially went badly for the allies and Pitt's government was weak and divided. Exhausted, he died in January 1806 just four months short of his forty-seventh birthday.

On Christmas Eve, 1802, Henry Dundas was ennobled and became Viscount Melville and Baron Dunira. Shortly afterwards, his luck began to run out when a commission of inquiry into the finances of the navy found unexplained shortfalls in the surplus from the budgets during the long period of Dundas's stewardship as treasurer. He was impeached and tried in Westminster Hall before his peers in April 1806. Although formally acquitted of all the charges, his parliamentary career was at an end. His biographer however notes, "Melville was, of course, guilty all along. He was guilty not as charged, for, in the impenetrable mass of cryptic evidence, his accusers simply did not know where to look." He goes on to quote a letter of Dundas in which the politician admits, "I have been thinking how far the examinations might not lead to a discovery of any of those secret political purposes which I have declared my determination never to disclose." Dundas lost office but not influence or political control of Scotland, which he exercised until his death in 1811. He was buried in the family plot at Lasswade kirk, near Melville Castle.

Robert Dundas was lord advocate of Scotland and MP for Midlothian until 1801, when he was promoted to the bench as lord chief baron of the Exchequer. He died in 1819.

Both Henry Dundas and William Pitt have statues in central Edinburgh, so in 1837 the radical MP Joseph Hume, who represented Montrose Burghs, started a campaign to have a monument erected to the "Scottish Martyrs", as they had become known. He was assisted by the reformer Francis Place; the journalist John Rutt, who had visited Palmer and Muir in the hulks, now 77 years of age; Thomas Muir Moffat, son of Muir's dearest friend William; and James Blair, Muir's nephew, son of his now-dead sister. The Edinburgh Tories strongly opposed the scheme and had it delayed for some time. They were content with the statues of Dundas and Pitt and their leader accused Muir in the pages of the *Scotsman* of having been a traitor. William Moffat bravely replied in his defence in pages of the same paper.

On 21 August 1844, three thousand people assembled close to Old Calton cemetery to see the memorial's foundation stone laid in that confined space by Hume. Four hundred members of the Complete Suffrage Association had first filed past the site of the old court-house in Parliament Square where the trials had taken place and the sentences of transportation had been handed down by Braxfield. William Moffat, now an old man, was there at the ceremony with Hume, as was a son of William Skirving, who was greeted with "thrilling cheers". In September 1845 the monument, a 90-foot obelisk, was completed. A second, smaller obelisk was erected in Nunhead cemetery in south-east London, in 1851.

The London memorial has a quotation from Joseph Gerrald's defence speech, "The experience of all ages should have taught our rulers that persecution can never efface principles. Individuals may perish but truth is eternal." On one side of the base of the Edinburgh obelisk are words from William Skirving's speech in the High Court of Justiciary, "I know that what has been done these two days will be rejudged." Below it, this from Thomas Muir: "I have devoted myself to the cause of the people; it is a good cause; it shall finally triumph."

REFERENCES

Abbreviations

Adm	Admiralty
BL	British Library
DIB	Dictionary of Irish Biography
FO	Foreign Office
HO	Home Office
NA	National Archives, England
NAS	National Archives of Scotland
NLS	National Library of Scotland
ODNB	Oxford Dictionary of National Biography
PH	The Parliamentary History of England
ST	State Trials
TS	Treasury solicitor

Title

For the complete version of Burns's *The Tree of Liberty* and a discussion of its provenance, Noble and Scott Hogg, 845–51.

Introduction

Page i

Thompson, 111, 111n.

Page ii

For Hutcheson, McIlvanney, 28–9.

Influence of Hume, Smith, Millar, and Stewart, Meikle, 15.

Page iii

Burns, *Parcel of Rogues in a Nation*, Noble and Scott Hogg, 393–4.

Feudal powers retained in the Act of Union, Davidson, 58; Fry, Scotland, 285.

Economic impact of Union, Fry, Scotland, 283, 304.

Representation in British parliament, Davidson, 99; Fry, Scotland, 286–289.
Feudal rights and the Stuart challenges, Davidson, 106–22.

Page iv

Dundas's patronage, Brown, 271–3.

Voting in the elections of 1790 and 1796, Meikle, 10, 27.

Letter, George Dempster to Dr Carlyle, quoted in Meikle, xviii.

Letter, Dundas to Robert Saunders Dundas, 11 July 1807, quoted in Brown, 269.

Page v

Kirk patronage, Noble and Scott Hogg, 556.

Attacks on customs houses, Fry, Scotland, 305.

Letter, Burns to a friend, quoted in Noble and Scott Hogg, xxviii.

Letter, Daer to Grey, 17 January 1793, E Hughes, 35; Noble and Scott Hogg, 635.

Locke, *Second Treatise*, section 149, quoted in Oxford Companion to Philosophy, 526.

Real Whigs, McIlvanney, 24–28.

Page vi

Burgh and county reform in 1780s, Meikle, 5–27.

Mackenzie, 35–7

Page vii

Gazette Nationale ou Le Moniteur, quoted in Yeoman, 290–92.

Meikle on Muir's escape and in France, 135, 172–77.

Johnston on the radical movement, 217–37.

Page ix

Bewley, x.

MacMillan, 9.

Page x

"*A Scottish constitution to serve the common weal*", Elliot Bulmer, *Herald,* 13 July 2013.

"*A statue for Muir*", Patrick Scott Hogg, *Scottish Review* online, 21 May 2010; Scottish Parliament public petition no PE1325; "*Call for Holyrood statue rethink*", BBC News online, 4 May 2010.

"*Posthumous pardon sought for Thomas Muir, the 'father of Scottish democracy'*," *The Times*, 27 February 2010.

Chapter 1 Riot

The narrative of the three days of rioting is contained in newspaper reports and depositions sent to the home secretary. This account is based on reports in the *Caledonian Mercury* covering events from Monday 4 June until Wednesday 13 June, followed by reports of the trial of John Bertram and Alexander Lockie on Monday 16 July and Thursday 19 July. This is supplemented by Home office correspondence addressed to Henry Dundas from Scotland, January–October 1792 (NA HO102/5), from Lord Provost Stirling of Edinburgh to Henry Dundas, June 5, 1792; the depositions of Sheriff Pringle, Admiral Adam Duncan, and Colonel Francis Dundas, Major Robert Matthews of the 53rd, Ensign George Hay of the 53rd; and 14 examples of "threatening letters and handbills" in the bundle. There is also a good account of the riot in Logue, 133–145, and Meikle, *The King's Birthday Riot, Scottish Historical Review*. Details of Lockie's trial are from *Caledonian Mercury* 19 July 1792 and the Home Office correspondence addressed to Henry Dundas mentioned above. The dialogue between Muir and Braxfield is fictitious. There is no verbatim record of the case but the trial papers, including the indictment and Lockie's deposition are in the High Court of Justiciary Book of Adjournal, 16 July 1792, 52–67 (NAS JC3/46).

Chapter 2 The Association

Page 13

Burns, *Here's a Health to Them That's Awa*. Although believed to have been written in December 1792, it was 1808 before a part of it was first published, and another ten years before the complete poem appeared in the *Scots Magazine*. Noble and Scott Hogg, 769–772 for complete text, provenance and context.

Page 14

For the founding of the London Corresponding Society, Thompson, 19–24. Origins of provincial radicalism in England, Goodwin, chapter 5.

A full description of Muir is given in his passport issued in Paris in 1793 and contained in the National Archives of Scotland (NAS JC26/1793/1/5/10), although his height is wrongly recorded as 5' 3". He was 5' 9".

Page 15

For a short biography of William Skirving, Macleod, *ODNB*.

The practice of creating 'parchment barons' is discussed Meikle, 9–10. The number of county votes, Watson, 281.

Page 16

For the position of Erskine and Fletcher on parliamentary reform, Brims, in Devine (ed), 35.

Page 17

Report of the Fortune tavern meeting, *Morning Chronicle* and *Caledonian Mercury*, 28 July, 1792. See also Bewley, 30; Brims, op cit, 36.

Page 18

Nor' Loch, Coghill, 73–4.

Page 19

Duns riot, Meikle, 81.

Page 20

Trongate and the Tontine Hotel, Daiches, 12, 57, 75–6, 122.

Chapter 3 Huntershill

Page 21

The Clerical Informer's Creed, set to the tune of Black Jock, was published in the *Edinburgh Gazetteer*, 10 September 1793.

Position of James Muir's shop, Insh, 19–20; description of university, Daiches, 89.

Ann Fisher, McKenzie, 66, 77; ST, vol 23, col 146.

Page 22
James Muir, Bewley, 1; Insh, 18n; MacMillan, 13.

Page 23
Description of Rottenrow, Daiches, page 120.

Popular and Moderate parties in the Church of Scotland, Burleigh, 291, 301, 324. "What difference does a piece of land make ..." is a quote from Ebenezer Erskine, leader of the Secession Church, in 1732, McIlvanney, 145.

Page 24
Scottish parliamentary representation, Bewley, 17–19; Johnston, 215.

Page 25
Muir's early life, Mackenzie, 1–3; Bewley, 1–6.
Muir and the 'parchment baron' controversy in Cadder, Bewley, 11; Donnelly, 7.

Pages 26–32
The conversation with Lapslie is fictional but the visit would not have been untypical. It is based on the following sources, Lapslie's brother-in-law, Joseph Stirling, commented on the minister's tendency to "greet" [cry] (Anecdotal information about Lapslie is on welcometolennoxtown.co.uk/campsonians); Lapslie's notice of his intention to move a loyal address at the Glasgow presbytery appeared in the *Morning Chronicle*, Saturday 16 June, 1792; Birmingham "Church and King" riots, Thompson, 79; Lapslie's remarks about licentiousness and high wages are paraphrased from his chapter on the parish of Campsie in the *Statistical Account of Scotland 1791–99*, vol.15, 380; Richard Sheridan introduced the petition for the reform of Scottish burghs on 18 April 1792, Meikle, 76–7; William Wilberforce's motion on abolition of the slave trade was introduced five days after the Burgh Reform motion, Meikle, 77–8; Lapslie's opposition to the Church of Scotland's involvement in the anti-slavery petition campaign, Whyte, 86; Gustavus Vassa, aka Olaudah Equiano, ix–xxx; 359–63.

Chapter 4 Equal representation
Page 33
Paine, Rights of Man, 239.

Pages 34—5

Extract from the *Bee* vol 10, No 85, quoted in Meikle, 80.

Daniel McArthur was called as a witness at Muir's trial and the conversation and location are based on his testimony in *ST*, vol 23, col 178. Part of Muir's reply to McArthur dealing with the differences between France and England are taken from an address published by the London Corresponding Society on 29 November 1792 (*Place Papers*, vol II, British Museum add mss 27,812. London Corresponding Society. *Original Journal or Minute Book*. April 1792 to 2 January, 1794, folio 27). The argument about whether James II was removed or abdicated is at the centre of the constitutional debate in this period and is reflected in most of the competing literature. The radicals argued that his removal demonstrated the constitution was a contract but it was not such a legal point of conflict in Scotland since James was not in the country at the time of the Glorious Revolution and Scotland's Claim of Right agreed in parliament is based on the assumption that he was indeed removed.

The coffee shop with a round window is described by William Wordsworth's sister Dorothy in a notebook she kept during their visit to Glasgow in 1803, "The shops in Glasgow are large, and like London shops, and we passed by the largest coffee-room I ever saw. You look across the piazza of the Exchange, and see to the end of the coffee-room, where there is a circular window, the width of the room. Perhaps there might be thirty gentlemen sitting on the circular bench of the window, each reading a newspaper." The passage is quoted in Daiches, 127.

Page 36

The increase in the numbers of Scottish newspapers, Meikle, 87.

Letter, Burns to Johnston, 13 November 1792, quoted in *Tait's Magazine*, 1837.

Page 37

Alexander Muir and Ann Fisher were both witnesses in Thomas's trial. Their conversations and Anne's behaviour are based on testimony (*ST*, op cit).

Page 38

The description of Paisley's manufacturing industry is from the *Statistical Account of Scotland 1791–99*, Paisley by Dr John Snodgrass (vol 7 62).

Muir and Dalrymple in Paisley and at Sinclair's Inn, testimony of William

Orr, *ST* vol 23, col 179.

Page 39

The Encyclopedia Club of Paisley is described by Harris, *The Scottish People*, 26.

The fictitious reader in the inn is quoting John Butler, *Brief Reflections Upon the Liberty of the British Subject*; in an *Address to the Right Honourable Edmund Burke, Occasioned by his Late Publication on the French Revolution* (1792), in Claeys, vol 3.

The *Statistical Account of Scotland* online contains descriptions of various towns and parishes for 1791. I have consulted Kirkintilloch by Rev William Dunn (vol 2, 275), Campsie by Rev James Lapslie (vol 15, 314), Cadder by William Barclay, schoolmaster (vol 8, 474), and Paisley by Dr John Snodgrass (vol 7, 62).

Page 40

Glasgow association founded in the Star Inn, 3 October 1792, Mackenzie, 5; Meikle, 92.

Growth of societies nationally, Harris, *Scottish People*, 75–77; Bewley, 32–3; figures for the 1790 general election, Jephson, 188.

Page 41

The formal proposal for a convention of all Scottish societies was actually made a little later than the Kirkintilloch meeting, at a meeting of delegates of the societies in and around Edinburgh on November 21. It was moved by Thomas Muir (*Morning Chronicle*, Saturday 24 November, 1792).

Pages 42–3

Newspaper reports of Dundas being burned in effigy at Peebles and Lanark are from reports to Henry Dundas quoted in Meikle, 81.

The Kirkintilloch meeting and the subsequent conversation in Wallace's tavern are from various statements or depositions at Muir's trial, *ST*, vol23.

Page 44

The meeting between Lord Daer and Muir may have been in the spring of 1792, Bewley, 29.

Anna Barbauld was toasted as a "lady defender of the revolution" by the British Club in Paris in November 1792. Alger, *Englishmen*, 99.

Daer's meeting with Robert Burns and Dugald Stewart, along with Burns's *Extempore Verses on Dining with Lord Daer*, Noble and Scott Hogg, 632.

Muir being "hopelessly in love with the daughter of an aristocratic landowner" is claimed to be "an unconfirmed rumour reported by Mackenzie", Bewley, 12.

Chapter 5 Wimbledon

This particular weekend in Dundas's Wimbledon home is fictional. However, as explained in the text, Pitt regularly and frequently spent his time there. Each of the incidents described happened at various times and are referenced below.

Pages 46—7

Letter, Watt to Dundas, 31 August, 1792 (NAS GD51/5/6).

For Evan Nepean see Sparrow, *ODNB*.

Page 48

For Pitt's character and appearance, Turner, 10.

The early authorised Tory account of Pitt's dying words ("I love my country") was later disputed by Disraeli's revision, "I think I could eat one of Bellamy's pies", Mori, 6.

For Lady Anne Lindsay, Grosart, revised by Trapido, *ODNB* under Barnard, Lady Anne.

Henry Dundas's affair with Anne Lindsay and contemporary ditty, Fry, 156. Their affair ended in 1793 when Dundas married Lady Jane Hope.

Page 49

Pitt's quote on the revolution in France is from his speech against Grey's proposed reform motion in the House of Commons in April 1792, Mori, 112. His phrase, "We have to keep ourselves quiet" is from a letter to Lord Auckland, 2 September 1791, "in the singular and uncertain state of Europe our chief business must be to watch events and keep ourselves quiet", Turner, 160.

The address from the London Corresponding Society had been included in a subsequent letter from Watt on 21 September 1792 (NAS GD51/5/6).

Page 50

Dundas's love of English beer, Fry, 106.

Pitt's love of port, Turner, 8.

Page 51

Dundas's entertaining, the turnpike road incident, and the case of Thurlow's anesthetised piles, Fry, 107.

Bottomless Pitt, Barrell, 18.

Page 52

The remark about Windham and Dundas, Fry, 157.

Chapter 6 Mad ideas

Page 53

Alexander Wilson, Leonard, 8–12.

Langholm, *Statistical Account of Scotland 1791*, 587.

Buccleuch, see Murdoch, *ODNB* under Henry Scott, third duke of.

Pages 54–5

Pulteney, see Roe and McBryde, *ODNB*; Fry, 46;

Correspondence relating to Dundas's Langholm visit NA HO102/5/6. The dialogue over dinner is based on these letters, which refer to two meetings at Langholm, the second one on Dundas's return to London in December. I have conflated the two.

Pages 56–7

The conversation between Dundas and Watt is based on Watt's reports sent to Henry and Robert (NAS GD51/5/6). The location of the meeting is unknown. Dundas said in a note to Nepean, "I took care to have a private interview with him and urged him if possible to learn from Mr Mackintosh who is his friend and informer, who the gentlemen were, and I told him he might confide his information to lord advocate and the sheriff Mr Pringle with equal safety as myself." (No 3 in 24 November bundle from Melville Castle to Nepean, NA HO102/5).

Dundas's comment on handbills in Edinburgh is from NAS GD51/5/6, letter with enclosures, H Dundas to Nepean, Melville Castle, 14 October 1792.

Page 58

The meeting in Robert Dundas's house is fictional, although we know that Dundas held various planning sessions with his chief lieutenants. The Home Office/Henry Dundas correspondence in NA HO102/5/6 and NAS GD51/5/6/7 has been used in constructing the dialogue at the meeting; the "French democrats" passage is quoted in Meikle, 94; the suggestion that Watt and JB may have been the same person is made by Macmillan, 32. He refers to Omond, 185, who says of JB, "A spy had been hired to attend the meetings, under the pretence of being a member, and report to the Lord Advocate everything that was done. Who or what this spy was it is impossible to say. His letters are anonymous. He may have been a man named Watt, who was afterward tried and executed for treason, and whose defence was that he was acting for government at the time he was arrested. He was certainly a person of talent and education, as the reports which he prepared are cleverly written. He was well informed of all that went on." However, this interpretation is disputed. Scott Hogg argues, 347n1, "The identity of the spy 'JB' has been a mystery for historians for two centuries. In my view he was Claude Irvine Boswell, Depute Sheriff of Fife and cousin of James Boswell. In early December 1792, Claude Irvine Boswell offered his services to spy on the Edinburgh Friends of the People in a letter to government and he is named as the source of a report on Edinburgh radicals in papers RH2/4/64 f255(b). The mystery surrounding his identity has been largely down to his signature where he employed only two initials, his middle name and surname only. Claude Irvine Boswell signed his name with a long slanted old fashioned 'I' for Irvine, which looks like a capital J. His signature was simply 'IB', for Irvine Boswell. The 'I' has been mistaken for a 'J' and his identity has remained a mystery until now – if I am correct."

Page 59

Lord Braxfield's remarks, Osborne.

Page 60

Military disposition in Scotland, NA HO102/5, Dundas to Nepean, No 2 in a bundle of correspondence from Melville Castle, 24 November, 1792.

Page 61
Government support for loyalist newspapers, Harris, 55–62, 127; Henry Mackenzie, Drescher, entry in *ODNB*.

Chapter 7 Panic

Pages 63–5
The Perth and Dundee riots are described in reports of the *Morning Chronicle*, Thursday 29 November 1792; Home Office correspondence relating to Scotland, November and December 1792 (NA HO102/6); Logue, *Popular Disturbances*, 149–154; Harris, *Political Protests*, 65–6.

The cry 'No Dundas! No Bishops! and no King!' is from Harris, *The Scottish People*, as is the *Edinburgh Gazetteer* description of the Jemappes victory as one for "the whole family of the human race", both 79; the phrase, "the most inflammatory set of scoundrels" is from a government agent, quoted on 82; the figure of 1,200 society members in Perth is contained in an anonymous letter to Henry Dundas, September 1792 (NAS GD51/5/6).

Pages 66–7
The 21 November Edinburgh delegates meeting is reported in a copy of letter from Edinburgh procurator fiscal William Scott, sent by Henry Dundas to his office in London, and also in a letter from Robert Watt to Robert Dundas (both NA HO102/5) and in the *Morning Chronicle* of Saturday 24 November 1792; Sheffield celebrations, *Edinburgh Gazetteer*, Friday 7 December, 1792 (NAS GD 99/228/5); a report of the Belhaven meeting, *Edinburgh Gazetteer*, Friday 30 November, 1792 (NAS GD 99/228/5).

The Lanark county meeting and Lord Kinnoul's attempt to gather support, Harris, *The Scottish People*, 130; George Meliss and the Perth resolution are on 128; Letter, Queensferry and Dalmeny parishes to Henry Dundas, 15 December, 1792 (NA HO102/5).

Page 68
Article on Earl of Kinnoul, *Edinburgh Gazetteer*, Friday 28 December, 1792 (NAS GD99/228/4).

Chapter 8 Liberty restrained

Pages 69–72

Again, this meeting is fictitious but is reconstructed from the following sources, letter, Adam Gordon to Henry Dundas, 26 November 1792, on troop movements (NA HO102/5); the names of Wylie and Meliss are provided by the sheriff of Perth in a letter to Henry Dundas, 24 November 1792 (NA HO102/5); news of a recruiting party at a reform meeting is contained in information transmitted to the lord advocate, undated but around 26 December 1792 (NAS GD51/5/7); the information on the loyalist association is in a letter from Pultney to Henry Dundas, 12 December, 1792 (NA HO102/5); subsidised publication of *Look Before Ye Loup*, and Oldys's hostile biography of Tom Paine is detailed in Harris, *The Scottish People*, 133; the appointment of Brown as editor of *Patriot's Weekly Chronicle* is from Meikle, 118; financial information on the loyalist campaign is in correspondence from Robert Dundas to Henry Dundas, 12 December 1792 (NA HO102/5); the Glasgow provost's expenditure is in Meikle, 116–7; for the subsidy to London papers see Turner, *Pitt the Younger*, 141; the interception of letters is requested by Henry Dundas in a letter to Evan Nepean, (NA HO102/6), see also Harris, *The Scottish People*, 119); arrests and subsequent prosecutions for sedition are detailed in *ST*, 1793–94, vol 23, Nos 587, 588, 589, 590, and 592; information on the Scheldt and activity in London is from *The Edinburgh Advertiser*, 7 December 1792 (NAS GD26/15/53); Dundas's assurance to Pitt is in a letter to Nepean, 24 November 1792 (NA HO102/5), Pultney's remark is from a letter, probably to Pitt, quoted in Harris, *The Scottish People*, 78.

Page 73

For Wight, Ritchie, *ODNB*.

Proceedings against those mentioned, *ST* vol 23, cols 1–116.

Pages 74–7

The delegation to the Lord Provost is recorded in the *Caledonian Mercury*, 8 December 1792, and quoted in Bewley, 41.

The conversation between Muir and Fletcher is based on Fletcher's letters to Graham of Gartmore (NAS GD22/1/315); a recollection of the meeting in *Autobiography of Mrs Fletcher* and its appendix, *Memoir of Archibald Fletcher, advocate*; and Macleod's *ODNB* for Fletcher. Fletcher's argument about "two evils" is from Meikle, 104–5; Muir's argument about rumours spread by loyalists is from *Edinburgh Gazetteer*, 7 December 1792; Fletcher's description of war preparations from the same edition of the *Gazetteer*; his suggestion it would be "prudent to abandon" reform for the moment, Omond, 183.

Chapter 9 The Scottish convention

Pages 78–84

The minutes of the December 1792 convention are in Appendix A of Meikle's *Scotland and the French Revolution*, 239–273. They cover the three days of the meeting "as contained in the spy's reports, Public Record Office, London,...and in the official minutes published at Edinburgh, 1793", reprinted in *PH*, vol 31, 871–9.

Cabinet meeting, Emsley, *London Insurrection*, 66.

Chapter 10 Phoney war

Pages 85–7

National Alarm, Thornton, 63.

The debate on the opening of the emergency session of parliament, *PH*, vol 30, cols 1–80. "These demands [for evidence of the existence of insurrection] were repeated regularly over the next two and a half months culminating on February 28, 1793 in a motion from Sheridan that the Commons should resolve itself into a committee to inquire into the truth of reports of seditious practices in the country. The only place where any details of insurrection plans were given, however, was not in parliament, but in the pro-government press." (Emsley, *The London 'Insurrection'*, 84.)

Page 88

Letter, Sir Gilbert Elliot to Lady Elliot, 13 December, 1792, Minto, 81.

Letter, Norman Macleod to Charles Grey, quoted by Bewley, 39.

Letter, William Grenville to Lord Auckland, quoted by Turner, 161.

Page 89

Letter, Robert Dundas to Henry Dundas, 15 December, 1792 (NA HO102/5).
Tytler, Russell's *ODNB*.

Pages 90–1

Muir's arrest, Edinburgh Gazetteer, Tuesday 8 January, 1793 (NAS GD311/7/21).

Interview with sheriffs Pringle and Honyman is in *ST*, vol 23, cols 162–3; Bewley, 51.

Membership figures Harris, *The Scottish People*, 81.

Page 92

Letter, Muir to Skirving, published in *Edinburgh Gazetteer,* 22 October 1793.

Chapter 11 Death of a king

Pages 93–5

Extract from *The Tree of Liberty*, Noble and Scott Hogg, 846

The description of Muir's entry into Paris and the conversation with a national guardsman and a sans-culottes is fictional. We do know that he arrived in France on 15 January and stayed in Hotel de Toulon, Rue des Fosses du Temple, when he reached Paris, Bewley, 56; we also know the membership of the British Club at White's Hotel, and Muir is listed, Alger, *Englishmen*, passim. Visitors routinely attended sessions of the National Convention (and the Jacobins Club) and it is unlikely that Muir would not have done the same, since one of the purposes of his visit was to add his weight to the lobby cautioning against the execution of Louis XVI.

For the narrative of the French revolution from July 1789–January 1793, Schama, 369–675; Jordan 1–79; Wright, 24–65.

The time taken for the Calais to Paris journey was between 27 and 33 hours in good weather, *A Journey from London to Paris, The European Magazine and London Review*, vol 83, 1823, page 225.

Twiss, 248, describes liberty trees in "in every one of the towns between Calais and Paris".

Lauderdale and his fancy coachwork, Alger, *Englishmen*, 131.

Page 96

We have no evidence about Muir's initial contacts in Paris so I have taken the liberty of directing him to the most well-known members of the British Club, Paine and Stone. Stone knew French and Paris well and was well known there, too. His friend Jérôme Pétion, then mayor of Paris, helped him establish a sal ammoniac factory there. See Rapport, *ODNB*; Alger, *Englishmen*; Graham, 25.

Descriptions of Paris, Alger, *Paris*, passim.

Page 97

The interior of the Convention is described in Jordan, 45. Jordan also quotes the journalist and convention deputy Louis-Sebastien Mercier, who described the scene, "The back of the hall was transformed into a theatre box where the women, in the most charming state of undress, ate ices, oranges, drank liqueurs", 182.

Pages 98–9

For the debate in the Convention on the king's execution, Jordan, 161–207.

Vergniaud's speech from the chair of the Convention which includes the sentence, "I hope that humanity will lead you to maintain the most profound silence," (Jordan, 190) was actually delivered the night before the revised voting figures were announced and I have conflated the procedure a little for the sake of brevity.

Page 100

"Louis XVI considered as an individual..." is part of the speech by Paine that was read to the Convention on 21 November 1792 (*On the Propriety of Bringing Louis XVI to Trial, The Writings of Thomas Paine*, vol 3, in the Online Library of Liberty, para 491).

Paine's proposal to exile the Capets in the United States of America, and his comments on the Stuarts was made to the Convention on 15 January 1793 (*Reasons for Preserving the Life of Louis Capet, Writings* op cit, paras 514, 516).

Pages 101–3

Paine's interventions on January 17–19, Keane, 367–9. For a complete narrative of the trial from the appearance of Louis before the convention on 10 December 1792 until the final vote, Jordan, 101–207.

The date of Paine's letter announcing his desire to leave France is uncertain. He wrote it sometime between the debate on the execution and his exile in Saint-Denis in the spring. It is quoted in Kean, 370.

Pages 104–6

For descriptions of the execution. Jordan, 208–221, Schama, 668–670.

Joseph-Ignace Guillotin, Schama, 619–23.

"Oswald…at the head of his infernal pikemen formed the guard which closely surrounded the scaffold on which the late king of France was guillotined. Immediately after the head of the unfortunate monarch fell into the basket, he and his whole troop struck up a hymn he had composed for the occasion, and danced and sung, like so many savages, round and round the scaffold!" Joseph Haslewood, *The Secret History of the Green Room*, 1795, quoted in Erdman, 245.

For Maxwell's role in the National Guard, McIlvanney, 210, and Erdman, 245.

Louis Mercier is quoted in Schama, 670.

The extract from Wollstonecraft's diary is quoted in Moore, 167.

Chapter 12 Liberty curtailed

Page 107

The trial of James Tytler *ST*, vol 23, cols 1–6. His escape, McFarland, 96, 136–8; MacMillan, 27.

Page 108

Letter Robert Dundas to Henry Dundas, 3 January 1793 (NA HO102/5).

Pages 109–10

Trial of Morton, Anderson, and Craig *ST* vol 23, cols 7–26; Elder and Stewart, cols 25–34.

Report of the printers' trial, *Edinburgh Gazetteer*, 18 January 1793.

Page 111

The *Gazetteer's* full report of the trial and the subsequent cases for contempt of court against Johnston, including Robert Dundas calling the attention of the judges to the article, *ST*, vol 23, cols 43–80.

Page 112

Opinion on the accuracy of the portrait of Braxfield, Cockburn, *Examination*, 119.

Trial of Callender, Berry, and Robertson, *ST*, vol 23, cols 79–116.

Page 113

Trial of Smith and Mennons, *ST*, vol 23, cols 33–42.

Chapter 13 Steady hands

Page 114

Meikle, 122–3, notes, "A visit from Lord Daer and Colonel Macleod towards the end of January infused new energy into the Friends of the People, and the work of circulating the reform petition was actively carried on in spite of strenuous opposition."

Macleod's two letters, *Edinburgh Gazetteer*, 18 January 1793.

Pages 115–7

Intimidation of society members, Brims, 43; Meikle, 123.

Daer's letter to Grey in reply to Grey's to Skirving, E Hughes, 33–7. Grey's impulsive nature is from Lord Grey by EA Smith, quoted in Amanda Foreman, *Georgiana Duchess of Devonshire*, 203.

Intimidation in England by loyalists, Emsley, *Repression*, 802–3.

Letter, Matthew Campbell Brown to Hardy, *Second Report of the Committee of Secrecy*; Harris, *The Scottish People*, 98.

Morthland's and Fowler's resolutions, JB to Henry Dundas, 3 January, 1793 (NA HO102/5); Brims, 44; Meikle, 122.

Loyalist organisations in Scotland, Harris, *The Scottish People*, 125.

Effigy burning in Sheffield, *Edinburgh Gazetteer*, Friday 18 January 1793.

Page 118

Reports of Edinburgh meeting of 23 January chaired by Lord Daer, and the Airdrie meeting of 4 January, *Edinburgh Gazetteer*, 25 January 1793.

Glasgow Society for Borough Reform, Bridgton society, *Edinburgh Gazetteer*, 18 January 1793.

Page 119

Propaganda value of Louis's execution, Barrell, 74–5.

The Confederacy of Kings, Claeys, 193.

Chapter 14 Outlaws

Page 120

The meeting of the British Club is fictional but Muir would have attended at least one. The club lasted from November 1792 until around May 1793. We have no minutes of its meetings but we know its membership from Alger, and Muir is included. Bewley notes, 56, "At least 40,000 foreigners were in the city and the British contingent was the largest."

Page 121

John Oswald, a Scot and a former British army officer, was formally appointed commandant of the first battalion of pike bearers in October 1792, Erdman, 178. On the title of Oswald's *Le Gouvernement du Peuple, ou Plan de Constitution Pour la République Universelle*, published in January 1793, he is described as "Anglo-Franc, Commandant du Premier Battalion de Piquiers", Erdman,179. *The Second Report of the Committee of Secrecy of the House of Lords*, 7 June 1794, notes that his battalion was stationed in old barracks in the Rue de Babylone near the Champs de Mars, where Oswald drilled recruits. Oswald became a vegetarian while serving with the British army in India. Paine's rebuff, Erdman, 8.

Burial of Louis's corpse, Jordan, 220. Paine's comment about the depth of the grave, Keane, 369.

For Perry, see Gee, *ODNB*.

Page 122

For Williams, see Kennedy, *ODNB*.

For Stone, Rapport, *ODNB*

Mme Roland on Louis on the scaffold, Moore, 249.

Mme Roland's comment on Jacobins and republicanism, Kates, 161.

Alger gives the figure of 100 at the Jemappes victory dinner in White's. Stone presided. Both Alger and Erdman agree that 13 toasts were drunk. Erdman,

230, lists them. To paraphrase, the French republic, founded on the rights of man; the French armies and the destruction of tyranny; the national convention; the coming convention of Britain and Ireland; the union of France, Britain, Belgium and other nations with similar sentiments; the republic of men (with an English song to the tune of the Marseillaise); the dissolution of the Germanic circle, may their inhabitants be free; abolition of hereditary titles, proposed by Lord Edward Fitzgerald and Sir Robert Smyth; a subsequent toast to Fitzgerald and Smyth; Thomas Paine and the new way of making good books known by royal proclamations and by prosecuting the authors; the women of Great Britain, particularly those who have written in favour of the French revolution; the women of France, especially those who have had the courage to take up arms in defence of liberty; universal peace and universal liberty.

Page 123
For Smyth, Weinglass, *ODNB*.

Edmund Burke produced the dagger during his contribution to the debate on the Aliens Act in the House of Commons on 29 December, 1792, *PH* vol 30, col 189; Thornton, 91–94. Burns wrote a satirical poem, *The Dagger*, which was published in the *Edinburgh Gazetteer*, 16 May, 1793, Noble and Scott Hogg, 456–462; McIlvanney, 210–11.

Page 124
Maxwell's comments on a mob invading his London house are from his own account of the event in the *Morning Post* of 17 September 1792, quoted in Thornton, 72–74. At the Jacobins Club on Sunday 30 September 1792, Oswald announced Maxwell's initiative to purchase arms from Birmingham and Sheffield to send to the republic. He also reported the interruption of a meeting in Maxwell's Portland Square house, Erdman, 205.

Letter, Muir to James Campbell, 23 January 1793, ST, vol 23, col 171.

Henry of Prussia's comment on the Palais Royal, Alger, *Paris*, 22.

Page 125
Description of the Palais Royal and the oratory of Camille Desmoulins, Moore, 4,5.

Alleged reports in British newspapers about paté made from the flesh of

Swiss Guards was raised at the Jacobins Club on 30 September 1792, the same evening on which Oswald spoke about Maxwell, Erdman, 208.

Social Circle's meetings in the Palais Royal, Kates, 77–78. The Social Circle, associated with the Girondists, became a publishing company with a programme of well-financed journals, books, pamphlets, posters and art. Its three most significant journals were "the *Chronique du mois*, which was aimed at intellectuals, the *Sentinelle*, posted on Paris streets for sans-culottes, and the *Bulletin des Amis de la Vérité*, a daily newspaper. The Imprimerie du Cercle Social was suppressed at the beginning of the Terror", Kates, 11. It had by then produced nearly 200 books, pamphlets and journals, many of them subsidised by the Roland ministry, Kates, 269.

Page 126

The content of the conversation between Muir and Maxwell in the Palais Royal is unknown, although James Smith's letter to Glasgow (see below, note for page 128) confirms it took place. I have used the opportunity to explain the work of the British Club.

Champ de Mars massacre, Moore, 101–2.

Maxwell's meetings with Servan, Thornton, 65–6; Erdman, 225–7.

Page 127

Fitzgerald's meetings with Lebrun, Erdman, 216; 264.

Address of the British Club to the National Convention, Erdman, 229 and note; Davis, *ODNB* on John Frost.

Page 128

Letter, Smith to the secretary of the Glasgow Friends of the People, Bewley, 57.

Page 129

The Williams's Sunday evening receptions in the Rue de Bac, Alger, *Englishmen*.

Condorcet's political influence, Kates, passim.

Condorcet's fond description of Muir, Bewley, 58. It may originally have come from Peter Mackenzie's *Reminiscences of Glasgow and the West of Scotland*, Glasgow, 1865, although the reference in Bewley is unclear.

Page 130

'War against the cabinet of St James', Erdman, 250.

'Planting the tree of liberty in London', Erdman 255.

William Maxwell's decision to return to Britain after the declaration of war, Thornton, 100.

Page 131

For the transfer of letters from Edinburgh to London and on to Paris, NAS JC26/1793/1, *Trial papers of Thomas Muir*, bundle 5.

Page 132

Letters, Campbell to Muir; Campbell to Macintosh (the London intermediary); Muir to Friends of the People, 13 February 1793, published in the *Gazetteer*, 1 March, 1793; *ST*, vol 23, cols 171–173.

Page 133

Letter, Smith to Glasgow society, 15 February 1793, MacMillan, 44.

Lord Braxfield's sentence of fugitation in Lallans, MacMillan, 45.

Chapter 15 Petitioners and conspirators

Page 134

A transcript of the House of Commons reform debate of 6 and 7 May 1793, including the debate on the admissibility of the Sheffield petition is in *PH* vol 30, cols 775–925. The quotations used in this chapter are from that source but have been converted to the present tense.

Number of petitions submitted to parliament, Goodwin, 280.

Page 135

Letter, Col Norman Macleod to William Skirving, 11 May 1793, NAS, High Court Papers 1793, JC26/280, bundle 8.

Page 136

The four letters between reform societies, Appendix E, *Second Report from the Committee of Secrecy of the House of Commons* (unnumbered, beginning after 72)

Anti-war resolutions from west Scotland societies January to March 1793,

Bridgeton, Renton, Irvine, Kilmarnock, Loch Mill, Lennox Town, Torrence, Campsie, Cambuslang, Darvel, Meikle, 124n, quoting *Glasgow Advertiser*.

Page 137

Convention numbers, Harris, Scottish People, 88.

Press gang reports, *Edinburgh Gazetteer*, Tuesday 30 April, Caledonian Chronicle, Tuesday 28 May; Glasgow enlistment, *Edinburgh Gazetteer*, Tuesday 30 April, 1793.

Letters, Wauchop to the Earl of Marchmont, 9 and 20 January 1793,(NAS GD158/2625, fols 72/3).

Watt's reports, MacMillan, 36, 38.

Chapter 16 The green bough

Page 145

Full text of the catechism of the United Irishmen, McFarland, flyleaf.

Letter, James to Thomas Muir, Bewley, 63. She explains that it is referred to in one of a series of *Aberdeen People's Journal* articles, *Martyrs of Reform in Scotland*, by AH Millar in July 1886. She notes that Millar had access to Muir's papers held by a family descendant, 196n.

Vergniaud, Schama, 714.

Page 146

Death of Oswald, Erdman.

Muir's receipt of travel documents, Bewley, 63.

Letter, Paine to Jefferson, 20 April 1793, Conway, vol 3, ch 17, Private letters to Jefferson.

Page 147

Robespierre's call for insurrection, Schama, 722.

The threat of the National Guard commander, Schama, 723.

"Horrid days of Robespierre", Conway, vol 3, ch 29, *The Eighteenth Fructidor. To the People of France and the French Armies.*

Page 148

Muir sails from Le Havre, Bewley 63; MacMillan 51.

Death of Marat, Schama, 735–7.

Page 149
Letter, Towers to James Muir has been lost. It is referred to in James Muir's reply, see note for page 174.

Descriptions of Archibald Hamilton Rowan, Knox, 38–9; Woods, *DIB*; Chambers *ODNB*.

Pages 150–1
The characterisation of Drennan as a "demure minister" is from Lady Morgan, *O'Briens and O'Flahertys*, vol 3, 75, quoted by McFarland, 100; Knox, 27.

Hamilton Rowan's part of this dialogue is taken from his *Autobiography*, 112–3 and 153.

Page 152
Figures for the sale of Tone's pamphlet, Knox, 26.

Page 153
Bewley speculates that Muir might have been intending to carry on to America but could have decided to return to a public trial in Edinburgh after his enthusiastic reception in Ireland, 65.

Letter, Drennan to Sam McTeir, 20 July 1793, *Drennan-McTeir Letters*, no 456, 556.

United Irishmen meeting place in Back Lane, Dublin, Knox, 41.

Tone, Fitzgerald in the country for the summer, Knox, 116–8; Tillyard 164–7.

Muir at Rathcoffey, Bewley, 63; McFarland, 101.

Page 154
Printing press and laboratory at Rathcoffey, Woods, *DIB*; Chambers, *ODNB*.

Hamilton Rowan's 'three great objects', Woods, *DIB*.

Hamilton Rowan's description of negotiations with France, *Autobiography*, 161; Tillyard, 154.

Page 155
Fitzgerald speaking for the volunteers in the Irish parliament, Tillyard 157;

his contemporary reputation as a radical, Whelan, *DIB*; his early rejection of parliamentary reform, Tillyard, 153.

Page 156

Letter, James Muir to George Towers, 21 July 1793, Mackenzie, 122; *The Trial of Thomas Muir*, 1793, appendix xiii, 13; *ST*, vol 23, cols 167–8, and in part, *Tait's Magazine*, 7.

Letter, Muir to Towers, 27 July 1793, ibid.

Hamilton Rowan to Macleod, McFarland, 102.

Page 157

The package of letters and literature that Muir carried to Scotland were confiscated at his arrest and are in a bundle at NAS, JC26/1793/1.

Chapter 17 The Heart of Midlothian

Pages 158–9

The narrative of Palmer's arrest and most of the dialogue are reconstructed from *ST*, vol 23, 594, columns 237–242, 256–260, 274, 281–2, and 30–382.

Page 160

The description of the position of the Tollbooth and its entrance is from Scott, *Heart of Midlothian*, 57. Scott acquired the stone gateway, door and fastenings of the Tollbooth when it was demolished in 1817 and re-erected them at the entrance to the kitchen court of his house at Abbotsford (Scott's Notes to this volume, 513).

Pages 161–2

Letters, R Dundas to Nepean, 21 June 1793; R Dundas to H Dundas, 2, 12, 29 July 1793; Meikle, 128–9.

Skirving's arrest, brief detention and examination about Palmer's handbill, *Edinburgh Gazetteer*, Tuesday 6 August, 1793.

Letter, Palmer to Ellis, 3 July 1793, *ST*, vol 23, col 329.

Page 163

The description of Portpatrick, its harbour, transport and economy, is from *The Statistical Account of Scotland*, 1791, volume 1, 37–47.

Page 164

Muir's arrest and incarceration at Stranraer and his transfer to the Tollbooth of Edinburgh are described in *ST*, vol 23, columns 163–4; *Trial papers of Thomas Muir* NAS JC26/1793/1; *Tait's Magazine*, 9; Bewley, 66–67; *Edinburgh Gazetteer*, Tuesday 6 August.

Page 165

Letters, Stranraer sheriff to R Dundas noting Muir's "confusion"; R Dundas to Nepean, Bewley, 66.

Skirving mentions moving house in a letter to Thomas Hardy, LCS secretary, in May 1793. It is reproduced in appendix E of the *Second Report from the Committee of Secrecy, 1794*.

Page 166

The religious and political affiliations of Skirving, Macleod, *ODNB*.

Letter, Hardy to Skirving, 17 May 1793, High Court papers, No 26, NAS, JC26/280. A draft of the same is in the Second Report from the Committee of Secrecy, appendix E. The correspondence concerning other English towns is there, too.

Page 167

Lockie's pardon, High court of Justiciary Book of Adjournal, 6 February 1793, remission to Alexander Lockie, pages 385–387, JC3/46; report, *Edinburgh Gazetteer*, 12 February 1793.

The circumstances of Skirving's arrest are in his pamphlet, *Complaint of Wrongous Imprisonment*, 6–8; and *Edinburgh Gazetteer*, 13 August 1793.

Pages 168–9

Muir's escort by soldiers, lord advocate's comments, release on bail, *Caledonian Mercury*, 15 August 1793; Bewley 67.

Skirving's "excessive bail" of 3,000 merks, *Edinburgh Gazetteer*, 20 August 1793.

Chapter 18 The trial of Thomas Muir

Page 170

Romilly, quoted by Bewley, 71

The narrative and dialogue in Muir's trial are taken mainly from *ST*, vol 23, cols 117–238, along with Cockburn, *Examination*, vol 1, 144–183, and Omond, 178–204.

Muir's dress in described in MacMillan, 67. There is no reference provided but I have gone along with the idea.

Moffat's presence as Muir's assistant in court, *Robertson's 1793 pamphlet*, 3. Muir "had become as part of the family" in Moffat's home, MacMillan, 33.

The mood and the weather that day is described by an eyewitness in *Tait's Magazine*, 8n, as follows, "A friend of ours, then a child, and bred among the most noted of the reformers of the period, gives a lively idea of the general state of feeling in Edinburgh, by recording his own notions. The day of the trial, or of the sentence, was thundery and exceedingly dark, and the rain fell in torrents. There was but one topic, one interest, Muir and the trial, and everyone had gone to witness it. A trial was beyond the comprehension of our friend but, gazing through the window, he felt that some awful thing was acting by wicked men." Macmillan has imagined the thundery weather breaking later in the day of the trial and I have taken his lead, 79.

Page 172

The interior of the inner hall and the fireplace, Cockburn, *Memorials*, 110; Insh, 2, 79.

Page 175

The unflattering estimates of the abilities of the lord advocate and the solicitor general are from Cockburn, *An Examination*, 91–2.

Page 176

The Lapslie ditty is *The Clerical Informer's Creed*. See note at chapter 3.

Page 177

Fisher's subsequent employment is reported in the *Edinburgh Gazetteer*, 3 September 1793.

Page 179

Fisher's claim that she was given presents by the Muir's on leaving their employment is contradicted in a report in the *Edinburgh Gazetteer*, 22

October 1793, "This part of Fisher's testimony, we have the authority to say, is totally false; she did not receive a farthing from Mrs Muir besides her wages, nor any article of clothes from Miss Muir; and she was not permitted to remain in the house after the term day." In the same issue it is reported, "We are also informed that she, like the Rev Mr Lapslie, was present at the precognition of other witnesses, and she was frequently closeted in the Star Inn, Glasgow, with an active sheriff of the west, who probably taught a certain judge to expiate so warmly on her singular abilities" (Sheriff Honyman was Braxfield's son-in-law).

Fisher and Lapslie left court together to "an universal hiss", *Edinburgh Gazetteer*, 3 September 1793.

Page 181
Horner, the juryman to whom Braxfield made the passing comment, told Lord Cockburn about it years later, *Memorials*, 117.

Pages 182–8
On the behaviour of the public, MacMillan notes, 67, "Though interjections are absent from the official record, it is known that the crowd jammed into that small courtroom and the vast hall beyond were not there to witness the proceedings in silence"; Bewley, 79 has, "When Muir sat down there was a unanimous burst of applause from the audience, who cheered three times"; *Robertson's pamphlet*, 131, has "an unanimous burst of applause"; the official records have both Braxfield and Henderland referring to the "indecent applause" in their speeches on the following morning.

Page 189
The quote from Braxfield on his way home appears in MacMillan, 96, but is not sourced.

Chapter 19 Defiance
Page 192
Burns, *Robert Bruce's Address to His Troops at Bannockburn*, Noble and Scott Hogg, 462–473. They note that the exact date and place of the composition of the poem is unknown, but that a letter from Burns to George

Thomson in August 1793 explains that he associated that historic event with "some other struggles of the same nature, not quite so ancient". Burns adds, "So may God ever defend the cause of truth and liberty, as he did that day!, Amen!" Two other poems by Burns on the Bruce and liberty theme were published under a pseudonym in the *Edinburgh Gazetteer* in 1793.

The episode concerning the jury is described by Cockburn, *Examinations*, 182. It is taken from a statement given to Cockburn by Sir James Gibson-Craig, who said, "On this I was informed by my uncle, Mr Balfour of Pilrig, who had been clerk to the jury."

Page 193
Linen and fresh-cut flowers brought by the Moffats is noted by MacMillan, 106, but is not referenced.

Page 194
The distress of Muir's parents when searched in the Tollbooth is recorded by Bewley, 86. The bible given to Muir is noted by Bewley, 91, and Mackenzie, 31.

Page 195
Robertson's edition is datelined, "Tollbooth, Edinburgh, September 16th 1793. Sixth month of my imprisonment".

Letters, Muir to Drennan and Rowan, McFarland, 105.

Page 196
The proceedings of the Canongate meeting on 3 September and the all-Edinburgh meeting on 5 September are from spies reports. Macmillan has extensive quotes, 103–4, as does Meikle, 137. JB's reports of 30 August, 4, 6, 7 and 8 September, are in NA HO 102/9, August-December 1793, folios 50–59.

The *Edinburgh Gazetteer*, Tuesday 10 September, has a report of threatening letters sent to members of Muir's jury.

Page 197
Letters, provost and sheriff to lord advocate and the home secretary, 7 and 9 September, NA HO 102/9, August-December 1793, folios 43 and 48.

Watt's visit to Muir in the Tollbooth, MacMillan, 105.

Page 198
Letter, Romilly to Bentham from Edinburgh, 2 September 1793, quoted by

Cockburn, *Examinations*, 183, and taken from vol 19 of Romilly's *Works*, 295. Palmer's trial is taken from *ST*, vol 23, cols 237–382; Cockburn, *Examinations*, 184–220; 1793 pamphlet with an introduction by Skirving . Palmer's background. Millar, *ODNB*.

Page 199
The unflattering description of Lord Eskgrove is from Cockburn, *Memorials*, 119.

Page 201
Skirving's letters were confiscated from him on his arrest in December 1793. Correspondence with other societies, *First Report of the Committee of Secrecy, 1794*, 53; full texts, *Second Report*, appendix F.

The rumour about Mrs Fletcher's guillotine Bewley, 86.

"The Siege of the Edinburgh Tollbooth", report, *Edinburgh Gazetteer* of Tuesday 1 October, 1793.

Page 202
James Maitland, Lord Lauderdale, Thorne, *ODNB*.

Lauderdale's visit to Muir in October 1793, Meikle, 136.

The Glasgow peace petition, reports, *Edinburgh Gazetteer*, 17 and 24 September 1793.

The conversation between the three men on the legality of the sentence of transportation is based on correspondence in Supplementary papers relating to the trials of Charles Sinclair, Muir, Palmer, and Gerrald, NAS GD164/1484, item 3, a letter from Braxfield to Dundas; item 4, a reply to that letter; item 5, extract of a paper sent to Dundas from Lauderdale, Grey, and Sheridan. In addition, Cockburn, *Examinations*, discusses the legality, or otherwise, of the sentence in his analysis of the cases of Anderson, Craig, and Morton (vol 1, 95–108), and Charles Sinclair (vol 2, 34–40).

Page 203
Resolution of the Friends' meeting in Blackfriar's Wynd, 4 October, *Edinburgh Gazetteer*, 8 October 1793; spy's report to Robert Dundas, MacMillan, 107.

Page 204
Letter, Hardy's to Skirving, 5 October, 1793, *Committee of Secrecy, First Report*, 54; full text, appendix E of the *Second Report*.

Chapter 20 Hackney
Page 205
Thelwall, *Poems*, Sonnet II, *To Tyranny*, page 2

The Hackney meeting of the LCS is reconstructed from the minute book of the society, *Place Papers* vol 2, BL add MSS 27812, fols 75, 184–191; Hardy, *A Sketch of the History of the London Corresponding Society*, Place Papers, vol 24, BL add MSS 27814, fols 57–9; Thale, 85–9.

Page 207
The Sheffield meeting is recorded in a letter to Skirving from the Constitutional Society of Sheffield, November 14, 1793, NAS JC26/280 High Court Papers 1793, No 62.

Letters from the societies in Leeds, Sheffield, and Birmingham are mentioned in Thompson, 137, and are contained in the *Second Report of the Committee of Secrecy*, appendix E.

Breillat's arrest, Hardy, op cit.

Chapter 21 The third Scottish convention
Page 209
Letter, R Dundas to H Dundas, 28 October 1793, Insh, 88, quoting Arniston papers, 239.

The numbers attending the third Scottish convention are from its minutes, which are reproduced in Skirving's trial, ST vol 23, 596, cols 391–413.

Page 210
Occupational analysis of the membership of the convention, Harris, *Scottish People*, 90, 264n.

The address from the Belfast branches of the United Irishmen is in McFarland, appendix iii, 253–5.

The letters to the convention from Paisley, Dunfermline, Montrose, Johnstone, Dunbar, and Glasgow are in the High Court papers 1793, NAS JC26/280.

The numbers on poor relief, enlisting in the military, and emigrating, plus the comments on those and government assistance to Glasgow, are from Harris, op cit, 90.

Page 211
Letter about weavers' wages, Lapslie to Dundas, 6 December 1793, NAS RH 2/4/73, folios 268–73; copy in NA HO102/9, August-December 1793, folios 268–273.

Letter, R Dundas to H Dundas, 28 October 1793, op cit.

Page 212
Margaret Beattie is mentioned in a letter from Muir to the lord provost, John Elder, 30 October 1793 (NAS JC26/280/1/58).

Letter, Scott to R Dundas on Muir's sleeping patterns, 2 November 1793 (NA HO102/9, August-December 1793, folio 107).

Muir's thank-you letter, 26 October, *Edinburgh Gazetteer*, 29 October 1793.

The restriction of Muir's visitors to two, report, *Edinburgh Gazetteer*, 5 November, 1793; also in minutes of the third convention, *ST* vol 23, trial of William Skirving, col 411.

Page 213
The incident concerning Binnie, Bryce, and Clarke is the subject of the letter from Muir to the lord provost, op cit; a letter to Skirving on the same date (JC26/280/1/57); and a report in the *Edinburgh Gazetteer* of 5 November 1793.

Hamilton Rowan's visit to Edinburgh is described in detail in his *Autobiography*, 170–182; *ST* vol 23, trial of Maurice Margarot, cols 750–57; Meikle, 140.

Page 215
The story of the two Belfast men and Carmichael is told by Martha McTeir in a letter to her brother, William Drennan, undated but between 11 October and 8 November, 1793, *Drennan-McTeir Letters*, vol 1, letter 464, 570–1.

500 The Liberty Tree

Page 216

Letter, Sheriff Pringle's to R Dundas, 9 November 1793,(NA HO102/9, August-December 1793, folio 139).

Muir's health is described in a letter from his father, dated 11 December, to lawyers in England inquiring whether a petition to the king could be presented in time, NA HO102/9, August-December 1793, folios 289–290.

The *Edinburgh Gazetteer* report of Muir being ordered on board the revenue cutter is dated 12 November 1793. The circumstances are disputed. A minute of the Edinburgh monthly committee of November 1793, notes, "Mr Scott announced to the meeting that he and Messrs Margarot and Taylor had the pleasure of accompanying Mr Muir on board the Royal George where they left in high spirits & in a more comfortable situation than he had been in for some time past" (NAS JC26/280 High Court Papers 1793, unfoliated bundle) and Bewley goes along with this, "His parents, Margarot, and another reformer, Taylor, watched him taken on board" (91). However, a letter from the procurator fiscal, William Scott to Robert Dundas, dated17 November, 1793, contains a post script in which Scott asserts, "It had almost escaped me to observe that although it was represented in the general committee of the Friends of the People here on the evening of the 14th inst that Messrs Scott, Margarot, and Taylor had the pleasure of accompanying Mr Muir that morning on ship-board, as mentioned in JB's letter of the 15th, yet not one of them were with Mr Muir that morning nor did any person accompany him on board except Wm Middleton and Geo Galloway, two of our sheriff officers with some of the ship's company. This I am positive of, as the sheriff and I accompanied the party from Edinb[urgh] and I saw Muir put into the boat at Newhaven. The only purpose then of reporting so gross a falsehood to that meeting must have been to call the attention of the Friends of the People to Muir and raise these three gentlemen in their estimation." The first version has not, to my knowledge, been disputed by any of those involved and Mackenzie's 1831 *Life of Thomas Muir* places his parents at the scene. Mackenzie had access to family papers that are now, as far as we know, lost. The dispute is semantic and probably arises from an inaccuracy in the committee minute. It uses the phrase "accompanying Mr Muir on board", when the delegates simply saw him off at the jetty.

Page 217
Mackenzie refers to James Muir being "struck with a shock of palsy" and tells of Mrs Muir frequently taking to sea in an open boat to catch sight of Muir on board the Royal George, both on 31.

Declaration of John Grant, NA HO102/9, August-December 1793, folio 258.

Palmer's removal from Perth by dragoons, report, Edinburgh Gazetteer, 26 November 1793.

Page 218
Ten convicts taken from Glasgow to the Royal George, report, Edinburgh Herald, 23 November 1793.

List of visitors to Palmer in Perth prison, NA HO102/9, August-December 1793, folios 228–230.

Chapter 22 The British convention

Pages 219–22
The proceedings of the British convention are taken from the minutes gathered from several sources and published in ST, vol 23, trial of Skirving, cols 414–471. Howell in ST, vol 23, col 391, notes that in 1817 he was given access by Robert Dundas to the minutes used in evidence in the trials. JB's longhand minutes are in NAS and contemporary copies of them are in NA HO102/9, August-December 1793, folios 162–226, 232–235, 238–242.

For Margarot's life, appearance and character, Emsley ODNB; Roe, A Radical in Two Hemispheres; Cockburn, Examinations, vol 2, 25.

For Gerrald, Davis, ODNB.

Pages 223–8
Dialogue in the arrests of Skirving, Margarot, Gerrald, and Sinclair, in the two subsequent emergency conventions, and at the scenes in the Grassmarket are reconstructed from evidence given in their trials, ST, vols 23 and 24.

Page 229

Letter, R Dundas to H Dundas, 6 December 1793, NA HO102/9, August-December 1793, folios 250–253).

The resolution of the United Irishmen is in the *Report of the Committee of Secrecy of the House of Commons, 1799*, 13.

Chapter 23 The hulks

Page 230

The opening quote from James Hardy Vaux is from his diary, quoted in Branch-Johnson, 31. This is also the source of the descriptive and historical references to the hulks, organisation of work gangs, gaol fever, and food provided.

Bewley, 92, reports the mutiny rumours spread by Grant.

Page 232

The conversation between Ogilvie and Erskine was reported in the *Edinburgh Gazetteer*, 10 December 1793.

Page 233

Muir's remarks about "having much to learn in this school" are taken from a letter written by him in Woolwich to Benjamin Flower, radical journalist and editor of the *Cambridge Intelligencer*, *Place Papers*, vol 26, fol 208.

Page 234

Muir's removal to the Prudentia is described in a letter from Palmer, 2 December, published in the *Edinburgh Gazetteer*, 10 December 1793.

The theft of Palmer's watch is described in one of his letters, published in the *Monthly Repository*, 1817, 261, with a commentary by JT Rutt.

Visitors are listed in two letters from Palmer published in the *Edinburgh Gazetteer*, 10 December 1794; a letter from Palmer to Rutt, 10 January 1794, quoted in Bladen, 837; Bewley, 93; Rutt, *Monthly Repository*, 1817, 203, 204, 261.

Page 235

Letter, R to H Dundas, NA HO102/9, folio 265. Nepean's reply is quoted in Bewley, 93.

The *Morning Post*, 6 January 1794, is quoted in Bladen, 834.

The suspicion that the hulks' captains were acting as spies is recorded by Rutt, op cit, 261.

Page 236
Pitt's comment on Godwin's book *Political Justice*, Grylls, 16.

Muir's illness is described by Rutt, ibid; Dr Hornsby's report, NA HO 102/10, folio 45; Bewley, 96 and 97, including the *Morning Post* article of 10 January.

Page 237
Letter, Home Office to Duncan Campbell, NA HO 102/10, folio 49.

Details of the meeting on 26 December 1793 are contained in a letter from William Moffat to the anonymous author of *A Life of Thomas Muir Esq*, xxxii, which is printed in the 1835 Glasgow pamphlet, *The Trial of Joseph Gerrald*.

Palmer's letter to Moffat was published in the *Edinburgh Gazetteer*, 10 December 1793. Muir's to Moffat from the Tollbooth is in Bladen, 91; Moffat's constant companionship with Muir from December until his departure for New South Wales is recorded in the *Morning Chronicle*, 14 March, 1794.

Ellis's arrival at Woolwich and his intention to travel with Palmer to New South Wales is reported in the *Glasgow Advertiser*, 17 January 1794.

Page 238
Palmer's letter "from his late congregation at Dundee" was published in the *Morning Chronicle*, 13 January 1794.

A discussion of the possibility of the authorities revoking the sentences of Muir and Palmer is in Bewley, 87 and MacMillan, 108.

Palmer's petition to the king (undated) from the Stanislaus vessel at Woolwich and drawn up by J Martin, solicitor [the Corresponding Society member who attended the magistrates at the Nag's Head in Hackney], Richmond buildings, Soho, is in NAS GD164/1484, item 11, supplementary papers relating to the trials of Charles Sinclair, Muir, Palmer, and Gerrald.

Page 239
Palmer's letter to Grey from Perth, 29 October 1793, is in Hughes, *Scottish*

Historical Review, No 35, 1956, 38. See also letter from Palmer to Rutt, 7 February 1794, *Monthly Repository* 1817, 576.

For the visit of Grey, Sheridan and Lauderdale to Dundas, see Bewley, 94; Harris, 122; *Edinburgh Gazetteer*, 17 December 1793; and related documents in NA HO102/9, folios 282–285; NAS GD164/1484, items 5 and 6.

The home secretary's letter to Robert Dundas is dated Wimbledon, 16 November 1793. He had two visits from the three opposition leaders up to that time. The letter is reprinted in Bladen, 827.

Page 240
Dundas's marriage, and the appointment of Barnard to post of colonial secretary, Fry, 157.

Chapter 24 Exemplary punishments

Pages 241–3
The description of a large crowd waiting to greet Skirving at his home is in Skirving's collected papers, undated letter, NAS RH4/52. The remainder of the description and dialogue in Skirving's trial is taken from *ST*, vol 23, cols 471–602; Cockburn, *Examinations*, vol 1, 222–292.

For details of those convention members arrested but not convicted to transportation see A Member, *Account of the Proceedings of the British Convention*, 58.

Page 244
The *Morning Chronicle* report of Margarot's procession on 9 January was published on 14 January 1794.

Letter, R to H Dundas, 10 January 1794, NA HO102/10, folios 76–7.

Page 245
Reports of Margarot's second procession and the fight on North Bridge are from *Glasgow Advertiser*, 10 and 13 January 1794; *Morning Chronicle* 17 January 1794; Cockburn, *Examinations*, vol 2, 23–25 (he witnessed it as a young boy).

Pages 246–9
Margarot's trial is reconstructed from *ST*, vol 23, cols 603–778; Cockburn, *Examinations*, vol 2, 1–34.

Letter, R to H Dundas, 15 January 1794, NA HO102/10, folios 83–84.

Letter, Margarot to Norwich, 18 January 1794, NA TS11/953, No 17.

Page 250

Letter, Elder to Dundas, 17 January 1794, NA HO102/10, folio 93

Reports from Sheffield and Paisley, *Glasgow Advertiser*, 10 January 1794.

Chapter 25 Newgate

Page 251

Dundas's instructions to remove Muir to Newgate were sent to the sheriffs of London and Middlesex, 16 January 1794, NA HO102/10, folio 85.

Page 252

The description of Newgate's wings, the rates for rooms, the prison shop, and the visiting times are from Thomas Lloyd, *Impositions and Abuses*, NA TS11/952, bundle 3496/2.

Famous inmates and outbreaks of gaol fever are from Grovier, xv, xvi, 209–216, 218–221.

Page 253

Rochemont Barbauld is in the list of visitors to Muir, Skirving, and Margarot in Newgate, NA HO102/10, folios 156–160.

For Thelwall's fund-raising lectures, Thompson, 141.

The SCI and LCS meetings are described in Thompson, 141–2; and Barrell, 182–3; Thale, 105–9; ST, vol 24, cols 359, 441–446, 799–802.

Pages 254–5

Letter, Martin to Margarot, 22 January 1794, NA TS11/3510, quoted by Thompson, 142n.

The conversation between Parr and Gerrald is from the anonymous 1835 Glasgow pamphlet, *The Trial of Joseph Gerrald*, which contains a *Memoir of Joseph Gerrald*, as an introduction, 4–5.

Letter, Godwin to Gerrald, *Memoir*, ibid, 115–117.

Page 256

Letter, Gerrald to Millar from Belford, *Memoir*, ibid, 118.

Movements of Skirving, Margarot, Gerrald and Sinclair, report, *Glasgow Advertiser*, 3 February, 1794.

Page 257
Stanhope's motion on the House of Lords, 31 January 1794, *PH*, vol 30, cols 1298–1310.

Page 258
Adam's motion on the House of Commons, 4 February 1794, *PH*, vol 30, cols 1346–1358.

Arrival of Margarot and Skirving at Newgate, *Glasgow Advertiser*, 7 February 1794.

For other radicals in Newgate see Davis, McCalman & Parolin (eds), passim.

The correspondence between Dundas and Braxfield on the legality of sentences, NAS GD164/1484, supplementary papers.

The *Morning Chronicle*, Saturday 11 January 1794 reported, "On Wednesday, the King in Council signed an order for the transportation of Messrs Muir and Palmer…"

Dundas's order to transfer Muir, Skirving and Margarot from Newgate to the transport ship is dated 8 February, NA HO102/10, folio 150.

Removal of the prisoners from Newgate to the Surprize is described in papers of an LCS member, Matt Swift, NA TS11/956, bundle 2.

Page 259
Letter, Palmer to Rutt, 10 February 1794, is reprinted in *Monthly Repository*, 1817, op cit, 204.

Letter, Palmer to Moffat, 7 December, was published in the *Edinburgh Gazetteer*, 10 December 1793.

Bladen lists 60 female convicts on board, 102n, as does Bewley, 103, although she has the wrong date for embarkation, at 13 February. It was 11 February.

Chapter 26 In the balance
Page 260
Thelwall, *Poems*, Sonnet V, *The Source of Slavery*, page 5.

Sinclair's appearances in court, *ST*, vol 23, cols 777–802 and Cockburn, *Examinations*, vol 2, 34–40.

Page 261
Morning Chronicle report on the discretion of judges, 1 March 1794.

Page 262
Letter, Theophilus Lindsey's to a friend, 20 February 1794, quoted in Belsham, 271n.

Visitors to Muir, Skirving and Margarot in Newgate from 17 January to 10 February, NA HO102/10 January to April 1794, folios 156–160.

Delay of Surprize at Deal and the damage to the hull, Bewley,104.

Sheridan's introduction of Palmer's petition in the House of Commons, *PH* vol 30, cols 1449–1461.

Pages 263–4
Gerrald's appearances in court and his eventual trial, *ST*, vol 23, cols 803–1012; Cockburn, Examinations, vol 2, 41–132.

R Dundas having to leave Edinburgh for London, *ST* vol 23, col 805.

House of Commons debate introduced by William Adam, 10 March 1794, *PH* vol 30, cols 1486–1576.

Pages 265–70
Gerrald's breakfast with the Fletchers, Cockburn, *Examinations*, vol 2, 43 (the story was related to him by Eliza Fletcher); description of Gerrald's dress, 43–4; character of Gillies and Laing, 45.

Trial report, *ST* vol 23, cols 808–1012.

The passage from Thomas Campbell, Cockburn, op cit, 83n.

Page 271
House of Commons debate introduced by William Adam, 25 March 1794, *PH* vol 31, cols 54–83.

Chapter 27 Chalk Farm
Pages 272–6
Hardy's circular letter is in the *First Report of the Committee of Secrecy*, 24–5.

The Chalk Farm meeting is reconstructed from documents in the *First Report of the Committee of Secrecy*, 20–40; *Second Report*, 59–72; Hardy, *A Sketch of the History*, *Place Papers*, op cit, folios 70–76; Hardy, *Memoir*; Thale, 133–140; *ST*, vol 24, trial of Thomas Hardy, cols 735–742. From the documents we know that Lovett chaired the meeting and that Thelwall spoke and Richter read some resolutions and documents, although there is no record of the speeches. Thelwall's is here taken from the handbills and letters of the LCS and I have assumed that Hardy would have been one of the other speakers. His contribution comes from his *Memoirs* and some of the circulars.

Goodwin points out that "although the occasion had been planned as part of the preparations for the eventual summons of a general convention, Thelwall saw to it that no formal resolution calling for such action was put." This was to avoid the meeting being proscribed in advance by magistrates, However, all of the relevant correspondence is about organising a national convention and the final resolution agreed at Chalk Farm gave "approbation and applause" to the proceedings of the Edinburgh convention (*ST*, vol 24, col 738, Goodwin, 328-9, 331).

House of Lords debate introduced by the Earl of Lauderdale, 15 April 1794, *PH* vol 31, cols 263–287; *Morning Chronicle*, 16 April 1794.

Chapter 28 The Motherbank

Page 277

Muir's (long) poem to Moffat was published in the *Constitutional* in 1837, as part of the campaign for funds to erect a memorial in Edinburgh, *Place Papers*, vol 28, BL add MSS 27816, fol 448.

The Surprize's complement and cargo, Bladen, 119–20.

Palmer's luggage, Bewley, 105.

Page 278

For negotiations concerning the Margarots' cabin, Bladen, 855; Bewley, 106; letter, officers to under-secretary King, Bladen, 855; Clune, 37–8.

Campbell's orders from the secretary of state, Skirving, collected papers, NAS RH4/52; letter Palmer to Joyce, 8 March 1794, NA TS11/952, bundle 3496/2.

Page 279

Palmer's dialogue with Campbell is based, in part, on Palmer's *Narrative*, 13.

Passage on the Canada for Palmer and Muir; Palmer, *Narrative*, 15; Bewley 105.

For the dispute about cabins on the Surprize (including Ellis's) Palmer, *Narrative*, 18, 19, 57; Skirving, collected papers, op cit; *Petition of Palmer and Skirving to Grose*, 26 October, 1794, Bladen 867.

Letter, Palmer to Joyce, op cit, describes living conditions with soldiers.

Page 280

Muir's letters from Deal are quoted, in part, by Bewley, 103–4. The letter to a friend in London was published in the *Dublin Evening Post* on 8 April 1794; his letter to Flower, along with earlier letters to the *Cambridge Intelligencer* editor, are in the *Place Collection*, vol 26, BL add MSS 27814, fols 208–11.

Palmer refers to his "long illness" in his *Narrative*, 17, 34; see also Bewley, 104;

Pages 281–3

The arrival of the extra detachment of soldiers at Portsmouth, the characters of Reddish and Draper, and the activities of Grant, Palmer, *Narrative*, 15–18.

The Surprize's cargo, see note for page 314.

Page 284

Letter, Muir to Joyce at Stanhope's, NA TS11/960, folder 3506/2.

Page 285

Campbell's refusal to give Ellis a cabin, Palmer, *Narrative*, 19.

The incident of a ship pulling alongside the Surprize to jeer at the reformers, Bewley, 104.

Encounter between Campbell and naval officer, *Morning Chronicle*, 17 March 1794.

Grant's theft and the presence of witnesses is described by Palmer, *Narrative*, 15.

Page 286

Grant's rumour, Palmer, *Narrative*, 18.

Grant's diary entry is from Captain Campbell's deposition on the mutiny, taken at Rio, Bladen, 865.

510 The Liberty Tree

Letter, Moffat to Thomas Maclean, Gosport, 30 April 1795, NA TS11/952, bundle 3496/2.

Page 287

Rev Russell Scott's last sighting of the fleet is contained in a letter from the Rev Theophilus Lindsey to a friend, 3 May 1794, quoted in Belsham, 271n.

Address from London Corresponding Society to the prisoners, *Tait's Magazine*, 32; paraphrased in Thale, 134.

Chapter 29 Treason and plot

Pages 288–90

John Thelwall's song, *Britain's Glory, or the Blessings of a Good Constitution*, was sung at a general meeting of the LCS in the Globe Tavern on the Strand on 20 January 1794. It is in reference to a fable of the King Chaunticlere in Daniel Isaac Eaton's periodical, *Hog's Wash*, of November 1793. See Barrell, 109–110.

There are accounts of Hardy's arrest in his *Memoirs*, 31–33; in a letter from Hardy to Francis Place in 1831, in Thale, 157–8; and in a contemporary LCS pamphlet, *An Account of the Arrest of Citizen Thomas Hardy*, 2–3. Mrs Hardy's first name, Lydia, is given in Alan Wharham, *The Treason Trials*, 22 (Leicester University Press 1992), and in Vincent Carretta's introduction to Equiano's *Interesting Narrative*, xxx.

Pages 291–2

Gerrald in Newgate, Thale,176–188, spies' reports; Davis, *ONDB* entry.

Radicals in Newgate, Davis et al, passim; Manogue, 268. Grylls mentions that Godwin took Coleridge to visit Gerrald, 56.

Smith had raised a subscription for Gerrald's upkeep and "Citizen Gerrald had made him his Treasurer, that he might neither spend or be robbed of it", Spy's report of LCS general committee meeting, 5 June 1794, Thale, 179–80. He was a regular visitor to Gerrald and it is merely possible he was the one to bring the news of Hardy's arrest but there is no evidence of how they got this particular information inside Newgate. It could have been one of many visitors who reported it.

Pages 293—4
Panic caused by Bow Street Runners in New Compton Street, Thale, 158–160, spies' reports.

Royal message to parliament, 12 May 1794, *PH* vol 31, col 471.

The suspected government attack on human rights, LCS pamphlet on Hardy's arrest, op cit, 3.

Thelwall's arrest, Thale, 162–3.

Page 295
House of Commons debate on the Committee of Secrecy, 13 May 1794, *PH* vol 31, cols 471–5.

Pages 296—8
Arrest of John Martin, Thale, 167.

Arrest of Jeremiah Joyce, Joyce, *An Account of*, passim; *Manchester Guardian*, 8 February 1892, 7.

For the "Watt plot" see Barrell, 252 et seq; Omond, 202–4; Harris, *ODNB* on Watt; Meikle, 149–153; Plowden, 240–249; *Life and Character*, passim; McEwen's evidence is taken from the report of Hardy's trial, *ST*, vol 24, cols 846–856.

Pages 299—300
Debate on the first report of the Committee of Secrecy and the suspension of habeas corpus, Commons and Lords, *PH*, vol 31, cols 475–605; *New Annual Register 1794*, 189–215.

Countrywide arrests, *First Report of Commons Committee of Secrecy*, 15; Thale, 157; Thompson, 144; Harris, *ODNB* for Mealmaker.

Page 301
Arrests of Irish leaders, McFarland, 116–17; Knox, 139.

Chapter 30 Mutiny
Pages 302—3
The broadside ballad is quoted by Keneally, 67, and Hughes, 68.

The conversation at the captain's table is fictional but based on the sources mentioned below. The people present in the roundhouse are recorded. The major sources for the voyage of the Surprize and the so-called mutiny plot are Palmer's *Narrative*, published in Cambridge by Joyce in 1797 and containing depositions from Thomson, Pattullo, Ryan, Pitt, Stirling, and Griffiths, along with additional material on Bet Carter from Skirving's journal; William Skirving's collected papers (NAS RH4/52); and Bladen, who has collected together letters and depositions from Campbell, Baker, Reddish, and Draper, letters from Muir, Palmer and Skirving to Rev James Joyce, an article from *Saunders's News-Letter* in 1795 entitled *Mutiny on the Surprize*, and the petition of Skirving and Palmer to Governor Grose (857–77). The motives ascribed to Campbell for his behaviour towards Muir and company, largely through McPherson, are conjectural. He was initially ordered by the Home office to treat the political prisoners as ordinary felons but this seems to have been rescinded, partially at least. However, there is no evidence, so far, of further interference from either Dundas, Nepean, or King in Campbell's decisions over how to treat the prisoners. On the imagined mutiny, was he genuinely afraid of Jacobinism? Why, then, was his treatment of Margarot different from the other three? Did he have fear and contempt of the "criminal classes"? Was he simply bamboozled by the lies of Grant and Draper? Or was his behaviour influenced by all or some of these things and, ultimately, irrational?

Voyage of the first, fleet, Keneally, 3, 49–89, 261–2, passim; Hughes, 61–76 and passim.

Sailing characteristics of the Surprize; Bateson, 127–8; Hughes 134.

Navigation to NSW, Hughes, 72.

Page 304
The order from the Committee of Public Safety for the interception of the vessel carrying Muir and the others offers "*un asile en France aux hommes persécutés pour la cause de la liberté; arête que le Ministre de la Marine prendra toutes les mesures necessaries pour délivrer Muir, Palmer et Margarot et intercepter le vaisseau qui les conduit en exil. Signé au register, St Just, B Barère, Jeanbon St André, CA Prieur, R Lindet, Carnot, Collot d'Herbois, Billaud-Varenne*", quoted by Meikle, 146n, from the Archives, French Foreign Office, Correspondance Politique (Angleterre), No 558, f.139.

Muir, in a letter to Branciforte, 20 August 1796, mentions that he had read the names of the French frigates looking for them in an Article in an American newspaper, Archive of the Indias, Seville, quoted in Masson and Jameson, 52n.

Page 305

The conversation between Muir and Loftus is fictional as is the character Ann Loftus and her companion Jane Simmons. They are composite characters based on four women sentenced for the crime described. The four, Jane Ison, Ann Dawson, Sarah Loft, and Ann Simmons, were convicted at Old Bailey, 17 December 1792; their sentence was death, commuted to transportation for life on 27 February 1793. They appear among the list of convicts on Surprize, NA HO1/11, pp 195–9, and their trial is at oldbaileyonline.org, ref, t17921215–15. I have constructed composite characters because there is only circumstantial evidence that Muir had a relationship with a woman on the voyage and, if he did, it could have been anyone on board. Each of the women named in the trial may still have relatives alive in Australia or in the United Kingdom and I want to avoid surprising or offending any of them. The idea that Muir might have formed a relationship on the Surprize comes from Earnshaw, who speculates "we may fondly imagine he had shared deeper ties than just those of a fellow convict and voyager." In fact he suggests that Muir may have managed to have the woman he met on board appointed as a servant at his farm on Milson's Point in Sydney Cove. Bewley adds to the speculation, "He may have associated with one of the women, which could be the reason why he separated from the others", 109. Elizabeth 'Bet' Carter, on the other hand, is real and we have evidence of her relationship with McPherson and her flogging. She is also on the ship's convict list and her trial is on the Old Bailey website, ref, t17921215-91. The practice of sailors taking 'sea wives' on convict ships was widespread, "The captain and each officer enjoy the right of selection," wrote a Captain Bertram in 1806. "Thus they continue the habit of concubinage until the convicts arrive at Sydney town. Each sailor or soldier is permitted to attach himself to a female" (James Bonwick, *The First Twenty Years of Australia*, London, 1882, quoted on page 86 of Richard Gott, *Britain's Empire, Resistance, Repression and Revolt*, Verso 2011).

Pages 306–7
Daily routine on convict ships, Brooke and Brandon, 139–141.

Page 308
The letters of Captain William Hill, captain of the guard on the Surprize in the second fleet, are in Bateson, 33, 74, 127, 128, and in Brooke and Brandon, 290.

Conditions in the Southern Ocean, Keneally, 3.

The Guardian encounters icepacks, Keneally, 262.

Surprize reaches Sydney Cove under jury masts, Keneally, 286.

Page 309
Voyage of the second fleet, Bateson 126–31; Keneally, 240–91; Hughes, 96–7, 133–6, and passim.

Treatment of convicts by Captain Anstis; Hill's comment on the slave trade, Bateson, 128.

Eyewitness report of Rev Richard Johnson, Brooke and Brandon, 145

Page 310
Surprize fitted with shackles from the slave voyages, Hughes, 134.

Improvements to contracts, Hughes, 136.

Page 311
Mutiny on the Scarborough, Bateson, 128.

The latitudes crossed by Surprize are included in one of the depositions contained in *Place Papers*, vol 28, BL add MSS 27816.

Pages 312–3
The encounter between Grant and Thomson is recorded in Thomson's deposition, Palmer, *Narrative*, 59–62.

Letter, Grant to Pringle, Palmer, 15.

Beer incident, Bladen, 862.

Pages 314–26
Major sources quoted in notes for pages 302–3

Page 327
Equatorial calms and squalls are described by Tuckey, 35–40.

Chapter 31 Ship of fear

Page 329

Ryan's declaration is from Palmer's *Narrative*, 66–7.

Contemporary description of the harbour at Rio, Tuckey, 41–2; Graham, 112.

Page 330

Letter, Campbell to Commissioners of the Navy, 2 August 1794, describes the breakdown of the harbour water pipes, as well as the parts played by Margarot and Muir in the alleged mutiny, Bladen, 857.

Letter, Baker to commissioners of the navy, 2 August 1794, lists the provisions taken on board, Bladen, 860.

Letter, John Grant to Sir James Grant, 9 July 1794, NAS GD248/687/2/1.

Letter, Campbell to Commissioners of the Navy, op cit.

Page 331

Somerville's story, Palmer, 40; Campbell's request for a court martial from the captain of Swift, 41.

George Pitt's declaration, Palmer, 70.

Page 332

Draper's confinements are in the deposition of William Pattullo, Palmer, 64.

McPherson's appointment as Suffolk's quartermaster is reported in *Mutiny on the Surprize, Saunders's News-Letter*, Thursday 5 March 1795, reprinted in Bladen, 874–7. How the news got back to the Surprize is uncertain, but it could only have been when she was in port in Rio.

Page 333

Contemporary descriptions of the town of Rio are from Graham, 114–19 and 134; and Tuckey, 45–54.

The inscription in the book presented by Muir to the Antonine monastery was recorded by Tuckey on his visit there in 1802 (page 50n).

Page 334

The outing with the Pattullos is fictional but we do know that Muir was frequently allowed on shore, accompanied by an officer. The two most likely and most friendly were Pattullo and Thomson.

The Vallongo slave market in 1823 is described by Graham, 159.

Page 335

Baker's assault on Muir following their argument is recorded in both Baker's statement, 28 July 1794, and Reddish's declaration, Bladen, 858–59.

Pages 336–7

Margarot's comments to Boston, Campbell's about hanging Casswell, Palmer 35; being prevented from playing with the Boston child, 35; confiscation of papers, 36–7; lurcher drowned, 38; Thomson's and Pattullo's admissions of fear and anxiety on the final leg of the voyage, Depositions, 62 and 65.

Page 338

Palmer's description of the wet conditions, *Narrative*, 32.

Sailing conditions in the Southern Ocean are described by Hughes, 76; Keneally, 3; Bateson, 127.

Bewley notes that the ships parted company near Amsterdam Island, no reference.

Page 339

Time and date of arrival of the Surprize in Sydney Cove, Palmer, *Narrative*, 47.

Chapter 32 Oyer and terminer

Page 340

Thelwall, *Poems*, Sonnet IX, *The Cell*, page 9.

Oyer and terminer was a commission issued to judges to try cases on assize, the forerunner of the English crown court. The assizes outside London took place only twice a year. A special commission of oyer and terminer was a useful legal tool for quick action in political crises and rebellions, where accused persons could be presented for trial from a grand jury, before whom a bill of indictment had to be placed. The term is from Anglo-Norman, *oyer*, to hear, and *terminer*, to determine or judge.

Page 341

Thelwall's belief that Gerrald was kept in England until the treason trials were over, Thale, 234n.

The conversation between Gerrald and Smith is fictional. For the full indictment against the Old Bailey prisoners tried for treason, *ST*, vol 24, cols 224–238.

Page 342

Letters, H Dundas's to Pitt about the Watt plot, 19, 23, 24, 27 May, 2 June, *Second Report of the Commons committee of Secrecy*, 10–19.

Lords and Commons debates on Second Reports of secret committees, *PH* vol 31, cols 688, 886, 909, and 915; address to the king from both houses, col 911.

Unification of the law of treason in Scotland and England, Meikle, 151; Barrell, 256.

Page 343

Letter, R to H Dundas, 20 June 1794, Meikle, 151.

Watt's trial, *ST*, vol 23, cols 1167–1404; Dundas's evidence, cols 1322–28; *Declaration and Confession of Robert Watt*, cols 1394–1404; Omond, 202–204; Meikle, 149–153; Barrell, 252–284.

Pages 344–7

Downie's trial, *ST*, vol 24, cols 1–200.

Watt's execution, *The Life and Character of Robert Watt*, 85–93.

Eyewitness report of Watt's execution, ibid, 93.

Chapter 33 Twelve good men

Page 348

Burns, *Here's a Health to Them That's Awa*. Tammie, the Norland laddie, is Thomas Erskine, defence lawyer in the treason trials. Burns wrote this after his earlier defence of Tom Paine. "At the lug (ear) o'the law", means that Erskine is intimate with and makes his living from the legal system. See also the reference in Chapter 2

Joyce describes walking on the roof of the Tower in his *Account*, 11, as does Hardy, *Memoir*, 41. This conversation, though, is fictional.

Pages 349–50

The trial of Thomas Walker, *ST*, vol 23, cols 1055–1166.

The death of Lydia, attack by a loyalist mob, Hardy, *Memoir*, 35–38; Thale, 183;

Page 351

Hardy's description of the felons' courtyard, *Memoir*, 53.

Hardy's trial, *ST*, vol 24, cols 199–1384.

For "constructive treason" see Barrell, passim; Thale, 232.

The lord chancellor's statement, Thale, 232.

Letter, Grey to his wife, *Life of Lord Grey*, 28, quoted in Jephson, 236.

Page 352

Pitt's assertion that his "head would be off" if he resigned, *Life of Wilberforce*, ii, 114, quoted in Emsley, Repression, 811.

Instances of arms mistakenly attributed to the LCS, Barrell, 218–9.

Page 354

The foreman of the jury being overcome is noted in an alternative contemporary version of Hardy's trial, "reported by a student in the temple", 274.

Description of the events following Hardy's acquittal, *New Annual Register 1794*, 272–275; Hardy, *Memoir*, 53–55.

Hardy's speech to the crowd is reconstructed from a paraphrase of it in *New Annual Register*, opt cit, 274.

Page 355

Existence of the additional warrants prepared by the government is claimed by Hardy, *Memoir*, 42.

Tooke's trial, *ST*, vol 25, cols 1–745; *New Annual Register*, op cit, 276–282.

Post-trial celebrations, ibid, 282–4.

The story of Davey from Norwich, Thompson, 148.

Page 356

The remaining acquittals are in *ST*, vol 25, cols 475–478. Thelwall's trial is not listed. Howell notes he was unable to obtain a correct report of it; there is a brief report in Thale, 234–5.

Letter, Cartwright to his wife, quoted by Emsley, op cit, 810, from *The Life and Correspondence of Major Cartwright* by his niece, 1826

Letter, Robert Burns to Mrs Dunlop, 12 January 1795, quoted in Scott Hogg, 296.

Gerrald's daughter in jail is mentioned in *Gerrald, A Fragment*, 16; Davis, *ODNB*.

The *Morning Chronicle* report of Stanhope's party at Chevening, is reprinted in Joyce's *Account*, 25.

Page 357
The Crown and Anchor celebration, Hardy, *Memoir*, 55.

Lord Daer death notice, *Morning Chronicle*, 20 November, 1794.

Hardy's new shop in Tavistock Street, *Memoir*, op cit, 58.

Page 358
For an assessment of the state of the LCS after the treason trials, Thale, 251.

Provincial prosecutions and dissolution of societies, Thompson 149–50.

Renewed low-level activity in Ireland and Scotland, McFarland, 131–2.

Paine was released from the Luxembourg on 9 November 1794, Keane, 419.

Victims of the terror and the end of Robespierre, Schama, 805–847 passim.

Gerrald's order for transportation, Thale, 234n.

Portland took over from Dundas as home secretary in July 1794 in a cabinet reshuffle. Portland had taken a section of the Whig opposition over to Pitt's benches and he was rewarded with the cabinet seat. Dundas became secretary for war and he remained as treasurer for the navy, president of the India board, and governor of the Bank of Scotland. His hold on patronage in Scotland was undiminished.

Chapter 34 The Rum Corps
Page 359
George Hamilton, *The Telegraph, A Consolatory Epistle from Thomas Muir Esq of Botany Bay to the Hon Henry Erskine, late Dean of Faculty*
The poem was published in January 1796 and is often misattributed to Muir, possibly because the original manuscript is in the Mitchell Library in Sydney. It is, in fact, an anti-Jacobin satire celebrating the defeat of the

Scottish radicals on the occasion of Henry Erskine's removal as Dean of the Faculty of Advocates in Edinburgh in late 1795, Leask, 59–62. Erskine had presided at a meeting opposing proposals in parliament to extend the laws of treason and to prevent political assemblies. As a result, a petition against the bills, which became known as the Two Acts, was signed by 8,000 in Edinburgh, 2,500 in Paisley, and 10,000 in Glasgow and Erskine was removed from his position for disloyalty to the faculty, Meikle, 159.

Surprize 15-gun salute, welcome by Collins, Clune, 72–3.

Page 360

Edinburgh prisoners remain on board Surprize until November, Earnshaw, 17.

Campbell went ashore with "a monstrous bag of papers containing the original charges, and copies of the evidence he had been able to procure against us", Palmer, *Narrative*, 47.

Letter, King to Lt Governor Grose, 14 February 1794, State Library of New South Wales, a1246002.

Letters of introduction, Earnshaw, 17.

For Macaulay, Keneally, 399.

Margarot's "birthright" demand, Clune, 74.

Page 361

Petition of Skirving and Palmer to Grose, and Grose's reply, Palmer, *Narrative*, 47, 55.

Page 362

Phillip's policy of sending new arrivals away from Sydney, Keneally, 425.

Treatment of women on arrival, Hughes, 233.

Page 363

The parting of Muir and Loftus is fictional.

Page 364

Population statistics, Bewley, 119; Bateson, appendix VIIa, Statistics of Male and Female Convicts 1788–1868, 379.

For a description of Sydney in 1794, engravings based on Watling's paintings, Paterson, passim; De Vries, 6–13; Ashton and Waterson, 6–15; Earnshaw, 16.

References 521

Origins of the Tank Stream, Ashton and Waterson, 12.

Page 365

The adjoining houses of Muir, Palmer, and Skirving are described by them in various letters to friends, 1794–96; Bewley, 129; and Clune, 75, who notes that they were on the west side of the site of present-day O'Connell Street.

Grose's offer to provide goods, Bewley, 119.

Palmer's *Narrative*, with additions from Skirving, was sent to Joyce with 60 depositions sworn before a magistrate. The attempt to have a case heard in England failed and in 1797 Joyce had the manuscript published together with six of the depositions, which he thought was sufficient to illustrate the case.

Palmer on Margarot and Campbell, *Narrative*, 57.

Page 366

John Stirling's deposition of 30 November 1794, Palmer's *Narrative*, 73.

Letter, Muir, Palmer and Skirving to Joyce, 9 November, 1794, Bladen, 868–9.

Page 367

Grose's enrichment of the Rum Corps, Hughes, 100.

MacArthur's creation of the spirits monopoly; ownership of livestock, Hughes, 101–2.

Purchase of farms by Muir, Palmer, and Skirving, Bewley, 121, Clune, 76–7. Clune provides evidence to show that Muir's land was on Milson's Point, now the site of the north pier of the Sydney Harbour Bridge.

Page 368

Letter, Skirving to his wife, undated, Clune, 95.

Letter, Palmer to Joyce, Sydney, 15 December 1794, (reprinted in *Morning Chronicle*, 27 July 1795), Bladen, 870–1.

Letter, Muir to Moffat, Sydney, 13 December 1794, *Monthly Repository* 12, 577–8.

Page 369

Letter, Palmer to Joyce, op cit.

Earnshaw, 19, argues that the artist who painted Muir's farm could only have been Watling, even although the painting has never been found.

Extracts from Watling's *Letters of an Exile at Botany Bay to his Aunt in Dumfries* (Perth c1794), Hughes, 95; de Vries, 8. An interesting article about him on the website of the Dumfries Museum, dumfriesmuseum.demon. co.uk/watling1.html, quotes White's instructions to the printer on the back of one of Watling's paintings.

Page 370

Collins's book was published in London with engravings made from Watling's work by Edwards Dayes. Watling was not attributed, de Vries, 8.

The description of harvesting wheat and the abundance of wood and seafood is from *A soldier's letter*, reprinted in *Saunders's News-Letter*, 31 July 1795, quoted in Bladen, 817.

We are fairly certain of the name of the young woman, Jean, who was sent to Muir's farm as a servant, as will become clear later. The boy's name is unknown.

Arrival of the Experiment, Paterson, 198.

Pages 371–2

Letter, Palmer to Lindsey, Sydney, 15 September 1795, tells of Boston being accused of Jacobinism, Lindsey's *Memoirs*, appendix XI, 403–6.

January's heavy rains, revenge attacks, Paterson 201.

Arrival of Britannia, Paterson, 204.

Boston and Ellis demand access to cargoes, punished, letter, Palmer to Rev Dr Disney, June 13 1795; *Monthly Repository* 12, 262–4; Palmer to a friend, 23 April 1796, Clune, 96. The location of this incident is unknown but from the timing it is likely to have been on the Britannia. The dialogue in the confrontation is based on the letters.

Events in March, April and May, including the arrival of Endeavour and Boston's production of salt, Paterson, 204–9.

Page 373

Letter, Palmer to Disney, op cit.

Expected arrival of new governor, letter, Palmer to Disney, op cit.

Page 374

Letter, Hunter to King, 17 January 1795, Clune, 79.

Arrival of HMS Providence, Paterson 210.

News of acquittal of Tooke, Hardy, etc, Clune, 90.

Arrival of Fancy, Supply, and Reliance, Paterson, 211, 212.

Hunter's public meeting, Paterson, 212; Collins 305.

Page 375
Letter, Palmer to Lindsey, 15 September 1795, Lindsey's *Memoirs*, op cit.

Hunter's census, Paterson, 214.

Arrival of Young William, Paterson, 212.

Chapter 35 Voice of the banished
Page 376
John Hunter, Frost, *ODNB*.

Letter, John Hunter to a friend in Leith, 16 October 1795, printed in the *True Briton*, 20 August 1796, and the *Edinburgh Advertiser*, 1796; quoted in part in Bladen, 882, and in full in Mackenzie, 33.

Pages 377–8
Letter, Palmer to Lindsey, 15 September 1795, on the commercial activities of Boston, Ellis, etc, Lindsey's *Memoirs*, appendix XI, 403–6.

Petition of Muir, Palmer and Skirving to Governor Hunter, Sydney 14 October, 1795, Bladen, 884. Lauderdale's motion, *PH* vol 31, 15 April 1794; Gillies's argument at Gerrald's trial, *ST*, vol 23, col 849.

Hunter to the Duke of Portland, 25 October 1795, Bladen 882–3.

Pages 379–80
Dialogue from the transcript of Boston v Laycock, McKellar and others, *Historical Record of Australia*, series 1, vol 1, 603–43.

Arrival of Sovereign, Paterson, 214; Wantrup, 299.

Page 381
Hunter to Portland, 30 April 1796, quoted in Clune, 93–4.

Margarot to Hardy, Bewley, 129, no reference, no date.

Page 382
Gerrald's explanation of his incarceration and treatment, *A Fragment*, 16 and 24; *Memoir of Joseph Gerrald*, 1835 Glasgow edition of his trial, 5, and letter to Gilbert Wakefield, 17 May 1795, 7; letter from Dr Parr to Gerrald, undated, reprinted in *Tait's Magazine*, 30–31; Davis, *ODNB*; Bateson, 147.

Page 383
The trial and appeal to the governor, *Historical Records of Australia*, op cit.

Page 384
News from Norfolk Island and failure of wheat harvest, arrival of Arthur and opening of theatre, Paterson, 216, 220, 225; activity in Sydney, MacMillan, 156.

Return of Gerrald from Farm Cove, behaviour of Balmain, letter, Palmer to a friend, 23 April 1796, in Clune, op cit.

Page 385
Arrival of Ceres and Péron, Paterson, 228; Collins 23.

Péron on Amsterdam Island, Earnshaw 4, 23.

Arrival of Experiment, Paterson 228; Dorr calls at Amsterdam Island, arrival of Otter, Péron taken on as first officer, deal over seal skins, Earnshaw 26.

Page 386
Escape plan, Wantrup 29; Earnshaw, 26.

Gerrald encourages Muir to escape, letter, Muir to John Millar, Monterey, 15 July 1796, NLS, *Insh papers*, Deo 344, box 1, bundle 4, pages 69–70.

Chapter 36 Escape

Page 387
Mémoires du Capitaine Péron sur ses Voyages, published in Paris in 1824 in two volumes, are an abridged version of his manuscript journals, which remain undiscovered. It is thought that more than a third of his entries were omitted. The Paris volumes were rediscovered by both Earnshaw and Insh, who translated sections of them for their works. Bewley translated parts of them, and it appears that MacMillan did, too.

Arrival of Marquis Cornwallis, Paterson, 229.

Last minute invitation to servants, Earnshaw, 27.

Page 388
Rendezvous with the Otter, Wantrup, 29.

Muir's letter to Hunter, Collins, 315.

Page 389
Letter, Palmer to a friend, 23 April 1796, attendance of Dr Bass, deaths of Gerrald and Skirving, Clune, 96.

Letter, Palmer to a friend, 23 April 1796, op cit.

Page 390
Hunter's reply from London on the sentences, undated, Bladen, 886.

Palmer to Joyce, 5 May 1796, Clune 97.

Pages 391–4
Péron's log entries are from MacMillan, 165–6.

The narrative is taken from Earnshaw's translation of *Péron*, vol 1, 267–282, quoted on 31–35 of his 1959 article.

The group of islands 'discovered' by Péron had been named the Danger Islands in 1765 by the captain of a passing ship but it is probable that the crew of the Otter were the first Europeans to land there. Today the islands are called Motu Ko, Pukapuka, and Motu Kotowa.

Dorr family and construction of the Otter, Masson and Jameson, 56n; Clune, 102.

Entry in Cook's journal, Weber, 285.

Pages 395–400
Nookta Convention, Weber, 288.

The continuation of the narrative is again from Earnshaw, 39–44, quoting *Péron*, vol 1, 294–315.

Captain Cuba's offer of a pilot and Dorr's passport from Charleston, Earnshaw, 45.

Negotiations for an exchange of crew, Muir's acceptance on the Sutil, Insh, 125–131; Earnshaw, 45–48; he quotes Tovar's letter to Branciforte from Statement by Tobar, enclosure 3, Branciforte to Godoy, 26 September 1796.

Documents Proceeding from the Minister of State, High Court of Mexico, File 6, Archive of the Indies, Seville.

Description of Monterey, Insh, 132–3.

Chapter 37 New Spain

Page 401

The 1623 poem *Canto Intitulado Mercurio*, by Arias de Villalobos, is quoted by Knight, 183.

Muir's relationship with Borica, Insh, 133; Earnshaw, 49–51; letter, Borica to Branciforte, 13 July 1796, one part quoted by Earnshaw, 51, another part by Insh, 133.

Pages 402–4

All eight letters written by Muir in Monterey on 14 and 15 July 1796 are in the Archive of the Indies in Seville, in English, and the Spanish translations kept by Branciforte are in the National Archives in Mexico City. Earnshaw has collected them in appendix 2 to his 1959 article, 59–70. Copies of the originals, along with other documents pertaining to Muir, including his letter to Branciforte of 17 July 1796, are in the *Insh papers* in the National Library of Scotland: 46 prints from Seville and 36 from Mexico.

For Upper and Lower California in 1796 and Borica's governorship, Weber, 217 and 264–5; Fages, 63–66.

Later in the year, Borica was to encounter Muir's former shipmates when the Otter put into Monterey in search of supplies. Dorr now had his hold full of furs and was making for China. He had no need of the numbers on board any more nor, it would appear, did some of them have any desire to be with Dorr. A group deserted but Borica's search party soon found six of them, who were returned to the ship. Five more surrendered to Borica when the Otter was out of sight. But later that day, Dorr took the ship near a beach at the Carmel mission and put ashore, at gunpoint, five "Englishmen" and a woman he no longer needed or wanted. They, too, presented themselves to Borica, who on 12 November 1796 prepared a list of the names and nationalities of everyone left in Monterey from the Otter. Andrew Lambert, John Rich, and James Smith were Americans, part of the original Boston crew. Thomas Moody of Lincoln in England, had been left at Nootka by a previous ship and picked up by Dorr in September. The other seven were convicts from New South Wales, Peter Pritchard, John Jones, John Turner, Joseph Hongate, John Gibson, originally a black Philadelphian, Nicholas Phillips, and Jean "Lambert". This last castaway was the young woman brought to the Otter by Muir. She told Borica that she was married to Andrew Lambert, presumably for protection, and that they had a child in Boston. Jean and Andrew stuck together and the two of them lived and worked in different parts of New Spain until 1802, when they were put on a ship for Spain. There is no record of them after that date. (Earnshaw, appendix 4, *The Otter Convicts in Monterey and New Spain*, 75–77).

Voyage from Monterey to San Blas, Insh, 137.

Page 405
Muir and Gibson, Insh, 140; influx of British textiles to Mexico, Knight, 270.

Letters, Muir to Branciforte, Tepic, 20 August and 19 September, 1796, Archive of the Indies, Seville, quoted in Insh, 138 and 142.

Page 406
Narrative of the journey from Tepic to Mexico City, Veracruz, Havana and Cadiz, Insh, 143–9.

Page 407
The view of Popocatepetl and Iztaccihuatl, Sevin, 48.

University of Mexico, Knight, 183; immigration from Spain, 209; social organisation of city, 112; suburbs, 115.

Page 408
Letter, Muir to Branciforte, Veracruz, 22 October 1796, Archive of the Indies, Seville, quoted by Insh, 146.

War with Spain, Watson, op cit, 372.

Page 409
Letter, Muir to Hamilton Rowan, Havana, 3 December 1796, quoted by Rowan in a letter to his wife from Wilmington, Delaware, 10 February, 1797. See Masson and Jameson, op cit, 65.

Letter, Muir to French Directory, 30 May 1797, Archive of Foreign Affairs, Paris, Corresp. Pol. Espagne, 648, f48, quoted by Insh, 149.

Approach of Spanish ships to Cadiz, Insh, 149.

Chapter 38 Citizen Thomas Muir

Pages 410–2

There is a detailed account of the chase and engagement at Conil Bay in the master's log of HMS Irresistible (NA Adm 52/3128) and an abridged version in the captain's log (NA Adm 51/1212). The officers' names are in the ship's muster roll (NA Adm 36/1 1775). See also James, *Naval History*, 93–4; Clowes, *The Royal Navy*, 507; letter, Capt George Martin to Admiral Sir John Jervis, 28 April 1797 (NA Adm 1/396, fol 71, also published in the *London Gazette*, 16 May 1797); letter, Muir to the Directory, 30 May 1797, op cit; letter, no signature, from the Orion, Cadiz, 29 April, published in *Caledonian Mercury*, 29 May 1797; news item, *Caledonian Mercury*, 1 June 1797; extract, letter from officer on Irresistible, *Caledonian Mercury*, 5 June and another on 10 June 1797; news item, *Caledonian Mercury*, 15 June 1797; article by William Moffat, *The Scotsman*, 17 December 1842. Muir's request to be set on shore or fight alongside the Spanish is contained in the report of Fonnerga, commander of the Ninfa, quoted in Masson, *Odyssey*, 65.

Page 413

Masson, op cit, 66, reports that Muir was taken to the Royal Hospital on the Isla de Leon and that the governor refused to release him to the English. Muir's presence there was reported to the consul by a French citizen called Tournée, see letter, Muir to the Directory, 30 May 1797, op cit.

Page 414

Request to governor of Cadiz for Muir's transfer to the English squadron, Wantrup 31.

Letter, Citizen Roquesant, consul at Cadiz, to the minister of foreign affairs, Delacroix, 2 May 1797 Archive of Foreign Affairs, Paris, AF III, 62, dossier 246, quoted in Insh 155.

Memorandum, Delacroix to the Directory, Archive of Foreign Affairs, Paris, political correspondence, Spain, 649, ff 405–6, quoted in Insh, 155.

For Godoy, Weber, 275.

Letter, Muir to Paine, 14 August 1797, quoted in MacMillan, 203, from original letter in NAS, MS1003, fol 37.

Page 415
Letter, Muir to Talleyrand, 15 August 1797, Archive of Foreign Affairs, Paris, political correspondence, Spain, 649, fols 194–5, quoted in Insh, 156–7.

Letter, Talleyrand to Muir, 10 September 1797, Archive of Foreign Affairs, Paris, political correspondence, Spain, 649, fol 330, quoted in Insh, 157–8.

Letter, Talleyrand to Roquesant, September 1797, Archive of Foreign Affairs, Paris, political correspondence, Spain, 649, fol 329, quoted in Insh, 158.

Page 416
Letter, Talleyrand to Pérignon, September 1797, Archive of Foreign Affairs, Paris, political correspondence, Spain, 649, fol 331, quoted in Insh, 158.

For Pérignon's letters to Godoy, and Godoy's note in Muir's file, see Masson, Odyssey, 67.

Letter, Muir to Talleyrand, 3 November, 1797, Archive of Foreign Affairs, Paris, political correspondence, Spain, 649, fols 209–10, quoted in Insh, 161.

Page 417
For Muir's Bordeaux reception see Meikle, 173–4, and Bewley, 160, who quotes his speech as reported in the *Edinburgh Advertiser*, 15 December, and *The Press*, Dublin, 16 December 1797.

Page 418
David, *Gazette Nationale ou le Moniteur Universel*, No 72, 2 December 1797, quoted by Insh, 166. There is another translation of the full article, using less excitable language in Yeoman, 290–3.

Chapter 39 Exile and intrigue
Page 419
Chorus from *Plant, Plant the Tree*, possibly by Robert Crossfield. It was read out at his trial for treason in May 1796, he was one of those acquitted in the farcical "pop-gun plot", *ST*, vol 26, cols 135–6.

Description of Talleyrand, R Harris, 4, 19–20, 45.

Muir's speech is taken from a letter of thanks he wrote to the Directory, 5 December 1797. MacMillan 210, and partly in Bewley 161, both quoting a version published in the *Edinburgh Advertiser*, 26 December 1797.

Pages 420–1

Letter, Muir to Talleyrand's private secretary, 29 December 1797, quoted in Insh 164–5 from the Archive of Foreign Affairs, Paris, political correspondence, England, 529, fols 144–5

Muir's address is given as Rue de Braque in an undated letter, Samuel Turner to Castlereagh, Vane, 398.

Page 422

Paine's visit to the apartment is fictional. How they were re-acquainted is uncertain but from subsequent events we know they spent a great deal of time together. There is a hilarious story told by Meikle of a visit of John and Benjamin Sword from Glasgow to Paine in Paris. He told them of Muir's presence there and they visited him, too, noting that he "appeared to live in style and kept his carriage". Later, the four men got together and the Sword brothers tell of Paine and Muir getting very drunk and arguing about organised religion (Meikle, *Two Glasgow Merchants*, 154–5). Paine's account of his imprisonment is from Keane, 409–414.

Paine's address is given by Keane, 433, "In spring 1797 he moved in with Nicolas de Bonneville at 4 Rue du Théatre Français and often frequented Putode's café on the Rue des Marais."

Page 423

Rue du Colombier is given as the address of the United Irish club by Elliott, 239.

Letter, Muir to Minister of General Police, 28 December 1797, reprinted in *Lloyd's Evening Post*, 5 January 1798, quoting "Paris papers"; followed by the *Morning Post and Gazetteer*, the *Oracle and Public Advertiser*, 6 January; *Bell's Weekly Messenger*, 7 January; and the *True Briton*, 8 January, which accused Muir of encouraging the French "to put to death one hundred of his countrymen" (Burney Collection, British Library).

Whig boycott of the Westminster and Dublin parliaments, Wells, 79.

Page 424

Description of Paris at the time of the Directory, Lefebvre, 151.

Tone in Philadelphia, Knox, 173, 176.

Description of Lewins, Knox 238; his background, Woods's entry on Edward Lewines (note different spelling) *DIB*; his appointment as official United Irish representative in Paris, *Commons Secret Committee Report, Ireland, 1798*, 15.

Page 425

Tone's account of the attempted landing at Bantry Bay, *Memoirs*, vol 2, 136–164.

Tone's Texel posting, *Memoirs*, 238–48.

Page 426

Planned invasion of Scotland, Woods, *A Plan*, 108–114

James Smith's permanent residence in France and his marriage, Bewley, 168.

For Williams see Kennedy, *ODNB*.

For Stone see Rapport, *ODNB*.

Page 427

The reform societies and the Two Acts, Thompson 153–163.

Page 428

United Scotsmen, Harris, *The Scottish People*, 147–180; McFarland 129–175; Meikle 186–193; Johnston 231–233; *Report of the Secret Committee of the House of Commons, March 1799*, 24–35.

Henry Harding was sent with information for the exiles to Hamburg by Robert Watson, Elliott 142.

The trial of George Mealmaker, *ST*, vol 26, cols 1135–64.

Page 429

Letter, Robert Dundas to Home Office, 6 May 1797, NA HO 102/16, fol 212. A second letter referring to "swarms from Ireland" is dated 14 July 1797 and quoted by Meikle, 186n.

United Scotsmen membership, McFarland 168; Elliott 145.

Militia riots, Logue 78–113; Meikle 178–183; Western 3–14; Johnston 230–31.

Paine's plan for an invasion of Britain, Aldridge 74–84; Keane 440–41.

Page 430

Williams's comments on the Directory are from her *Sketches of the State of Manners and Opinions in the French Republic*, 1801, quoted in Moore, 342 and 388–89.

Paine supported the coup of 4 September 1797 against an Anglo-royalist plot. In a pamphlet published by Bonneville in October that year, he praised the constitution of 1795 but criticised its narrowing of the franchise. Keane 435; Paine, *Letter to the People of France*, Conway 231; speech in the French National Convention, 7 July 1795, Conway 187.

Rue de Condé meeting place is mentioned by McFarland, 166.

Page 431

Tandy, Woods, *DIB*. Invitation to Paris, Coughlan 113.

Madgett, Woods, *DIB*.

Tone's comment on Madgett, *Memoirs*, quoted in Knox, 187.

Tandy's reception in Paris by Tone, Coughlan, 114.

Tandy's communications with Ireland, Elliott 170–80.

Page 432

Muir's memorial to Talleyrand, February 1798, Bewley 170–1; MacMillan 227; Insh 167; Meikle 174, quoting *Memoir of Muir of the Government of England*, Archive of Foreign Affairs, Paris, political correspondence, England, 592, fol 161.

Tone's January meeting with Napoleon, Knox 239. His two 1795 memorials on the state of Ireland are in an appendix to his *Memoirs*, 433–5.

Page 433

Talleyrand-Napoleon correspondence; memo to Directory, R Harris 99 and 101.

Napoleon's review of the army of invasion, letter, Turner to Castlereagh, 13–15 February 1798, quoted in Vane 165.

Report, Napoleon to Directory, 28 February 1798, Insh 168, quoting JH Rose, *Life of Napoleon* (1913).

Page 434

Talleyrand's opportunism, ibid, 89.

On December 14–15 1797, Paine argued in *Le Bien Informé* for an invasion of England, Keane 440.

The report of Muir's intervention on behalf of Irish prisoners is from the *London Packet or New Lloyd's Evening Post*, 22 February, 1798, BL Burney Collection.

Turner reported to Castlereagh, who passed the information to Grenville, that Madgett had permission to recruit Irish prisoners of war, 16 August 1798, Vane 309, and again in an undated report, Vane, 398.

Tone's comment on Tandy and Coigly, *Memoir*, 1 February 1798, 273.

Page 435

Turner's report, Tone-Tandy quarrel, Coughlan 121, Vane 309.

Tone's report of the disagreeable meeting with Tandy, Madgett, Muir, and Stone, then subsequently with Muir, *Memoirs* 273–5;

Page 436

Directories of three republics, *Secret intelligence from France, extract, January 1798, Fortescue, Historical Manuscripts Commission*, vol 4, *Dropmore mss*, 69–70.

Loyalist article, "Mr Gifford's address", *Lloyd's Evening Post*, 4–7 May 1798 (BL Burney Collection).

Tone's comment on articles in *Le Bien Informé*, *Memoirs*, 3 March, 278; on Paine, 3 March 1797, 173; On Tone and Muir, 1 February 1798, 274.

Pages 437–8

General Lake's martial law in Ulster, Tillyard 258.

For pre-May activity in Ireland in 1798, see Knox, 239–251; Tillyard, 239–276; McFarland, 188–191.

Factions in Ireland for and against a rising before a French invasion, McFarland, 184.

Messenger sent by O'Connor to Tandy, Elliott, 179.

Page 439

Coigly in London, Ireland, and Lancashire, McFarland, 184–186; *Commons Committee of Secrecy, 1799*, 23–4; Goodwin, 438–441.

Ashley arrives from London Corresponding Society, scepticism over his figures, Bewley, 169; Thale, 400n, 422; *Commons Committee of Secrecy, 1799*, 24–5.

Talleyrand's/Napoleon's plans approved by the Directory, Lefebvre, 166.

Page 440

Coigly and O'Connor were arrested at the King's Head Tavern in Margate on 28 February 1798, McFarland, 185.

Chapter 40 A flame extinguished

Page 441

Letter from Muir, recipient and precise date unknown, quoted by Donnelly, 24.

Watson's background, Forbes, 324–34; Chase, *ODNB*.

Muir's new address at Hôtel de la Marine, Bewley,169.

Mass arrests in England and Scotland, Elliott, 188; Thompson, 187–192; McFarland, 187–8; Thale, 428–37.

Deposition from spy [Powell?], c 15 April 1798, Thale, 427–8.

Page 442

Watson's rank in Washington's army, Forbes, 328; Chase.

Watson's escape, Forbes, 326.

Watson's memorial to the Directory, 19 July 1799, names himself and Williams as representatives of the English associations and Cameron and Kennedy as the Scots delegates. French Foreign Office archives, Mémoires et Documents (Angl.), 53, f. 361, quoted in Meikle, *Scotland and the French Revolution*, 192n.

Kennedy and the British Convention, Meikle, 192n. Called as a witness in the trials of Watt and Downie, *ST* vol 23, cols 1181–2.

Page 443

Cameron and the militia riots, Logue, 96–112; Johnston, 231–2; Penny, 84; Meikle, 182, 191, 192n.

Trials of Angus Cameron and James Menzies, 15 and 17 January 1798, *ST*, vol 26, cols 1165–80.

Trial of George Mealmaker, 10–12 January 1798, *ST*, vol 26, cols 1135–64.

Statistics on those charged during the militia riots, Logue, 100–1.

Trials of Coigly, O'Connor, et al, 21–22 May 1798, *ST*, vol 26, cols 1191–1432, and *ST*, vol 27, cols 1–254.

Page 444
Arrests in March of United Irish leadership, Tillyard, 253; McFarland, 190; Knox, 247.

UI membership figures from national executive paper dated 26 February 1798, quoted by Tillyard, 245.

20 April entry in Tone's Memoirs, 293.

Napoleon's departure from Paris and on to Malta, R Harris, 101.

Date for Irish rising, Tillyard, 265; McFarland, 191; arrest of new Irish Directory on 21 May, Vane, 148; rising uncoordinated, Tillyard, 277–8; McFarland, 191–3; Wells, 142–5.

Page 445
Highland lairds and recruitment to the British army, Penny, 49. Rumours of being sent abroad, Logue, 79; Western, 2–3.

Muir's May memorandum to Talleyrand, Bewley, 171–5; MacMillan, 227; Insh, 167; Meikle, 174–5, quoting Archive of Foreign Affairs, Paris, memoirs and documents, England, ii, 153.

Page 446
Hôtel Gallifet is described by R Harris, 97.

"Great doubt prevailed as to whether an invasion of Ireland was really to be attempted. The First Consul blew hot and cold upon it… Why Bonaparte, at first so anxious for invasion, should have changed his mind, is explained in the recently published memoirs of Gouverneur Morris, as due to the conflicting reports of Irish envoys. At St Helena he told Las Cases that his mistake in '98 was to have gone to Egypt and not to Ireland." Fitzpatrick, 32.

"By April 1796 he [Tone] was protesting that a force was being considered for Scotland and remained convinced that 'nothing will ever be done unless we first begin in Ireland'." McFarland, 172.

The incident outside the Foreign Ministry is conjecture, a reminder of what he must have been suffering. Muir was weakening daily at this point but there are no records of how this affected him.

Page 447

Tone learns of May rebellion while in Le Havre, Knox, 240. His feeling of isolation and Lewins's absence from Paris, Elliott, 215–6.

Talleyrand's new submission to the Directory, R Harris, 104.

Tone learns of latest postponement of invasion, Knox, 241 and 255.

Rebellion, McFarland, 188–193; Tillyard, 277–8; Wells, 142–5, and associated naval mutinies, 150.

Page 448

The expeditions of Humbert, Tandy, Hardy and Tone, McFarland,193; Knox, 255–6; Wells, 160–1; Coughlan, 122–125.

Page 449

A translation of Muir's petition to the Directory for a country property is in Insh, 169–71, from Archive of Foreign Affairs, Paris, political correspondence, England, 590, fols 321–2.

Letter, Turner to Portland and Castlereagh, 16 August 1798, Vane, 308.

For background to Turner, Fitzpatrick, 8–13; Woods, *DIB*.

Page 450

For a discussion of the failure of the expected diversionary risings in Scotland and London, Wells, 151–3.

Pages 451

Substantial parts of Muir's final memorandum to Talleyrand on 18 October 1789 are translated and discussed by MacMillan in appendix C, 256–63. See also Bewley, 180–1; Meikle, 175–6, quoting Archive of Foreign Affairs, Paris, political correspondence, England, 594, fol 53 et seq. This document, he notes (as does MacMillan), is wrongly dated 1800 instead of 1798.

Page 453

Muir in Chantilly, Meikle, *The Death of Thomas Muir*.

Chapter 41 Epilogue

Page 454

Meikle, op cit.

Obituary quoted by Bewley, 183.

Page 455

Mackenzie, 43.

Verbal evidence from Michael Donnelly, May 2013.

Inscription and portrait, Bewley, 183.

Letter, Dollan to Insh, NLS, Dep 344, box 1, bundle 4.

Page 456

Disposition and settlement of James Muir, 8 April 1801, Huntershill estate titles 1801–1849, Glasgow archives, Mitchell library, TD276/1/ 3.

Hardy, *Memoir*, 49–51.

Bewley, ix–x.

Page 457

Lockhart, 49.

Note on Muir's application for property, MacMillan, 231.

Verdicts on Muir's memos, Meikle, 176; Insh, 167; Bewley, 174, 193; MacMillan, 219.

Pages 458–9

1799–1806, Ireland, McFarland, 206–228; England, Wells, 152, 188–252; McFarland, 215, 222; Elliott, *The 'Despard Conspiracy' Reconsidered*; Scotland, McFarland, 200, 206, 217–24.

Page 460

Canning, Wells, 265, quoting PJV Rolo, *George Canning*, 1965, 165.

1806–1819, McFarland, 236–7; Foot, 59–62; Thompson, chapters 14–16.

Page 461

Radical war, Berresford Ellis and Mac a' Ghobhainn, passim; Meikle, 227–8; McFarland, 238–241; Johnston, 238–44.

Muir's transparency in Glasgow celebrations, Meikle, 236n, quoting *Scotsman*, 30 March 1831.

Reform Act in Scotland, Meikle, 237; MacMillan, 242.

Pages 462–3

Celebrations in Edinburgh, Meikle, 238 and Bewley, 185, both quoting the *Scotsman*, 11 August 1832; see also "Edinburgh Reform Jubilee", *Caledonian Mercury*, 11 August 1832 (BL Burney Collection).

For a detailed history of Palmer's later years, Clune, 131–158. Some of his letters to Rutt and Disney during this time are in the *Monthly Repository*, 1817, 264–7. The note on Ellis from Dundee Celebrities is quoted by Clune, 158.

For Margarot see Roe, 72–8; Clune, 159–175; Emsley *ODNB*; Hill-Reid, 53–7, 117, 140–5, 153.

Page 464

For Mealmaker, Clune, 161–2.

For Paine, see Keane, 429–433 and 456–536.

Pages 465–6

For Tandy, see Coughlan, 124 et seq; Woods, *DIB*.

For Watson, see Bain, passim; Forbes, 326; Chase, *ODNB*.

For Williams, see Kennedy, *ODNB*.

For Stone, see Rapport, *ODNB*.

For Ashley, see Davis, *ODNB* on the London Corresponding Society.

For Smith, see Bain, 31–2; FO 43/16.

For Madgett, Lewins, Turner, see their respective entries by Woods, *DIB*.

For Pitt, see Turner, 206–273.

For Henry Dundas, Fry, 253, 268–75, 305.

Page 467

For Robert Dundas, Omond, 204.

Report of a speech by Sir William Drysdale, *Scotsman*, 7 December 1842; reply by William Moffat, *Scotsman*, 10 December 1842.

Memorials campaign, Bewley, 185–7; Clune, 184–6.

BIBLIOGRAPHY

Main works concerning the 'Scottish Martyrs'

Bewley, Christina, *Muir of Huntershill, A Scottish Patriot's Adventures Around the World* (OUP 1981).

Clune, Frank, *The Scottish Martyrs, Their Trials and Transportation to Botany Bay* (Sydney 1969).

Donnelly, M, *Thomas Muir of Huntershill* (pamphlet, Bishopbriggs Town Council, 1975).

Earnshaw, John, *Thomas Muir, Scottish Martyr* (Studies in Australian and Pacific History 1, Cremorne, NSW, 1959).

Insh, George Pratt, *Thomas Muir of Huntershill* (unpublished mss, 1952, in GP Insh papers, National Library of Scotland, Dep 344, box 1. These papers also contain photographs and photocopies of correspondence by or relating to Muir from the French, Spanish, and Mexican archives, as well as Inch's research correspondence about the book.

Insh, George Pratt, *Thomas Muir of Huntershill* (pamphlet, Glasgow 1949).

Mackenzie, Peter, *The Life of Thomas Muir Esq, Advocate, Younger of Huntershill* (Glasgow and London, 1831, reprinted by Kessinger Publishing).

MacMillan, Hector, *Handful of Rogues, Thomas Muir's Enemies of the People* (Argyll Publishing 2005).

Masson, Marjorie and Jameson, JF, *The Odyssey of Thomas Muir* (The American Historical Review, vol 29, no 1, October 1923, pages 49–72).

Meikle, HW, *Scotland and the French Revolution* (Glasgow, J Maclehose & Sons, 1912).

Wantrup, Jonathan (translated and with introduction and notes), *The Transportation Exile and Escape of Thomas Muir. A Scottish Radical's Account of Governor Hunter's New South Wales published at Paris in 1798* (Melbourne 1990).

Scotland, biography

Anon, *Memoirs and Trials of the Political Martyrs of Scotland* (*Tait's Magazine*, Edinburgh, 1837).

Anon, *The Life and Character of Robert Watt, who was executed for high treason at Edinburgh, the 15ᵗʰ October 1794* (London and Edinburgh 1795).

Anon, *Thomas Muir of Huntershill*, (pamphlet, The Fight for Freedom Series, reprinted from Springburn Pioneer News, 1946).

Chase, Malcolm, *Robert Watson*, ODNB online, 2008.

Dawson, Elizabeth (ed), *Autobiography of Mrs E Fletcher of Edinburgh* (Carlisle, 1874).

Drescher, HW, *Henry Mackenzie*, Oxford Dictionary of National Biography, Oxford University Press, online edition, 2004.

Forbes, Alexander P, *Some Account of Robert Watson with reference to a portrait of him, painted by Professor Vogel von Vogelstein*, in Proceedings of the Society of Antiquaries of Scotland, vol 7, 1866–7 to 1867–8, pages 324–34, (Edinburgh 1870).

Grosart, AB, revised Stanley Trapido, *Lady Anne Barnard (1750–1825)*, Oxford Dictionary of National Biography, Oxford University Press, online edition, 2004.

Harris, Bob, *George Mealmaker*, Oxford Dictionary of National Biography, OUP 2004, online edition 2008.

Harris, Bob, *Robert Watt (1761x8–1794)*, Oxford Dictionary of National Biography, OUP 2004, online edition.

Logue, Ken, *Thomas Muir*, in Gordon Menzies (ed), *History is My Witness* (BBC 1976).

McIlvanney, Liam, *Burns the Radical* (Tuckwell Press 2002).

Macleod, Emma Vincent, *Archibald Fletcher (1746–1828)*, Oxford Dictionary of National Biography, Oxford University Press, online edition, 2004.

Macleod, Emma Vincent, *William Skirving (d. 1796)*, Oxford Dictionary of National Biography, Oxford University Press, online edition, 2004.

Murdoch, Alexander, *Henry Scott, third duke of Buccleuch*, Oxford Dictionary of National Biography, Oxford University Press, online edition, 2009.

Osborne, Brian D, *Braxfield* (Argyll Publishing, 1997).

Ritchie, Lionel Alexander, *Alexander Wight* d. *1793*, Oxford Dictionary of National Biography, Oxford University Press, 2004; online edition, October 2007.

Roe, MJ, and McBryde, *William Pulteney*, Oxford Dictionary of National Biography, Oxford University Press, online edition, 2008.

Russell, Meg, *James Tytler (1745–1804)*, Oxford Dictionary of National Biography, Oxford University Press, 2004; online edition, January 2008.

Scott Hogg, Patrick, *Robert Burns the Patriot Bard* (Mainstream 2009).

Scotland, general

Berresford Ellis, P, and Mac a' Ghobhainn, Seumas, *The Scottish Insurrection of 1820* (Victor Gollancz 1970).

Brims, John, *From Reformers to 'Jacobins', The Scottish Association of the Friends of the People*, in Devine TM (ed), *Conflict and Stability in Scottish Society 1700–1850* (Edinburgh, John Donald, 1990).

Burleigh, JHD, *A Church History of Scotland*, (Edinburgh, 1988).

Coghill, Hamish, *Lost Edinburgh* (Edinburgh, Birlinn, 2010).

Cockburn, Henry, *Examination of Trials for Sedition in Scotland* (Edinburgh, 1853).

Cockburn, Henry, *Memorials of His Time* (1856, facsimilie edition James Thin, Edinburgh, 1988).

Daiches, David, *Glasgow* (Granada 1989).

Davidson, Neil, *Scotland's Bourgeois Revolution*, in Bambery, Chris (ed), *Scotland, Class and Nation* (Bookmarks, 1999)

Fry, Michael, *The Dundas Despotism* (Edinburgh UP, 1992).

Fry, Michael, *The Union. England, Scotland and the Treaty of 1707* (Birlinn, 2006).

Harris, Bob, *Political Protests in the Year of Liberty, 1792*, in *Scotland in the Age of the French Revolution*, edited by Bob Harris (Edinburgh, John Donald, 2005).

Harris, Bob, *The Scottish People and the French Revolution* (Pickering and Chatto, 2008).

Johnston, Thomas, *The History of the Working Classes in Scotland* (Forward Publishing, Glasgow, 1920).

Leonard, Tom, *Radical Renfrew* (Polygon, Edinburgh, 1990).

Logue, Kenneth J, *Popular Disturbances in Scotland 1780–1815* (John Donald, Edinburgh, 1979).

Noble, Andrew, and Hogg, Patrick Scott (eds), *The Canongate Burns* (Canongate Books 2001).

Omond, George WT, *The Lord Advocates of Scotland* (Edinburgh 1833).

Penny, George, *Traditions of Perth During the Last Century* (Perth 1836).

Smout, TC, *A History of the Scottish People 1560–1830* (1969, this edition Fontana 1989).

Thornton, Robert Donald, *William Maxwell to Robert Burns* (Edinburgh, 1979).

Various, *The Statistical Account of Scotland 1791–99*, online, (http://stat-acc-scot.edina.ac.uk/ link/1791–99).

Whyte, Iain, *Scotland and the Abolition of Black Slavery 1756–1838* (Edinburgh University Press, 2006).

Yeoman, Louise (ed), *Reportage Scotland* (Luath Press, Edinburgh 2000), *Thomas Muir*, 289–292.

England, biography

Belsham, Thomas, *Memoirs of the Late Theophilus Lindsey MA*, London 1820.

Davis, Michael T, *Joseph Gerrald (1763–1796)*, Oxford Dictionary of National Biography, Oxford University Press, online edition, 2004.

Equiano, Olaudah (aka Gustavus Vassa), *The Interesting Narrative and Other Writings*, edited with an introduction and notes by Vincent Carretta (Penguin 2003).

Keane, John, *Tom Paine, A Political Life* (Bloomsbury 1995, this edition Grove Press, undated).

Kennedy, Deborah F, *Helen Maria Williams (1761–1827)*, Oxford Dictionary of National Biography, Oxford University Press, September 2004; online edition, May 2006.

Millar, AH, revised GM Ditchfield, *Thomas Fyshe Palmer*, Oxford Dictionary of National Biography, Oxford University Press, online edition, 2004.

Rapport, Michael, *John Hurford Stone (1763–1818)*, Oxford Dictionary of National Biography, Oxford University Press, September 2004; online edition, January 2008.

Sparrow, Elizabeth, *Sir Evan Nepean, first baronet (1752–1822)*, Oxford Dictionary of National Biography, Oxford University Press, online edition, 2009.

Taylor, Barbara, *Mary Wollstonecraft, (1759–1797)*, Oxford Dictionary of National Biography, Oxford University Press, September 2004; online edition, May 2007.

Turner, Michael J, *Pitt the Younger, A Life* (Hambledon & London, 2003).

Weinglass, DH, *Sir Robert Smyth, fifth baronet (1744–1802)*, Oxford Dictionary of National Biography, Oxford University Press, 2004, online edition.

England and UK, general

Barrell, John, *Imagining the King's Death, Figurative Treason, Fantasies of Regicide 1793–1796* (Oxford 2000).

Branch-Johnson, W, *The English Prison Hulks*, (London 1957).

Claeys, Geoffrey (ed), *Political Writings of the 1790s* (London, William Pickering, 1995), vol 3, *Radicalism and Reform 1790–1792*.

Clowes, William Laird, *The Royal Navy, A History* (London 1899).

Davis, Michael T, McCalman, Iain, and Parolin, Christina (eds), *Newgate in Revolution, An Anthology of Radical Prison Literature in the Age of Revolution* (Continuum 2005).

Fitzpatrick, WJ, *Secret Service Under Pitt* (London 1892).

Foot, Paul, *The Vote, How it was Won and how it was Undermined* (Viking 2005).

Goodwin, Albert, *The Friends of Liberty, The English Democratic Movement in the Age of the French Revolution* (Hutchinson 1979).

Grovier, Kelly, *The Gaol, The Story of Newgate, London's Most Notorious Prison* (John Murray, 2008).

Grylls, Rosalie Glynn, *William Godwin and his World* (London 1953).

Hardy, Thomas, *Memoir* (London 1832).

Hardy, Thomas, *A Sketch of the History of the London Corresponding Society*, *Place Papers*, vol 24, BM add mss 27814.

James, William, *The Naval History of Great Britain*, vol 2 (London,1860).

Jephson, Henry, *The Platform, Its Rise and Progress*, vol 1 (London 1892).

Mori, Jennifer, *William Pitt and the French Revolution 1785–1795* (Keele University Press 1997).

Paine, Thomas, *Rights of Man* (Folio Society, 2007).

Thale Mary (ed), *Selections from the Papers of the London Corresponding Society 1792–1799* (Cambridge 1983).

Thompson, EP, *The Making of the English Working Class* (1963, this edition Penguin 1991).

Watson, J Steven, *The Reign of George III 1760–1815*, OUP 1960.

Wells, Roger, *Insurrection, the British Experience 1795–1803* (Allan Sutton, 1983).

Wollstonecraft, Mary, *A Vindication of the Rights of Woman*, 1796 edition.

Ireland, biography

Bartlett, Thomas, *Theobald Wolfe Tone*, Dictionary of Irish Biography, Cambridge University Press, 2009.

Chambers, Liam, *Archibald Hamilton Rowan (1751–1834)*, Oxford Dictionary of National Biography, Oxford University Press, 2004; online edition, January 2008.

Coughlan, Rupert J, *Napper Tandy* (Anvil Books, Dublin 1976).

McBride, IR, *William Drennan (1754–1820)*, Oxford Dictionary of National Biography, OUP, 2004; online edition, January 2008.

Rowan, Archibald Hamilton, *Autobiography* (Dublin, 1840, facsimile by Nabu Public Domain Reprints, 2011).

Stewart, ATQ, *William Drennan*, Dictionary of Irish Biography, Cambridge University Press, 2009.

Tillyard, Stella, *Citizen Lord, The Life of Edward Fitzgerald, Irish*

Revolutionary (Farrar, Straus and Giroux, New York, 1998).

Tone, Theobald Wolfe, *Memoirs*, vol 2 (London 1827).

Whelan, Kevin, *Lord Edward Fitzgerald*, Dictionary of Irish Biography, Cambridge University Press, 2009.

Woods, CJ, *Archibald Hamilton Rowan*, Dictionary of Irish Biography, Cambridge University Press, 2009.

Woods, CJ, *James Napper Tandy*, Dictionary of Irish Biography, Cambridge University Press, 2009.

Woods, CJ, *Edward Lewines*, Dictionary of Irish Biography, Cambridge University Press, 2012.

Woods, CJ, *Nicholas Madgett*, Dictionary of Irish Biography, Cambridge University Press, 2009.

Woods, CJ, *Samuel Turner*, Dictionary of Irish Biography, Cambridge University Press, 2012.

Ireland, general

Agnew, Jean (ed), *The Drennan-McTeir Letters*, vol 1, 1776–1793 (The Women's History Project in association with the Irish Manuscripts Commission, 1998).

Elliott, Marianne, *Partners in Revolution. The United Irishmen and France* (Yale 1982).

Knox, Oliver, *Rebels and Informers, Stirrings of Irish Independence* (John Murray, London 1997).

McFarland, EW, *Ireland and Scotland in the Age of Revolution* (Edinburgh University Press 1994).

Vane, Charles (ed), *Memoirs and Correspondence of Viscount Castlereagh*, vol 1, *The Irish Rebellion* (London 1848).

France

Alger, JG, *Englishmen in the French Revolution* (London 1889).

Alger, JG, *Paris in 1789–94* (George Allen, 1902).

Carlyle, Thomas, *The French Revolution*, vol II, 1867.

Erdman, David V, *Commerce des Lumières, John Oswald and the British in Paris, 1790–1793* (University of Missouri Press, 1986).

Harris, Robin, *Talleyrand, Betrayer and Saviour of France* (John Murray 2007).

Jordan, David P, *The King's Trial, Louis XVI vs the French Revolution* (University of California Press, 1979, this edition 1981 paperback).

Kates, Gary, *The Cercle Social, the Girondins, and the French Revolution* (Princeton University Press, 1985).

Lefebvre, George, *The Directory* (London 1965).

Meikle, Henry W, *Two Glasgow Merchants in the French Revolution* (The Scottish Historical Review, vol 8, no 30, January 1911, 148–158).

Moore, Lucy, *Liberty, The Lives and Times of Six Women in Revolutionary France* (Harper 2007).

Schama, Simon, *Citizens* (Penguin 1989).

Twiss, Richard, *A Trip to Paris July–August 1792*, in John Carey (ed), *The Faber Book of Reportage (1987)*.

Wright, DG, *Revolution and Terror in France 1789–1795* (Longman, 1992).

Australia

Ashton, Paul and Waterson, Duncan, *Sydney Takes Shape, A History in Maps* (Hema Maps, Brisbane, 2000).

Bateson, Charles, *The Convict Ships* (Glasgow 1969).

Bladen, FM (ed), *Historical records of New South Wales*, vol 2, *Grose and Paterson, 1793–1795* (Lansdown Slattery & Co, Mona Vale, NSW, 1978, facsimile edition. Originally published by the Australian government in 1893).

Brooke, Alan and Brandon, David, *Bound for Botany Bay* (The National Archives, 2005).

Collins, David, *An Account of the English Colony in New South Wales* (London, 1801).

de Vries, Susanna, *Historic Sydney, The Founding of Australia* (Pandanus Press, Brisbane, 1999).

Frost, Alan, *John Hunter*, ODNB , Oxford University Press, online January 2008.

Hill-Reid, WS, *John Grant's Journey, A Convict's Story 1803–1811* (Heinemann, 1957).

Hughes, Robert, *The Fatal Shore* (Folio Society edition 1998).

Keneally, Tom, *The Commonwealth of Thieves* (Vintage 2007).

Library Committee of the Commonwealth Parliament, *Historical Records of Australia*, series 1, vol 1, 1788–96.

Paterson, William, *The History of New South Wales from its First Discovery to the Present Time* (Newcastle-upon-Tyne, 1811).

Péron, Pierre Francois, *Mémoires du Capitaine Péron sur ses Voyages* (Paris 1824). Translated independently by Earnshaw and Insh for their works, with additional translation by Bewley and MacMillan.

Colonial Spain

Fages, Pedro (translated by Herbert Ingram Priestley), *A Historical, Political, and Natural Description of California in the Year 1775* (University of California Press, Berkeley 1937).

Knight, Alan, *Mexico, The Colonial Era* (Cambridge 2002).

Weber, David J, *The Spanish Frontier in North America* (Yale 1992).

Brazil

Graham, Maria, *Journal of a Voyage To Brazil, and Residence There* (Echo 2010, first published London 1824).

Tuckey, JH, *An Account of a Voyage to Establish a Colony at Port Phillip in Bass's Strait on the South Coast of New South Wales* (London 1805).

Journals

Aldridge, Alfred Owen, *Thomas Paine's Plan for a Descent on England*, William and Mary Quarterly, third series, vol 14, no 1, January 1957, pages 74–84.

Alger, JG, The British Colony in Paris 1792–93, The English Historical Review, vol. 13, No. 52 (October 1898), pp. 672–694 (Oxford University Press).

Brown, David J, *The Government of Scotland under Henry Dundas and William Pitt* (History 1998, 265–79, The Historical Association/ Blackwell).

Elliott, Marianne, *The 'Despard Conspiracy' Reconsidered*, Past and Present, 75, May 1977, pages 46–61 (OUP).

Emsley, Clive, *An Aspect of Pitt's 'Terror', Prosecutions for Sedition during the 1790s*, Social History, vol. 6, No. 2 (May, 1981), pp. 155–184 (Taylor & Francis, Ltd).

Emsley, Clive, *The Home Office and Its Sources of Information and Investigation 1791–1801*, The English Historical Review, vol. 94, No. 372 (July 1979), pp. 532–561 (Oxford University Press).

Emsley, Clive, *The London 'Insurrection' of December 1792, Fact, Fiction, or Fantasy?* The Journal of British Studies, vol 17, No. 2, spring 1978, pp 66–86, (The University of Chicago Press).

Emsley, Clive, *Repression, 'Terror' and the Rule of Law in England during the Decade of the French Revolution*, The English Historical Review, vol. 100, No. 397 (October 1985), pp. 801–825 (Oxford University Press).

Graham, Jenny, *Revolutionary in Exile, The Emigration of Joseph Priestley to America 1794–1804* (Transactions of the American Philosophical Society, New Series, vol. 85, No. 2, 1995, pp. i–213.

Hughes, Edward, *The Scottish Reform Movement and Charles Grey 1792– 94, Some Fresh Correspondence* (Scottish Historical Review, 35, 1956).

Kennedy, Catriona, *Womanish Epistles? Martha McTier, Female Epistolarity and Late Eighteenth-Century Irish Radicalism* (Women's History Review, volume 13, Number 4, 2004).

Leask, Nigel, *Thomas Muir and the Telegraph, Radical Cosmopolitanism in 1790s Scotland*, History Workshop Journal, 63 (OUP 2007).

McIlvanney, Liam, *Robert Burns and the Calvinist Radical Tradition*, History Workshop, 40, 1995, pages 133–149 (OUP).

Manogue, Ralph A, *James Ridgeway and America, Early American Literature*, vol. 31, No 3, pages 264–288 (University of North Carolina Press, 1996).

Masson, Marjorie, *Thomas Fyshe Palmer, a Political Exile, 1793*, The Scottish Historical Review, vol. 13, No. 50, January 1916, pp. 159–167 (Edinburgh University Press).

Meikle, Henry W, *The Death of Thomas Muir*, Scottish Historical Review, vol 27, no 104, October 1948, pages 201–202.

Meikle, Henry W, *The King's Birthday Riot*, Scottish Historical Review, vol 7, no 25, October 1909, pages 21–28.

Roe, Michael, *Maurice Margarot, A Radical in Two Hemispheres 1792–1815*, Historical Research, volume 31, Issue 83, article first published online 12 October 2007.

Sevin, Charles, *Journey to Mexico in 1856* (Journal of the Royal Geographical Society, volume 30, 1860).

Western, JR, *The Formation of the Scottish Militia in 1797*, vol 34, no 117, April 1955, pages 1–18 (Edinburgh University Press).

Woods CJ, *A Plan for the Dutch Invasion of Scotland* (The Scottish Historical Review, vol 53, no 155, part 1, April 1974, 108–114.

Newspapers

Caledonian Chronicle 1794 (National Archives of Scotland GD99/228/9).

Caledonian Mercury, Edinburgh Evening Courant, Glasgow Courier, Edinburgh Gazetteer, Caledonian Chronicle, Edinburgh Advertiser, Edinburgh Herald, The Star, 1784–1793 (National Archives of Scotland, Bound volumes of various newspapers, GD311/7/21).

Caledonian Mercury 1792, 1797 (British Library, Colindale Newspaper Library).

Edinburgh Advertiser, 7 December 1792 (National Archives of Scotland GD26/15/53).

Edinburgh Gazetteer, (National Archives of Scotland, 1792 (GD99/228/5); January–June 1793 (GD99/228/6); July–Dec 1793 (GD99/228/7); January–June 1794 (GD99/228/8).

Miscellaneous cuttings (some undated) relating to various matters, including activities of Friends of People in Scotland, 1793 (National Archives of Scotland, GD99/228/4).

Manchester Guardian, 8 February 1892 (ProQuest Historical Newspapers: *The Guardian*, 1821–2003, and *The Observer* 1791–2003).

Morning Chronicle 1792–9 and other contemporary newspapers (British Library, 17th–18th Century Burney Collection).

The Scotsman, 10, 17 December 1842 (British Library, Colindale Newspaper Library).

Letters and papers

Admiralty papers concerning the sea battle at Conil Bay (National Archives Adm 1/396, 36/1 1775, 51/1212, 52/3128).

An Account of the trial of Thomas Muir, younger, of Huntershill, before the High Court of Justiciary at Edinburgh on the 30th and 31st days of August, 1793, for sedition ('Robertson's edition', 1793 pamphlet).

A Member, *An Account of the Proceedings of the British Convention* (1793).

Anon, *The Trial of Joseph Gerrald* (Glasgow 1835), appears to be compiled from various contemporary sources and contains not only the transcript of the trials of Gerrald, Skirving, and Muir, but also memoirs on the lives of all three, including many letters, and notes on the trials of Palmer, Margarot, Watt and Downie.

Anon, *The Trial of Thomas Hardy, reported by a student in the Temple* (London 1794).

Committees of Secrecy, *The First Report of the Committee of Secrecy of the House of Commons*, London 1794; *The Second Report of the Committee of Secrecy of the House of Commons (with the first and second reports of the House of Lords)*, London 1794; *Report of the Committee of Secrecy of the House of Commons in Ireland* (London

1798); *Report of the Committee of Secrecy of the House of Commons* (London 1799).

Conway, Moncure Daniel, *The Writings of Thomas Paine* (New York, G.P. Putnam's Sons, 1894, vol. 3, in the Online Library of Liberty).

Correspondence on Friends of the People in the National Archives of Scotland (NAS GD51/5/6/7).

Fletcher, Archibald, *Letters to Graham of Gartmore* (NAS GD22/1/315).

Fortescue, JB, *Historical Manuscripts Commission, Report on the Manuscripts of JB Fortescue Esq, preserved at Dropmore*, vol 4 (HMSO 1905).

Grant papers, *letter, John Grant to Sir James Grant MP, 9 July 1794* (NAS GD248/687/2/1); *letter, John Grant to Lady Grant, NSW, 19 December 1794* (NAS GD248/351/7, folios 27 & 28).

Home Office correspondence addressed to Henry Dundas from Scotland, January to October, 1792 (National Archives HO102/5).

Home Office correspondence relating to Scotland, November 1792 to December 1794 (National Archives HO102/6-11).

Howell, Thomas Jones, *State Trials 1793 & 1794*, vol 23 (London 1817); 1794, vol 24 (1818); 1794–96, vol 25 (1818); 1796–98, vol 26 (1819).

Joyce, Jeremiah, *An Account of Mr Joyce's Arrest for Treasonable Practices* (London 1795).

Lockhart, JG, *A Skeleton in the Cupboard* (Blackwood's Magazine, vol 268, July 1950, 36–49).

London Corresponding Society, *An Account of the Seizure of Citizen Thomas Hardy with some remarks on the suspension of the Habeas Corpus Act* (1794).

London Corresponding Society, *Gerrald, A Fragment, Containing Some Account of the Life of This Devoted Citizen* (London 1795?).

Muir, Thomas, *Letters from Monterey, Tepic, Veracruz* together with documents relating to Muir (Archivo General de las Indias, Seville, and Archivo General de la Nacion, Mexico City, contained in GP Insh papers, Dep 344, National Library of Scotland; the Monterey letters are also collected in Earnshaw, op cit, appendix 2, pages 59–70.

Minto, Countess of (ed), *Life and Letters of Sir Gilbert Elliot*, vol II, (Longmans Green & Co, 1874).

Palmer, Thomas Fyshe, *A Narrative of the Sufferings of TF Palmer and W Skirving During a Voyage to New South Wales on Board the Surprize Transport* (Cambridge 1797).

Place, Francis, *Papers* (vol 2, British Museum additional manuscript 27,812; vol 18, add mss 27816; vol 24, add mss 27808; vol 28, add mss 27816).

Plowden, Francis, *A Short History of the British Empire During the Year 1794* (London 1795).

Rutt, JT, *Monthly Repository of Theology and General Literature,* vol 12 (Hackney, 1817). Many original letters from Muir and Palmer to the author.

Skirving, W, *Complaint of Wrongous Imprisonment* (Edinburgh 1793, facsimile from Eighteenth Century Collections Online, print edition).

Skirving William, *Collected papers* (NAS RH4/52).

The Parliamentary History of England from the Earliest Period to the Year 1803, vols 30 1792–94, and 31 1794–95 (London 1817).

The Trial of the Rev Thomas Fyshe Palmer, held at Perth on the 12th and 13th September 1793, with an introduction by William Skirving (Edinburgh 1793).

Trial papers relating to Thomas Muir, younger of Huntershill for the crime of sedition (National Archives of Scotland NAS JC26/1793/1).